50 Years Offshore

50 years

offshore

Hans Veldman
George Lagers

1997 *Foundation for Offshore Studies, Delft*

Written by:	Hans Veldman & George Lagers
Initiative:	Jan Vugts
Book Design:	Piet van Meijl
Printing:	Drukkerij en Uitgeversbedrijf Lecturis BV, Eindhoven
Published on behalf of:	Foundation for Offshore Studies, Delft

Research was made possible by financial support of the following companies and organisations:

Main sponsors:

Shell International Exploration and Production, The Hague   Texaco Worldwide Exploration & Production, Houston
Brown & Root, Houston   Maersk Olie og Gas, Copenhagen
IHC Caland, Schiedam   ING Barings, Amsterdam
Heerema, Meer

Sponsors:

Nederlandse Aardolie Maatschappij, Assen   Laboratorium Soete, Universiteit Gent, Gent
Allseas Group, Chatel-St. Denis   INTEC Engineering, Houston
Phillips Petroleum Norway, Tananger   HSM, Fabrication Contractors, Gouda
Bluewater Engineering, Hoofddorp   KLM ERA Helicopters, Den Helder
Stork Engineers & Contractors, Amsterdam   Noble Drilling (Nederland), Rotterdam
Bataafsch Genootschap, Rotterdam   MARIN, Wageningen
Smit International, Rotterdam   United Offshore Services, Zevenbergen
Fugro, Leidschendam   Röntgen Technische Dienst, Rotterdam
Nationaal Instituut voor Scheepvaart en Scheepsbouw, Rotterdam   Wijsmuller, IJmuiden
Germanischer Lloyd, Hamburg   Kværner John Brown/ZEETECH Engineering, Zoetermeer
Clyde Petroleum Exploratie, The Hague   Vryhof Ankers, Krimpen a/d IJssel
Lloyd's Register, Rotterdam   Bob Fleumer Aerial Photography, Westzaan
RWE-DEA Aktiengesellschaft für Mineralöl und Chemie, Hamburg   Photo Sea Sky Martin, Rotterdam
MeesPierson, Rotterdam   Oilfield Publications Limited, Ledbury

Advisory Committee:

IR. J.M.H. VAN ENGELSHOVEN (CHAIRMAN)
    President of the Royal Institution of Engineers in The Netherlands,
    member of the Supervisory Board of the Royal Dutch Petroleum Company

PROF.DR.IR. H.W. LINTSEN
    Foundation of the History of Technology,
    Professor of History of Technology at Delft University of Technology
    and Eindhoven University of Technology

W.L.C. VAN DAM
    former Member of the Board of Management of Heerema Engineering Service BV,
    Managing Director of Van Dam Marine Contracting

W.A. MULOCK HOUWER
    former Member of the Board of Nedlloyd, former Managing Director of Neddrill,
    President of the Maritime Platform in The Netherlands

P.J.M. VERSCHURE
    former General Manager of Verschure & Co Shipyard,
    former Member of the Board of Management of IHC Holland NV,
    former General Manager of Technip Geoproduction

Distributor:
Veldman Bureau voor Bedrijfsontwikkeling
Kapellerweg 13, 6132 AT Sittard, The Netherlands
Tel.: +31 46 458 9010, fax: +31 46 458 9088

ISBN 90-803677-1-0
© 1997 Hans Veldman, George Lagers.

Preface

By Prof.dr.ir. J.H. Vugts;
Offshore Technology, Delft University of Technology

When I went to university in the mid 1950s I had a general fascination for ships and the sea. The notion 'offshore' was then still unheard of in The Netherlands and more generally in Europe. I chose naval architecture in Delft. Having completed my studies, done some 6 to 7 years of research in Delft's ship hydromechanics laboratory and finished my doctoral dissertation it was time to look for a job in industry. It was 1969; a time in which engineers with a good education had ample opportunities. Among those that were available to me was an offer from Shell in The Hague for their offshore department. I accepted, which is how I entered the offshore world, more by accident than by design, and I have never regretted it since. My fascination became focused on the ocean environment and man-made structures, floating and fixed, that would defy the whims of the sea and withstand the mightiest gales. In short, a fascination with offshore engineering.

I realise that luck was on my side. I happened to be in the right circumstances, at the right time and at the right place. Developments in the North Sea were about to explode, providing immense challenges and requiring space-age technology to make many of them come true. It was only after the second World War that the oil industry ventured into the open sea. From then on progress has been revolutionary. Begun in the Gulf of Mexico at a distance of 17 km offshore and in a water depth of as little as 6 m, offshore oil and gas developments are now taking place in more than 40 countries, at distances from shore of several hundreds of kilometres and in ever increasing water depths. For more than 25 years I was part of these developments or at least witnessed them from nearby; being an employee

of a large multinational corporation further provided me with an unparalleled opportunity for exposure to world-wide activities, both in respect of the seemingly easy successes and the hard struggles to solve technical problems when they arose.

Most of these developments were (and are) largely unknown to the general public; even within the profession knowledge is fragmented. By their very nature these activities and the offshore 'monuments' that were created are far away from population centres and in inhospitable places. And if they could be visited they would largely be hidden from view; they are like icebergs: 90 per cent or more is under water and invisible to the human eye. Of course they have been written about, but again in a fragmented manner, generally lacking adequate overview and the context in which these developments took place. Unfortunate as this is, it is very understandable: the people involved simply did their job and were not disposed to herald their achievements. Moreover, they were far too busy to be concerned with writing history.

Since quite some time I had felt the lack of a reliable history of the offshore as a deficiency. The 50th anniversary of the commonly accepted birth of the offshore in 1947 suggested itself as an excellent opportunity to stop thinking about it; it was time to get into action and have a book produced. The occasion of the BOSS (Behaviour of Off-Shore Structures) conference, which happened to be in Delft in 1997, only provided an additional stimulus to get after it. At this point, however, two questions needed serious answering, i.e. why did I want such a book to be

Jan Vugts has taken the initiative for the writing of this book.

written and how should one go about producing it? I feel that this preface should present the answers to these questions so that readers can put the book in the proper perspective.

The why is in fact simple. First and foremost, the spectacular achievements as well as the companies and people who did it simply deserve to be saved from obscurity. Secondly, fifty years is a critical time: it is long enough to take the necessary distance and see the developments from a broader perspective than was possible at the time they took place, while it is short enough for many of those who were actively involved to be still alive and provide first hand information. Given the state of public and company archives the task will become more and more difficult, if at all possible, the longer we postpone it. Thirdly, as in many other fields, there is a much closer interaction between the offshore and society today than there has ever been before. It is therefore important that mutual awareness and knowledge are improved.

The answer to the how is a bit more involved. There would appear to be many different ways to approach the task. Having no experience with a project of this nature I contacted Harry Lintsen, professor of History of Technology at the technical universities of Delft and Eindhoven. After a number of discussions and the completion of a pre-study executed by the same two investigators who wrote this book we laid down the basic rules as follows:
The focus should be on technical developments; these should however be viewed against the background of the general technical, social, economic and political developments in the world over the years.
The historical review should cover the entire world but the emphasis should be on the Gulf of Mexico and the North Sea, the two areas that have largely shaped the offshore into what it is today.

The book should be a fully reliable and well-founded historical account; however, it should not aim for completeness or consist of a dry summing up of dates and facts. Well written and amply illustrated it should be highly informative for a wide audience, ranging from the interested 'man in the street' to the informed professional, and be a pleasure to read.

The book in front of you is a first class achievement of Hans Veldman and George Lagers. Circumstances were difficult, the budget (too) tight and the time (too) limited but they nevertheless did it, in the right tradition of the offshore. As it was always intended, it has become a history which is painted in broad strokes of the brush with selective colouring of a number of details. It is not and cannot be a definitive account of these first fifty years of offshore history. I believe, however, that it does provide a very good picture of what happened and why, and if it stimulates others to add to it we can all only be very pleased.

Other than Hans and George I want to thank the members of the Advisory Committee for their critical comments and general assistance. Also a word of thanks to Dick van Leeuwen, a former boss in Shell, who after his retirement and out of sheer interest studied and obtained a degree in history. Together with his original technical degree and his first hand knowledge of offshore developments from about the 1950s to the mid 1980s he was the perfect person to try out the drafts. Last but certainly not least I want to thank the sponsors who made this book possible. The funds have come from oil companies, contractors, engineering consultants and financial institutions. Thanks to the interest in our cause of those who contributed and to the trust they invested in us we managed to bring this challenging undertaking to a successful end. The reader should now judge for himself whether the book meets his expectations.

Introduction

Two years ago, at the time Greenpeace climbed the Brent Spar, we were invited by Jan Vugts to talk about his idea to have us write the history of offshore technology. Prof. Vugts would chair the 1997 BOSS conference in Delft, which was to be held exactly 50 years after the first offshore oil was found out of sight of land, and as we soon found out exactly 100 years after the first structures were built to drill for oil under the sea. It provided an excellent opportunity to do something special.

For both of us this project was a huge challenge. Time was short and there were no comparable general offshore histories written so far. For George the challenge was to step back and look at a development in which he had taken part. For Hans, who read about the Spar commotion in the train to the first meeting with Jan, the challenge was to step forward and get over his amazement that there was something called 'offshore' out there at sea.

Writing the history of a business sector worldwide usually asks for leaving out details and even some main events. Authors simply should not dare to confront people with thousands of pages of text, adding that at least it is complete. Also in this case, we decided to stick to main lines, but use detailed developments to illustrate mechanisms. This means that some names and events are highlighted and others not even mentioned. We know, that in this way we do not provide justice to the innumerable contributions, large and small, to the development of this industry. We hope that our readers who do not find their role described, will understand that we had to limit ourselves enormously. What came out is a story, which starts in 1897 in Summerland California and which still continues in varions offshore areas, a hundred years later. We concentrated on the development of technology in the two main offshore areas of our world, the Gulf of Mexico and the North Sea. We hope that this book will contribute to the history of business and technology and will be a starting point to get more done on the history of offshore technology, the offshore sector and offshore companies.

During our research we received a great deal of support from many people and companies. Among them, we feel that we should mention a few. First of all we like to salute Jan Vugts who dared to take the initiative to do something never done before. We further thank the members of the Advisory Committee formed by Jan for their comments on our drafts. We thank our wifes and children who suffered through weekends and evenings in which we preferred to struggle through articles and books instead of being caring fathers. Special thanks are for Joe Pratt and Bruce Collipp. They helped us understand general American oil history. Joe gave valuable advices and provided us with the opportunity to use his archive.

Last but not least we thank all people within the offshore sector, who in the past century made it to what it is today. They actually did things. We just had the opportunity to write things down.

Hans Veldman & George Lagers,
May 26, 1997

Contents

Chapter 1

The underwater game
The early years offshore

On Sunday 4 October 1947, around 9 a.m., Kerr-McGee struck oil in the Gulf of Mexico. The drilling attempt in the Gulf had been a bit of a gamble, inspired by the desire to grow, but perhaps even more by the need to survive.

'And high drama it was. On a platform in eighteen feet of water, ten and a half miles from the nearest land, the play reached its climax before even the cast realized what had happened. As [Chief Engineer] Seale later described it, "We didn't know at first we had encountered oil… The first we knew we had encountered oil sands at such a shallow depth (between 1500 and 1700 feet) was when oil covered the mud pits inside the barge." Instead of pumping the drilling mud back out, they were pumping out mud and oil. Someone informed the tool pusher, and he in turn reported to Seale. Seale listened to the complaint and told the tool pusher to get a skimmer and skim it off. The reply to this was, "Skim it off, hell! There's barrels of it." '[1]

J.S. Ezell, who wrote this in the biography of the Kerr-McGee company, adds that the firm's reaction remained one of modesty. The press, however, called it a historical event, comparable with Col. Drake's first on land oil discovery in 1859. Besides, Kerr-McGee was portrayed as a major inventor of a revolutionary type of drilling equipment.[2]
Kerr-McGee's find was labelled the first to be made out of sight of land. 'It has become a symbol of oilmen who dared to sever their natural ties to the land, and venture into a strange and fickle environment, with reliance on nothing familiar except themselves.'[3]
But this was neither the first well being drilled so far

from the shore, nor the first discovery of oil in the Gulf of Mexico or the first one under water. Besides, Kerr-McGee wasn't the only company exploring in the Gulf of Mexico. But it was their success that presented oil-exploring America with a new and immense area. This and consecutive finds drew the attention of a number of large oil companies which until then had hardly shown any interest; new markets opened up to shipyards and engineering firms; discussions on the ownership of the sea bed flared up, and investors got interested. The success of Kerr-McGee was historic in an economical and political sense. Technologically, it was of much less importance. Technology, for that matter, had its origins half a century earlier.

1. Early developments

Summerland
A first rather embryonic kind of offshore technology can be found by the end of the nineteenth century. In 1883 H.L. Williams bought a piece of land along the shore a few miles south east of Santa Barbara, California, with the idea to set up a colony of spiritualists, *'a haven to escape the confusion of commercial society.'*[4] His Summerland turned into something more than a spiritualists' settlement. Williams discovered oil shortly after his arrival, but he kept it silent until 1887, when he announced the drilling of a number of wells in the Santa Barbara Newspaper. Summerland became a boom town, having 28 wells in production by 1895. The finds were not really a surprise. Oil and gas came to the surface at various spots on the beach, and in the 1860s natural

The first successful offshore well was drilled at Block 32 in the Ship Shoal area, off Cameron (Louisiana).

Henry E. Huntington Library and Art Gallery

Shell International - Photographic Services London

A view of pioneering offshore wells at Summerland, as the abandoned derricks and piers appeared around 1930. The first piers were built by H.L. Williams in 1897. By 1903, 198 wells were producing in this field.

A typical derrick of the first offshore days at Summerland, converted into a production platform. Oil is pumped up by means of a cable driven by an engine onshore. In the centre of the platform the cable can be seen to enter into the conductor. The thin pipeline to the right is large enough for the low production of these wells.

asphalt was collected there. Williams must have known this. When the search for oil had reached the beach in 1897, Williams took the initiative to continue on the water. He had a wooden pier built with a common drilling rig at its end. His idea became a success: the underwater oil turned out to be of much higher quality than the oil found on land. A new boom was sparked off. Within two years more than 10 piers were built, each supporting 6 to 20 derricks. The piers were linked by three wharves. The longest pier was designed by J.B. Treadwell and built by the Southern Pacific Railroad. Measuring over 450 yards in length and standing in some 35 ft of water, it was considered the pride of Summerland.[5]

Drilling was done with cable tools.[6] Rotary drilling was not yet generally accepted in those days. A relatively wide casing between pier and seabed was used, which the drillers called the conductor. The conductor was driven through a layer of sand into the deeper clay. It acted as a fixed point so that the actual drilling could take place as if it was done on land. Generally, the wells were a good deal deeper than on land.[7]

The Summerland offshore wells were large in number, but small in production. The most productive well gave a maximum of 75 bbls. a day, while the average Summerland well produced less than 2 bbls., which compares dramatically with the daily 100,000 bbls. from the famous Lucas gusher in Spindletop (1901). Because of these low rates, the bulk of equipment was concentrated on the shore,[8] and rigs were being centrally powered by petrol engines on the beach. It is doubtful whether the Summerland offshore enterprise has been profitable at all. As early as 1899 the construction of new piers and drilling of new wells was stopped. Storms seriously damaged the piers and the waves caused conductors to break. The very low production discouraged the operators to go further offshore. In 1903 less than half the number of wells still were in operation. The Summerland Refinery, which had been specially built for this field, was abandoned by its operator, California Liquid Asphalt.[9]

The Summerland Advance-Courier of February 1900 has an interesting item, recommending investment in Summerland's oil wells as *'almost as sure of a reason-*

At Huntington Beach, near Los Angeles, bathers and oil derricks shared the beach. Wells were drilled directionally under the seabed.

able return on the money invested as United States Bonds'[10]. It was calculated that a well producing 2 bbls a day and operating 335 days annually for five years, would give a $ 495 return every year, after deducting operational expenses. The Courier estimated the cost of sinking a well at $ 552.65,[11] but this amount probably did not contain the major investment, viz. of building a pier. Hence, it remains doubtful if ever anyone really made money through the Summerland adventure. Summerland as an oilfield reached its peak in 1902, and then it rapidly dwindled, leaving behind a jungle of derricks and piers.

A primitive kind of offshore technology was developed, using piers to support conventional wooden derricks and long casings extending above the water (the conductors), to facilitate the use of common drilling technology. Apart from pumps, all production equipment remained ashore. There was no need for real exploration in Summerland, since the oil simply gave away its presence by bubbling up from the soil.

In 1921 the State of California passed a tidelands leasing act, which regulated the leasing of state owned waters for the commercial winning of oil. The act attracted numerous wildcatters and brought various new areas under development. However, the public worried about this use of the coast and after 1926 the government felt obliged to take back hundreds of concessions. By that time, some fields, like Elwood, had fully developed. The use of wooden piers was extended, both in time and physically: Elwood had some piers of 1800 ft in 30 ft of water.[12]

A new technology was developed in those years and used by Barnsdall Oil, acting as an operator for Rio Grande Oil. Expecting underwater oil in the Elwood field, Rio Grande Oil bought onshore rights from private owners. In a short time, Rio Grande managed to sink underwater wells from locations onshore, by so called *directional* drilling.[13] An attempt to secure rights for the sea area based on these findings, failed because of a procedural mistake. In the end, an attentive lawyer, D. Faries, obtained the rights and sold them to Honolulu Oil. Barnsdall reacted by denying Honolulu

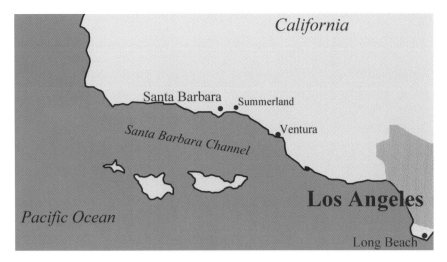

access to its area. Honolulu's answer was the building of a pier that did not reach back as far as the coastline. From a point that could just be reached at low tide by tractors, the pier was built. There, too, 'floated' a vessel containing all equipment.[14]
Apparently the use of piers in California had developed into a strong tradition. The connection with the shore was left intact, in spite of the great effort it required.[15]

California was the first to practise underwater oil exploration and with it a technological tradition. Piers built on wooden piles reached far into the sea. On land derricks were used to sink directional wells under the sea bed. Summerland's operators learned the high price of offshore operations. But also the Californian oil community and government came to face a population which was less than enthusiastic about these enterprises and its derelict remains of rigs and structures.

Lake Erie
Searching for oil around the turn of the century was to some extent comparable to the gold rush. Finding oil was a matter of fortune, and when fortune struck, the site of a new oil find exerted an irresistible attraction to both established firms and newcomers. Successful wildcats could change an uninhabited area into a boom town. Summerland was no exception to this rule. The presence of oil at a particular site boosted expectations for the adjacent lands and often triggered speculative drilling activity. Most prone

to speculation were those companies, persons and authorities which for one reason or another could not participate in established exploration or exploitation areas. This sometimes led to experiments never shown before.

A telling example of this phenomenon is the search for gas under Lake Erie, an effort dating early in this century, and almost forgotten in the history of oil. Lake Erie separates the United States from Canada between Buffalo and Detroit. The Northern (Canadian) shore was a gas producing area. A gas field named after the city of Tilbury, some 80 kilometres east of Detroit, was the most important one. On the south side, the lake is bordered by Pennsylvania and Ohio, the cradle of the oil industry. This fact was enough, early in the century, to make the lake and in particular the northern shoreline subject of speculation.[16] *'Experts in many instances are strongly of the opinion that [ ] gas veins extend under the lake and emerge on the North shore, in the vicinity of Leamington. That the biggest oil or gas flow in the history of Canada will be disclosed when these veins are tapped, is the optimistic view of several of the operators who have discussed the project'.*[17] Such wrote a journalist, W.E. Park in 1913. Equally strong was the conviction of a veteran oil man, who stated that *'if we could drill a well in the bottom of Lake Erie, we would strike a richer gas flow than we have in Canada or elsewhere in the United States.'*[18]

'If we could', because technology to drill in the bottom of the lake was non existent, and plans to explore in or near Lake Erie met with general resistance. The Vulcan Oil and Gas Company had already been forced to abandon her activities on the lake shore. In a court case it was established that private land which had washed into the lake in the course of years should remain property of its original owner, and that by consequence Vulcan was drilling on terrain on which it had no rights or not the proper ones.[19]
The Glenwood Natural Gas Company then decided to prepare for exploration on the lake itself. Ten holes would be drilled and to that end installations would be built on the lake. Not much is known today of the specifications for these installations. Documents

mention *'a number of pile and timber wharves, and trestles and steel and concrete piers',*[20] as well as *'a concrete crib 24 feet square'.*[21] During the spring of 1913 Glenwood started drilling of several wells. Two of them, probably very near shore, *'opposite the Coffel farm'* and *'opposite the Baldwin farm'*, encountered gas.[22]

Shortly after drilling had started, public resistance made itself felt. Landowners and fishermen filed protests with the Government of the Dominion against the drilling activities. Landowners claimed rights to the drilling sites, and fishermen were afraid that Glenwood would chase away their catch, or at least disturb their tracks. Following these protests, the authorities ruled that drilling had to be suspended until the matter had been investigated and a decision had been taken. This investigation took place in the summer of 1913.[23]

Glenwood had stopped most activity, but could complete the Baldwin well, after convincing the Baldwin farm owner that *'completion would be followed by the taking away of the temporary portion of the outfit, leaving only the concrete pier'.*[24] On August 12, 1913, the Chatham City Council voted in large majority, that the Minister of Public Works should be advised to forbid further exploration in Lake Erie. Glenwood moved its activities to on shore areas, and Lake Erie was forgotten for a while.[25]

Only in 1943, drilling in the lake was resumed. Consolidated West Petroleum hit gas in 48 of 49 wells drilled in the Canadian portion of the Lake. In the United States part of it, activities started in 1958. By that time, offshore technology was well advanced, but in Lake Erie the operators seemed unaware of this. Consolidated West used cable tool drilling apparatus and wooden platforms, concepts which already had been abandoned elsewhere. On the other hand, all wells were underwater completions, a choice imposed by the fear that structures above water would be damaged by ice flows in winter. In the Gulf of Mexico, it would still take years for the first underwater completion to appear.[26]

Altogether, the role of Lake Erie in the development of

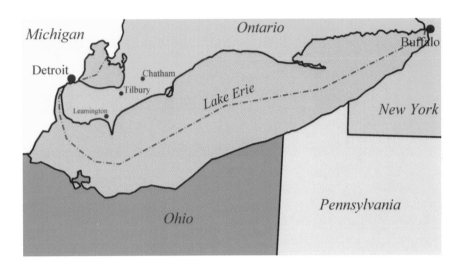

offshore technology has been small, and its most remarkable feat seems to be its isolation.

Lake Caddo

The area around Lake Caddo, on the border of Louisiana and Texas, was a place where oil seemed easy to find. Gas bubbled up from the lake, and on the shore oil came to the surface. In 1870 gas was accidently found in a well that was intended to supply water to an ice factory in Shreveport.[27]

In 1904 oil exploration started. A well was struck but it did not come into production. A next attempt took place in the spring of 1905, but this led to disaster. High pressure gas came up around the casing and caught fire. Similar accidents happened time and again during the six years that followed. Rigs were left behind, fully ablaze. Some wells continued to burn for several years and gas was lost in great quantities because there were hardly any technical means to put out the flames and close the wells. Since there was only a very limited market for gas, it was considered an unwanted by-product, and consequently no serious attempts were made to develop closing-in techniques for burning gas wells. The drillers were merely interested in oil, and it was thought that once the gas had ceased flowing, oil might follow.[28] For years drilling for oil around Lake Caddo remained a dangerous enterprise with severe consequences for the natural environment. Big blasts marked the derricks catching fire, but even heavier were the explosions that were used to stop the flow of gas. One

Drilling techniques

A three cone bit for rotary drilling. Picture taken in 1977.

In our days, the word *drilling* is strongly associated with *rotary* drilling. This applies to simple tools for use at home and hobbyist appliances up to the drilling for oil and gas. The meaning of the word *drill* however is broader: 'a tool or implement with cutting edges or a pointed end, for boring holes'. The action of drilling may be either *repeated blows* or *rotating abrasion*.

Cable tool drilling

The early drilling for oil was by repeated blows. *Cable tools* repeatedly dropped or 'spudded' a drill bit attached to a drill stem - a heavy length of steel - and suspended from a wire rope, or 'cable', to make a hole. Another term for this method was *percussion drilling*. Cuttings of this process had to be removed from the hole by periodically lowering a bailer. This drilling method has been in use for many centuries, mostly to drill for water.

A rocking or 'walking' beam was used to impart the up and down motion to the suspended bit. A wooden mast or derrick supporting a crown block was built over the drilling site and served for vertical handling of all tools. Around 1900, steel derricks started to appear.

A variation to the cable tool was first used in Galicia (Poland). Instead of a cable, a string of rods was used to move the bit up and then let it fall. In either case, heavy pieces of pipe were added just above the drillbit to create sufficient weight to pound through rock formations.

Rotary drilling

Rotary drilling was introduced in the oilfields early in the twentieth century and has nearly completely replaced the use of cable tools for its higher speed and efficiency, and its far deeper reach. In rotary drilling, the drill bit is continuously rotated by means of a pipestring between the bit and a rotary table at the surface. The string is assembled by joining 30 feet long pipe sections or joints with threaded ends. The torque needed to rotate the bit is exerted by the rotary table in combination with a hexagonal rod, the so-called kelly. A fairly recent development is to drill with a top drive, in which case the kelly and the rotary table are not used. Early bits for rotary drilling looked like fishtails. They would quickly get dull and a drilling operation needed a standby blacksmith for dressing the bits. An enormous boost to the application of rotary drilling was given by the invention of the cone bit in 1909 by Howard R. Hughes Sr. Further improvements, such as the introduction of the tungsten carbide bit in 1952, were all based on Hughes' concept.

Drilling in hard materials requires cooling to achieve a reasonable lifetime of the bits. In oilwell drilling, a fluid called mud is pumped down through the drillstring and returns to the surface through the hole. It cools the bit, provides lubrication and takes cuttings with it up to the surface. It can carry chemical additives, but most importantly it provides a hydrostatic balance with the water-, gas- or oil pressures in deep layers. This prevents a blow-out of the well which was unavoidable and therefore taken for granted in the days of the cable tools. Also, it prevents the wall of the hole from caving in. It requires that the mud is heavier than water, which is achieved by adding heavy clays, in particular baryte and bentonite.

Horizontal drilling

Originally, holes happened to be drilled vertically, or, in other words, non vertical drilling was not intentional. At a later stage it was even forbidden in some places to drill under a neighbour's terrain. For offshore drilling, the ability of men and equipment to drill slanted or deviated holes has become essential to penetrate a reservoir at different, horizontally spaced locations from a single platform, since platforms are expensive. From large angle deviations to horizontal drilling seems to be no more than a gradual step, although the technology is far more demanding and expensive. An important condition is knowing where the drill bit is, which has been made practical by the introduction of 'measurement while drilling'.

Since the late 1980s, horizontal wells make exploitation of thin layers economically viable. In some cases, highly deviated and horizontal wells have been made to substitute step out wells at considerable distances. In others, like at Wytch Farm in the UK, they serve to produce an under-sea formation from land. In the Wytch Farm case, a record horizontal distance of 8 km has been reached by BP in 1996.

even tried to bomb a well, but without success.[29]
The situation around Lake Caddo did not go unnoticed
by the American federal officials, who became concerned about the waste in general and the effect on oil
and gas which might be beneath the adjacent federal
lands.[30] Testifying for a federal inquiry in 1908, D.T. Day,
a known US Geological Survey geologist, called it
*'the most flagrant abuse of natural wealth yet recorded
in this industry'.*[31] During the two preceding years the
State of Louisiana had tried to secure conservation of
gas by means of legislation, but without success. The
federal inquiry led to immediate action by the federal
Department of Interior, resulting in a first conservation
law which, among other things, stated that wells must
be capped, and a cement plug must be set before
abandonment.[32]

This did not frustrate the search for oil in the Lake
Caddo district, which attracted the attention of a
growing number of companies. In 1908 the district's
Board of Commissioners was charged with the
granting of land for exploration and production, and
two years later this Board invited companies to bid for
the lake itself. The Gulf Oil Corporation obtained the
exploration rights. Gulf's interest dated from 1907,
when J.B. McCann, a Gulf staff member, made a boat
trip on the lake. By setting fire to the gas bubbling up
from the water McCann tried to locate the field and
the place where it crossed the shore.[33]

Gulf's drilling superintendent, H.A. Melat, worked out a
plan for drilling on water. Shortly after the exploration
rights were granted, the plan was carried out. Drilling
equipment was brought in by barge along the
Mississippi and Red Rivers. Cypress trees growing on
the shore were used as piles for a platform and a pipe
rack. On the platform a derrick was built, similar to the
ones used for on land drilling. A wooden tank acted as
a slush pit. In the spring of 1911 drilling could start and
in May Melat struck oil. The first producing well on
Lake Caddo was a fact. Before the end of the year Gulf
had eight wells in production.[34]

Exploration and production on Lake Caddo would
expand enormously. The activities developed into a
real industry. Gulf operated a special fleet for construction work. The experience of the first years led to
certain fixed habits in building platforms and their

equipment. A platform consisted of 140 wooden piles
with diagonal beams on top. A 10 inch pipe with a
length of 180 ft was used as a conductor. Production
platforms were equipped with their own pumps, gas
engines and flow tanks. The oil was brought to four
collecting stations through 3 inch pipes.[35]

On Lake Caddo, Gulf developed a method of working
on water that would become a tradition. Platforms
built on more than one hundred piles, containing all
equipment and wooden derricks like the ones used on
land, were to be used in later years on many other
locations. These structures were generally considered
adequate and they contributed to a general routine
in drilling on water. In those days wood could be used
without restrictions, since it was available in abundant
quantities, it was strong enough and it could be
handled easily. However, structures of piles, driven in
the Lake bottom, creating a solid and dry working area
for drillers, were not new at all. On land, operators
used pile foundations for the same reason, since the

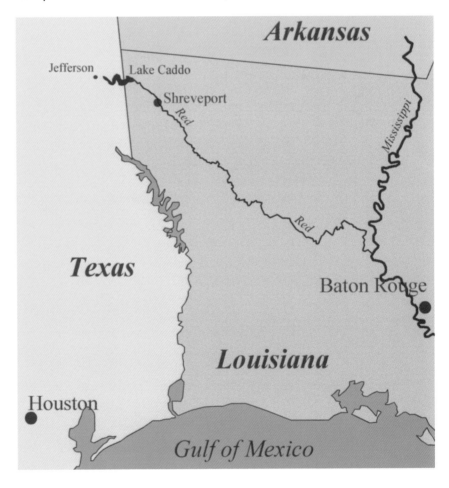

Louisiana State Library

By 1919 Lake Caddo was thickly covered with wells.

Caddo district was swampy.[36] This swampiness, which may have caused most of the problems in initial drilling activities, forced operators towards piling. Platforms built on piles in Lake Caddo thus became a logical step as a permutation of a concept proved 'on land'.

Still, Lake Caddo was a first basis for the development of an appropriate technology for offshore drilling and led to experience with working on water.

Oil drilling on water spread out to other areas in the 1920s. For the history of offshore technology, Lake Maracaibo in Venezuela is of major importance. There, the oil industry was confronted for the first time with the constraints of wood in the construction of platforms. Lake Maracaibo is subject of section 2. First we will give an account of remarkable and therefore noteworthy developments in the Caspian Sea.

Caspian Sea

The area near Baku, on the west coast of the Caspian Sea, had been a prolific oil producing province since 1877, providing over half of the world petroleum production in 1901.[37] Like in California, oil men ultimately formulated ideas to explore offshore. Near Baku, in the bay of Bibi-Eibat, these ideas however differed drastically from the early methods in the Americas. In 1900, a mining engineer, Sglenitzky, proposed to start drilling the Bibi-Eibat formation in the bay. His plans were only approved after it had been decided that for this purpose the bay would be filled

in. The commercial interest for the plan was low, and it took until 1911 before dumping of stone for the purpose started. In 1916 the work halted altogether, because all ships were requisitioned by the military. The Russian revolutions and the following civil war caused this standstill to continue. In 1920 Baku fell in the hands of the Bolsheviks. On the land so far filled in, drilling started early 1923. A racy detail was the name of the filled-in bay: Vassily Iliytch Oulianoff, the real name of Lenin.[38]

When the attention moved to the more open water in the 1930s, other concepts were needed. The economic order in the new Soviet Union was not like the American or Western European, and this may have contributed to the choice of technology. The October Revolution had isolated the Soviets from the technical developments elsewhere, and moreover, the contemporary development of offshore technology in the United States did take place in waters which were much more quiet than the wind-swept Caspian.[39] In his book Soviet Oil, Lewarne makes a very illustrating comment when he describes the first steel platforms in the waters north of the Arthem Islands: *'The early platforms were no more than large metal trestles, crudely constructed onshore, then dropped offshore in a hit-and-miss fashion.'*[40]

Only after World War II, offshore operations grew towards substantial scale. In 1949, the Neftianye Kamni field was discovered, 100 km offshore. For exploitation of this field, the usual production platforms were built, plus an infrastructure of piers. These piers were built onshore in sections and assembled at sea, and contained walkways, vehicle roads, train tracks, pipelines for water supply and crude transport, electricity and telephone lines. By 1960 the field was surrounded by a complex of some 40 square kilometre platform decks and 240 km piers, on which 5000 people were working.[41]

The Caspian Sea is one of the oldest oil producing areas of the world, and is still in full swing. Its influence on offshore technology, however, has been very small and its particular methods have not been copied in other continents.

In the Neftianye Kamni field, 100 km offshore in the Caspian Sea, an infra-structure of platforms and 240 km of piers were built. The photo was probably taken in the 1960's.

Pont Royal

2. Lake Maracaibo

Around Lake Maracaibo it was Shell that struck oil first in 1917 and subsequently managed to get hold of the entire east shore of the lake. In 1922 a large oilfield was discovered near the shore. This caused other oil companies in the area to direct their attention to the Lake itself, which with its shallow depth and the knowledge and experience obtained at Lake Caddo, appeared to offer enough opportunities.

In 1923 Lago Petroleum Corporation obtained concessions on a large part of the lake. The next year a first experimental drilling attempt was made just two metres off the shore. Further attempts followed shortly afterwards and at a greater distance from the shore. The technology used was similar to that of Lake Caddo: the platforms stood on wooden piles and carried all necessary equipment. The shallow water was tideless, and the platforms were not damaged by the tropical storms which occurred during the wet season. However, there was one factor in the environment that

in one blow rendered useless any wooden structure: the Teredo. This shipworm works its way into wooden piles and starts to eat them from within. Entire colonies of Teredos can do their work unnoticed, until the final moment when a wooden structure collapses. Once an oil platform was found by Teredos, it would survive for six to eight months at most, which perhaps was long enough for drilling but definitely too short for production.

This experience was gained quickly after the first explorations on Lake Maracaibo. Harder types of wood were tried, and in the end a type of wood was found that could withstand the worm. However, the natural length and diameter of this wood were insufficient for platform construction. A temporary solution was found in imported pinewood from the United States. When tarred, it could resist the Teredo fairly well. However, the cost of imported wood and the tarring pushed up the price of platforms, so the oil companies were stimulated to look for new construction materials.[42]

For drilling in Lake Maracaibo, platform-tender combinations were used. The tender was carrying most of the drilling equipment and could be reused at other locations. The platform was kept small and its foundation served as a base for production equipment after completion of a well.

Shell International - Photographic Services London

A more permanent solution to the platform construction problem was found in the use of concrete. The idea was to build platforms on a concrete foundation, consisting of piles supporting a concrete table a few metres above the water. The piles were made on land, all of the same diameter. They were driven into the ground in groups of three, four groups making a square. In the centre of this square, four other piles made up the foundation of the drilling table, whereas on one side of the square one pile was to support the drawworks. On this configuration of piles the formwork for a reinforced concrete table was made. After a thirty days' drying period, the building of a conventional wooden derrick started.[43]
After a well was sunk the derrick usually was removed and the concrete structure served as a platform for production. *'Once the well is taken in production, the foundation keeps its value for all operations that turn out to be necessary; in case the well would not produce oil, it is important that the initial, but unproductive costs of foundation have been as low as possible.'*[44]
The first concrete based platforms appeared in 1927 on

Lake Maracaibo. In the following two years another 160 were built. Concrete turned out to be a successful replacement of wood.
The concrete piles were produced by the Raymond Concrete Pile Co. of New York, who had started to build a concrete wall for the Venezuelan government in 1926. The application of concrete piles for offshore structures therefore lay at hand, because the material was locally available, albeit for a different purpose. In those years, Raymond set up a factory on Toas Island, 40 km from Maracaibo town, to produce the concrete it needed.[45]

In 1934, for the first time steel was used in structures on Lake Maracaibo. Instead of a concrete table made on the spot, the piles came to support a steel framework. In this way the pouring of concrete out on the lake was avoided, and the piles to support the rotary and drawworks became unnecessary. In all, it meant a considerable reduction of foundation costs.[46]
Another cost reduction was found in the use of drilling tenders, vessels that were moored head-on to the

A platform and drilling tender in Lake Maracaibo in the 1950s.

Shell International - Photographic Services London

*A Maracaibo platform after
well completion. In the centre
of the foundation, a
Christmas tree can be seen.
The ramp to the right is the
so-called widow maker,
which served for access from
the tender to the platform.*

platform and carried a major part of the drilling equipment. This led to an important simplification of platforms and foundations, and the fact that the equipment on these barges could be used at other locations immediately after sinking a well, added to the efficiency of operations.[47] Moreover, in case of a sudden heavy storm, Shell wrote in *De Ingenieur* in 1946, *'a barge could rapidly be pulled back by its anchor winches.'*[48]

Lake Maracaibo was rich in oil. Exploration and production activities grew immensely. The start was made by the Lago Petroleum Company (later taken over by the Creole Oil Company), which in 1923 obtained a concession more or less along the shore of the lake. Mene Grande Company was also working along the shore, whereas Shell, already active on land east of the lake, managed to obtain large concessions on areas farther off the coast, west and southwest of the fields first explored by Creole. Gradually, companies were facing the unavoidable challenge of drilling in deeper water.[49]

By the end of the 1930s the constraints of concrete pile production were felt: the maximum available length was insufficient for the requirements of the oil companies. Creole worked in 20 metres of water. Any greater depth would preclude the applicability of concrete piles. This fact led the company to use concrete caissons. In 1946 Shell wrote:

'For some ten years, this company uses its 'caisson' foundation, which in our terms is not a caisson foundation but a foundation of hollow concrete piles. Four of these piles, with a normal length of some 42 metres and a diameter at the top of 1.23 metre, slightly increasing towards the bottom, are placed in a 7.30 metre square and linked with steel girders, thus making the table on which the drilling floor with the derrick is placed.'[50]

Shell had an even greater challenge to meet, as its concessions covered areas with 30 metres deep water. Although concrete foundations were considered, Shell decided for a steel foundation in 1946. Steel was not unknown as a construction material, but, especially in

Lake Maracaibo, it was not favoured because of its sensitivity to corrosion. Shell's decision must *'in this case be attributed to the financial and economic advantages of steel over concrete'.*[51] *'We did not desire to follow this system* [of concrete piles or caissons] *which required a great capital outlay for a concrete yard and in our view it was not suitable for the greater depths of water',* remembers A. Kranendonk.[52]

In 1957, J. Ray McDermott installed four aluminum jackets, hoping for a lifetime of 72 years as compared to four years for steel.[53]

Nevertheless concrete remained most used in Lake Maracaibo. In the 1950s prestressed concrete piles were developed, that made it possible to build larger structures for deeper water. Both Raymond and

Heerema set up highly efficient processes to fabricate such piles.

The developments on Lake Maracaibo before World War II led to a number of characteristic trends in offshore technology. The use of other materials than wood and the development of tender-platform combinations are the most evident. More interesting, however, is the way in which technologies were applied. Here we find parallels with California and Lake Caddo. In all three areas the experience to build on was very limited at the start and almost solely encompassed the technology of on land drilling. Everywhere we see an almost immediate tradition to build a platform for every well to be drilled, and very little inclination

Hundreds of platforms were lined up in the Gulf of Maracaibo.

among the operators to change a proven concept. In California the use of piers remained common, even when there was in fact no real connection with the shore. On Lake Caddo there was a concept developed at the first attempt which was being copied many times in the following years. The concrete piles that were available at Lake Maracaibo presented a good alternative for the perishing wooden structures of Lake Caddo. Operators looked for ways to reduce technical risks and tried to use both technologies and materials that were already available on the spot. An equally important argument was found in costs: *'In the first place one had to take into account the explorative nature of these wells being drilled, viz., investments had to be minimal, as long as it was not clear that the concession was commercial indeed; and even after that, when it was decided that a mass production of the type chosen should take place, the cost per foundation were to remain as low as possible.'*[54]

Designing a structure in those years was a bit of a gamble, and once a concession had shown its value, the technology used at the first well was mostly adhered to.

3. The Gulf of Mexico coast

In the 1920s geophysical surveying made the attention of oil searching America focus on the southern part of Louisiana, where the land gradually becomes the Gulf of Mexico. It was an impassable and uninhabited area. Rivers and lakes were surrounded by swamps, where land was water and water was land. Since nobody had any reason to cultivate it, the region could not ordinarily be reached by land, neither by sea. But the surveys indicated the presence of salt domes, and it was known from experience that underneath these domes the presence of oil was very likely.[55]

'In the 1920s the task in south Louisiana was immense. Several oil companies were convinced that major discoveries awaited those who could get over the oil with a rig and get into it with a drill', R.L. Lankford writes in his much cited chapter on Offshore in J.E. Brantly's *History of Oil Well Drilling*.[56] He considered the bringing on location of equipment to be the greatest problem. His perception of a *'task'* suggests that there was a great need for oil, which seems to be in contradiction with the growing oilglut. Although it

Oil derricks built on cement piers in a Southern Louisiana bayou.

was a seemingly impossible task, the area was successfully explored on a large scale during the decades after 1920. But the challenge was not for everyone.[57]

'Activity in 1946 continued to show that South Louisiana is a territory for major companies with great financial backing', the *Bulletin of the American Association of Petroleum Geologists* reports in its 1947 annual review of developments in the area.[58] No less than 83% of the wells had been sunk by the major companies, and many of the activities of the smaller ones were supported by them. Apart from costs of working in this natural environment, an important reason for the dominance of the bigger companies was the higher risk of dry holes. This was caused by the fact that oil in South Louisiana was to be found at greater depth than normal, and that salt dome structures at such depth usually are more complex. *'In many fields of this type each well can be justly considered a wildcat, as production trends can not be mapped with enough assurance to permit normal development drilling.'*[59] Although wildcat drilling was a fairly normal phenomenon during the 1920s[60], investments in this area were too high to allow for lighthearted gambling.

In South Louisiana three techniques were used for drilling during the 1920s and 1930s.

When the swamp was more like land, derricks were built on wooden mattings, and the work much resembled common on land drilling. When the swamp was more like water, derricks stood on a foundation of wooden piles, comparable to the ones in the Caddo area, but the number of supporting piles was much larger. In both cases, the major problem was to get the equipment on location. Operators faced high costs for building passable roads or digging canals. Both wheel and barge transport were used, and each demanded equally high investments.[61]

A third technology resulted from a different approach to the problem. By 1930 a number of oil companies, when drilling in shallow water, used floating vessels containing all equipment.[62] This method is of limited importance to offshore technology as it could only be used in shallow water without current, waves, tides and wind. However, for this chapter the vessels are important. They introduce us to one of the most important developments in offshore drilling: the mobile drilling rig.

This site in Nigeria in 1963 is representative of drilling in swamps, as started in Louisiana in the 1930s.

The Submersible

One of the firms with a major interest in South Louisiana was the Texas Company (or Texaco, as it is called today). This major company had obtained concessions for a considerable area of swamps, lakes, bays and a part of the Gulf of Mexico. To carry out its explorations, the Texas Company was looking for solutions that would make matting or piles redundant. The reason for this was obvious. Matting and pile structures were expensive due to their high costs of transportation and installation. The area held the serious risk of unsuccessful attempts and loss of investments occurred more frequently than else-where.[63]

G.E. McBride, a Texas Company employee, came up with a solution that was based on the use of barges which were being used in the field. His concept consisted of a floating vessel carrying a platform for a derrick and equipment. The vessel was to be towed to the location and sunk on the spot, thus acting as a fixed foundation for the platform, which remained above the water.

Fearing infringing of patent rights of others, the Texas Company started to search for patent literature. And indeed, in the end a patent was found, granted to Louis Giliasso in 1928, which covered the concept of McBride.[64] The Texas Company decided to turn to Giliasso, but he could not be found. In order to carry out the idea rapidly, the Texas Company contacted Giliasso's lawyer Phillip McLean. McLean agreed to the building of a vessel based on Giliasso's patent, on the condition that the Texas Company would submit the detailed plans. At last, the firm could start developing its concept and build its first submersible vessel. In the autumn of 1932 an order was placed with the McClintic-Marshall Engineering Corporation. In the meantime, the Texas Company continued its search for Giliasso in order to settle the matter.[65]

Louis Giliasso, an American Italian, served in the US Navy during World War I and then became captain in the merchant marine. After 1920, acting as a marine superintendent for the Mexican Seaboard Company, he came to know the oil world. His presence in Venezuela in 1927 may have contributed to his invention. He applied for a patent in the United States and in Venezuela in 1928, and he tried to raise interest for his concept among oil companies. However, all potential customers rejected the idea as impracticable. It was thought that, once it had been sunk, the vessel would remain stuck in the mud and be lost forever. Giliasso failed to make money with his patent, and moved to Panama where he started a saloon. There the Texas Company found him in January 1933. After his return to the States in July of that year Giliasso reached an agreement with the company, in which the latter obtained the exclusive right to use the idea and to grant licences to third parties. In honour of the inventor the Texas Company named its first sub-mersible 'Giliasso'.[66]

The Giliasso was first used on Lake Pelto in November 1933. In its final shape, the design showed careful foresight. Instead of a specially shaped submersible vessel, two standard barges were used that could be re-used for other purposes in case the experiment failed. These vessels were linked, but a certain distance between them was kept free to allow manoeuvring the assembly around the drilling spot and safely abandoning the well. On the vessels a superstructure was welded which was to support the derrick, drilling machinery and pipe racks. Mud tanks and pumps were placed on the barges. A second submersible was used to carry a steam boiler, which would provide power to the entire installation. Two rows of piles were driven into the ground to fix the Giliasso and protect the blow-out preventers and the well conductor during drilling. Once positioned, the entire structure was anchored with spuds. The vessels were subdivided into closed compartments, which were filled through valves in order to sink the unit in a controlled way.

The idea of a submersible was that it would leave the location after the well was drilled. In Giliasso's concept, emptying the compartments would be sufficient to refloat the barges. However, the Texas Company had added jets to the structure which were to be used in case the vessels would stick to the bottom. They have never been used.

Already at the first attempt Giliasso turned out to be a success. The average time needed to build and dismantle a drilling rig in the water locations of Louisiana was 17 days, but Giliasso needed only two. Besides, much more equipment remained fit for further employment when the submersible was used.[67]

With the use of a new concept, the Texas Company developed a number of new ideas on oil exploration and production on water. We have seen how on Lake Caddo and on Lake Maracaibo structures were built and installed in series. The Texas Company built one structure that would drill a series of wells. Whereas on other locations a once installed drilling platform also served as a foundation for production, Giliasso was merely drilling equipment. During drilling, it was a fixed platform, but it could be remobilised without much effort and its value was not diminished after the operation. The well drilled by this mobile platform became the location for permanent production equipment. There was just one restriction to its use, viz., the depth of the water. The height of the super-structure carrying the derrick was limited by stability considerations. This meant that the submersible could only be employed in relatively shallow waters. In deeper water a fixed platform remained the solution.

4. Offshore in the Gulf of Mexico

In the early 1920s the United States managed to overcome an oil shortage which until then had been seemingly chronical. In a few years, this shortage even changed into a surplus, a situation that was not to change until World War II. This was an entirely new experience for the oil industry. Never before had the industry been confronted by a selling problem - its focus had always been on the supply side. Even when the main consumers, oil lamps, had been replaced by electric lamps, no fall in demand was felt, because of the simultaneous rise of internal combustion engines and the coming of the motor car as a mass product. In fact, demand had only risen since. The existence of an oil surplus in the 1920s was caused by a slower increase in demand as well as technological and organisational developments within the oil industry itself.[68]

Texaco

A better understanding of potential locations for oilfields and an increasingly strong position of geologists within the major companies led, over the years, to a more planned approach. Wildcatting became less common as a method to locate oil, although the selection of promising fields remained a matter of experience rather than of technology - but the experience grew richer and richer.[69] A second development can be found in the actual drilling. One of the most important contributions to drilling technique was called rotary drilling, which dated from the turn of the century but became much used during the 1920s. Rotary drilling allowed for faster and deeper drilling at lower costs than the use of cable tools.[70]

The Giliasso was the first mobile drilling rig, a submersible. It was built by the Texas Company, later Texaco, and was named after the inventor Louis Giliasso.

The industry as a whole evolved into a larger and more professional sector. The growth is shown by the increasing number of small companies on the one hand, and the development of a number of large oil companies into giant integrated corporations on the other hand. In due course, the smaller companies, also known as the independents, concentrated on new areas and on existing fields that were not considered worthwhile by the majors. To stay in business they remained active in less promising areas, but in this way they did contribute to extensive exploration. The majors were able to obtain large concessions and to explore on a massive scale. The more they expanded, the greater the risks these companies dared to take. They ventured into areas where great opportunities were linked to high investments.[71]

In spite of the oil surplus exploration and production in the coastal Gulf of Mexico went on.[72] The swamps, bays and lakes of Louisiana even experienced their major development in the 1920s. This may seem strange, since oil winning in this area was both expensive and uncertain. The explanation for the increasing activities in the Gulf can be found in the fact that the most promising concessions on land had been granted at an earlier stage, which made the majors go out on the water in their continuous attempt to reinforce their position. The geologists greatly added to the already existing belief that the area contained more than enough for everyone, thereby raising hopes among the independents to strike rich wells and obtain a higher ranking within the industry as a whole. It was a *'fight for new production'* as Shell put it succinctly in its 1920 annual report: *'we must not be outstripped in this struggle to obtain new territory [ ] our geologists are everywhere where any chance of success exists.'*[73] The great expectations and the enthusiasm with which specially the majors continued their activities, inspired governments in Texas and Louisiana to grant large concessions. This was mostly stimulated by the results of geophysical surveys made by, or for, the big oil companies.

In 1936 the State of Louisiana for the first time granted concessions for areas in the Gulf of Mexico. These

offshore concessions amounted to 121,000 acres and covered an area where, four years earlier, unsuccessful wells were drilled from a platform, standing in 4 m water, 100 m offshore. In 1934 the Pure Oil Company had carried out seismographic research in that same area.[74]

Pure Oil was, not surprisingly, one of the concessionaries who together with Superior Oil Company obtained an area of 33,000 acres offshore.[75]

These two companies planned a first test well in 1937, just one mile off the Cameron Parish coastline in 4 m water. Unlike other oil and drilling companies before them who planned to drill in water, not only the construction but also the design of the platform was left to a contracting engineering firm for which they chose Brown & Root, Inc.

Brown & Root came up with a platform on wooden piles that could resist waves, tides and any occurring hurricane. It could be fitted with all necessary equipment. The platform measured 100 x 300 ft, standing 13 ft above the average water level. Compared to the Lake Caddo and Maracaibo platforms this was a very large one.

On 6 October 1937 Pure and Superior began sinking their first well, and drilling lasted until March 1938. Drilling at sea went with some problems. Although the shore was but one mile away, supply vessels had to cover 13 miles to reach the platform. Personnel working on the platform rested in Cameron. New equipment and supplies were towed from Cameron on barges. For the transportation of personnel and supplies, an appeal was made to shrimpers. The platform had no radio, so the arrival of a new boat had to be awaited before spares and new tools could be ordered - and their delivery would be by the next boat at the earliest.[76]

In March 1938 oil was found in what was named the Creole field. After extending the platform, Pure and Superior drilled ten more wells directionally. However, the platform did not produce much. In 1954 the entire production totalled less than 4 million barrels.[77]

In April 1938 Humble Oil and Refining Company drilled one mile off McFaddin Beach, Texas. It was not a commercially successful attempt, nor were two subsequent ones.[78] In the same year, Standard Oil of

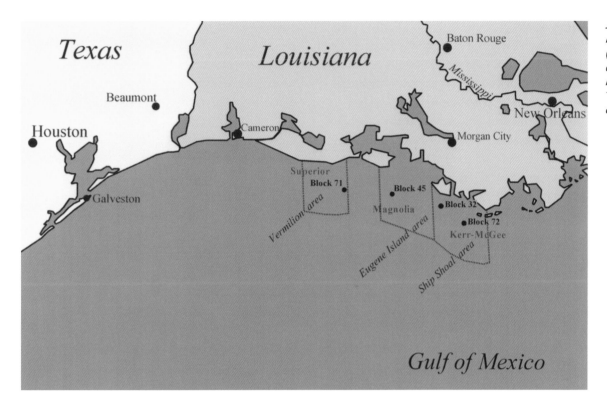

Texas · Louisiana · Baton Rouge · Beaumont · Cameron · New Orleans · Houston · Morgan City · Superior Block 71 · Block 45 · Galveston · Magnolia · Block 32 · Block 72 · Vermilion area · Eugene Island area · Kerr-McGee · Ship Shoal area · Gulf of Mexico

Just after World War II, Magnolia (1946), Superior (1947) and Kerr-McGee (1947) drilled wells in the Gulf of Mexico, offshore Louisiana. The map shows the location of their Blocks.

Texas had better results in Galveston Bay, also one mile offshore.[79]

From 1937 until the end of World War II some 25 wells were drilled.[80] Each drilling platform stood on wooden piles, and in that sense technology might be called conventional. The difference with previous attempts, elsewhere, was the larger size of the platforms and the occasional use of separate platforms for storage of equipment.[81]

However, during this period the Gulf area was discovered as potentially rewarding. Numerous small finds seemed to confirm the correctness of the geologists' expectations. The number of big finds on land was decreasing. Although operating in the Gulf of Mexico was expensive, the investments were not dramatically different from those for on land drilling in South Louisiana:[82]

'Drilling costs onshore were mounting; 36.5 percent of the wells drilled in 1946 were really in water locations and required such expensive measures as putting down matting and corduroy roads, driving piling or building artificial islands, digging canals and using drilling barges. Some of the existing fields were in open bays

and were 'onshore' only by courtesy of drawing a line connecting the nearest islands.'[83]

If one analyses the development of offshore technology, the move towards offshore operations in the Gulf of Mexico cannot be seen as a revolutionary step. On land drilling near Lake Caddo needed pile foundations, which led to pile supported platforms on the lake. This concept succeeded in the Louisiana swamps on a bigger scale, even while facing more difficulties. Pile and mat structures were merely preparations for the application of on land drilling practise. Near coast Gulf of Mexico drilling during the 1930s followed the same principle, however tides and depth forced towards more attention to pile driving and platform building. Technology developed within a pattern and adapted gradually to ever bigger tasks. In a way on land drilling transitioned into offshore drilling. But when oil companies planned to move their activities out of sight of land, things became different psychologically and environmentally.

Magnolia

In 1944 Magnolia Petroleum Company got permission from the State of Louisiana to carry out a geophysical survey in the Gulf, this time at a much larger distance from the shore than had been done so far. Other companies followed soon, leading to a survey peak in 1947, when no less than 37 parties were active there. Refraction seismic and gravity measurements led to the discovery of salt domes under the sea bed, an indication of oil fields under the Gulf.[84]

From 1945 to 1948 concessions were given, to a total of 3,164,000 acres, for the major part being situated off the coast.[85]

Magnolia was the first to venture into this really *offshore* area. In 1945 it was the only bidder on a lease sale by the State of Louisiana, and it acquired 149,000 acres offshore Point Au Fer. In 1946 the company built a platform 8 km off the coast at Morgan City in 5 m deep water. The superstructure was constructed in a way which was new to the Gulf of Mexico. It measured 160 x 70 ft and it was built in parts on land, in the relatively short time of 60 days. This superstructure stood on 338 wooden piles, but the derrick was supported by 52 steel piles. The derrick could be moved horizontally, which made it possible to drill three wells. Apart from the derrick, the platform had room for diesel engines, mudpumps, a mudpit, a freshwater tank, a mud mixing installation, a cementing pump, fuel tanks, a tool shed, a drilling shed, a radio and an office. A high deck at the drilling floor level had room for pipe racks and equipment for well logging. A 25 man crew either worked on the platform or rested on a ship nicknamed Magnolia Inn, moored by the coast. Two shrimpers ferried continuously between this houseboat and the platform.[86]

Magnolia had great plans. By the time the first well was sunk, preparations were under way for a similar platform that was to stand in deeper water, almost 40 km offshore.[87]

Although Magnolia made a big step both techno-logically and in conceptions, it was not rewarded by economic success: *'the Magnolia well proved to be a dry hole, it nevertheless represented the first major effort to drill in waters far from the shore in the Gulf of Mexico.'*[88]

Superior

A second attempt to find oil far off the coast in the Gulf of Mexico was made by the Superior Oil Company in 1947. This company was familiar with Gulf operations, since in 1937 it had drilled one of the first wells near the shore, in cooperation with Pure Oil.[89] Superior's new activities took place in recently obtained concessions in the Vermilion area. It was planned to drill at a location indicated as Block 71, almost 30 km off the coast, in 6 m water. This time design and construction of the platform was left to the engineering contractor J. Ray McDermott & Co., of Harvey, La. Their chief engineer M.B. Willey was charged with designing the structure, in which he was assisted by R. Wilson of Superior.

Willey had to develop a platform capable of working far off the coast in a region that was harassed frequently by hurricanes. Consequently the platform had to be strong and large, it should resist wind and waves and provide room to all sorts of equipment, stores and installations. And apart from all that, building the entire structure had to remain within reasonable limits of time and costs.

Willey's solution might be called revolutionary and beautiful in its simplicity. It was to become the standard method for the building of fixed offshore platforms in the years to come. He proposed to build steel structures on land, consisting of vertical tubulars linked by horizontal and diagonal members all along their length. These structures would be strong enough by themselves to be shipped as a whole to the drilling location. There they were to be lifted and placed on the bottom, where piles would be driven through the verticals and act as anchoring.

This concept had many advantages. The structures, called templates or jackets, could be built on land, under controllable circumstances. They made up a complete platform foundation. Earlier examples had already shown the advantage of prefabrication of steel parts on land, but in those cases the work had been limited to the platform's superstructure which later on had to be positioned on a configuration of wooden piles that had been driven into the bottom at the location.[90]

Building a complete foundation on land also allowed

for a stronger structure to be made. '*The old type platforms were braced above the water and proved substantial enough only because of the relative short distance between the above-water bracing to the water bottoms of the shallow areas. However, the lateral stability of a platform decreases as the distance from the bracing to the water bottom increases. Therefore, the prefabricated templates, crossbraced from top to bottom as used by Superior, offer a platform of much greater rigidity than could be obtained under the old method [ ].*'[91]

Perhaps the most striking advantage of Willey's concept was the short period at sea needed to install a platform. '*Whereas other offshore drilling platforms of the conventional type have required months for completion, the Superior platform was in place, with piling all driven, in a period of only 9 working days*', said E.H. Short in The Oil and Gas Journal of 1947.[92] And if it had not stormed, he added, it might have succeeded within a week.

Here he indicated one of the most time consuming aspects of platform construction offshore: the frequent occurrence of gales. Building offshore was expensive, dangerous and could lead to much damage and loss of time. Constructing on land and rapid installation on location led to major reductions in time and risk, which immediately influenced the cost of offshore platforms.

In 1947 Superior was one of the first to sink a well far out in the Gulf of Mexico. Because it took them some time to actually find oil, another oil company became the first to make a discovery. Superiors platform and drilling activities were quickly forgotten. Still its platform, designed by J. Ray McDermott, was the first template structure used, and therefore one of the most important innovations in offshore history.

J. Ray McDermott

J. Ray McDermott

Driving piles through the guides of a template structure in 1949. In this same way, Superior's templates were installed in 1947.

This picture, taken in 1957, gives an idea of early jacket transportation. As jackets became larger, it became common to transport them in horizontal position. The picture, however shows the traditional method, with four big, aluminium structures on a barge.

Superior's offshore platform was made of six jackets and fitted with 268 piles. It provided room for all equipment, stores and accommodations. Close to this platform Superior had a second platform built. Linked by a footbridge to the main platform, it acted as a hotel for personnel. It was installed in June 1947 and later that year drilling started.[93] But the exploration was not successful at the beginning. The well was abandoned before the end of 1947. After a new start, the discovery of a new field could be reported in June 1948.[94] However, by that time the prize for the first one to strike oil really offshore in the Gulf of Mexico had already been given to a small oil company, using a different approach.

Kerr-McGee

The Kerr-McGee oil company was a small but integrated company, smaller than most independents and much smaller than the majors. It started shortly before 1930 as Anderson & Kerr Drilling Company, just one of many small firms working in the oil industry. Not long after, the owners set up a production company of their own, A&K Petroleum Company. J.L. Anderson left both firms in 1936, and R.S. Kerr engaged two geologists, R.H. Lynn and D.A. McGee, who had both been working for Phillips Petroleum Company. The company names Anderson & Kerr and A&K were changed into Kerr-Lynn and Kerlyn, and in 1946 both firms merged into a new company, Kerr-McGee Oil Industries. In the early years Anderson had been responsible for the know-how in the starting company. Kerr, and later his successor Lynn, made the firm expand, and led by McGee the firm would develop into a large, integrated independent. Kerr-McGee was not unknown in the United States. This was probably due to Kerr's career as a Democratic Governor and Senator.[95]

Like many other smaller companies, Kerr-McGee had the explicit aim to grow within the American oil sector. Interesting opportunities for expansion were offered several times through contracts with Phillips, for whom Kerr was an important driller. In spite of the continuing growth, there were frequent worries about the firm's oil reserves and financial situation. Basically, these were the motives behind Kerr-McGee's attempt to find oil in the Gulf of Mexico, at a time when hardly any concessions had been given and chances of economic success were by no means obvious.
D.A. McGee had a simple explanation for his ambition: *'We decided to explore the areas where the really potential prolific production might be - salt domes - the good ones on land were gone, but we could move out in the shallow water and, in effect, get into a virgin area where we could find the real class-one type salt dome prospect.'*[96]

Like many others Kerr-McGee started in 1946 by doing a seismographic survey in the Gulf. It also tried to find out what the cost of operating offshore would be.
In the end, it was decided that Kerr-McGee was unable

to finance an offshore project properly on its own. To overcome this problem, McGee presented its plans to Phillips, with whom it had concluded a drilling contract in 1943 that allowed Phillips to participate in any of Kerr-McGee's oil operations. After some hesitation Phillips agreed to take part, as did Stanolind Oil and Gas Company. On 8 March 1947 the contracts were signed, in which Phillips and Stanolind declared to take part in the project for 50% and 37,5% respectively. Kerr-McGee acted as driller and operator, with a modest 12,5% participation.

In May 1947 Kerr-McGee got concessions in three blocks in the Ship Shoal Area. It was agreed that drilling would start in blocks 28 and 32 before 12 September of the same year.[97]

Although the financial risk of this exploration project in the Gulf had been reduced to reasonable proportions due to the participation of the bigger partners, Kerr-McGee was 'chronically short of working capital' and therefore forced to keep investment costs at the lowest possible level.[98] Apart from the financial complications, there were some technical problems to be solved as well. Although it had been agreed that sinking the wells was to begin in September, hardly any thought had been spent on the actual technical side of the project. In fact, the whole project might be called rather audacious as Kerr-McGee had no experience of its own with comparable offshore activities.

These two aspects, shortage of money and time, greatly influenced the technical choices Kerr-McGee made in order to comply with their contract. Shortly before the actual concessions were obtained in May 1947, A.T.F. Seale was charged with the execution of the project. He contacted G. Brown of Brown & Root in Houston, and asked him whether Brown & Root could help with the design and carry out the construction of a platform.[99] Brown & Root was familiar with offshore operations, as they had worked for companies in the Louisiana coastal area. Together with J. Ray McDermott, Brown & Root was specialist in this field, and worked as contractor for various oil companies. In their pioneering role as service companies to the new offshore oil industry, these two engineering firms were archenemies. In 1947, J. Ray McDermott worked in the Gulf for Superior, and Brown & Root was engaged by Kerr-McGee.

Seale and Brown came to the conclusion that the smallest possible platform combined with a floating vessel would be the most appropriate solution, both for the principal and for the situation. This combination had been used on Lake Maracaibo and it could be built quite easily and fast. In all, risks involved in this approach were considered to be small. F. Hauber, a civil engineer, was charged with designing the structures.

By making the platform very small, typical open sea problems like wind and deep water, could be reduced in a simple and cheap manner. A US War Department

In 1947, the State of Louisiana offered areas offshore in the Gulf of Mexico for lease. With Permit to drill for minerals no. 18402 Louisiana authorized Kerr-McGee to drill in Ship Shoal Area block 32.

The 'Frank Phillips' moored at Kerr-McGee's drilling platform on block 32.

Kerr-McGee Corporation

Kerr-McGee's drilling spread on block 32 included a piled platform, a converted LST as the drilling tender and support vessels.

Kerr-McGee Corporation

requirement, that all fixed structures at sea must be removed to a depth of 6 ft under the sea bed after abandonment, did also contribute to the choice.

In case of an unsuccessful attempt, the cost of underwater demolition would be limited when only a small platform was used.[100] The risk of losing expensive equipment in a gale or hurricane was reduced by storing this on a floating vessel, which also could be sold again when the project would fail.

In spite of their small size of 38 x 71 ft and 46 x 80 ft respectively, the building of the two platforms for Blocks 28 and 32 took four months. Driving the 24 steel piles for each platform lasted a month, and the remaining time was spent completing the platforms. The still unknown conditions of wind and water were incorporated in the design through substantial overdimensioning, or, according to Seale, *'we made some assumptions, and by brute strength we got them built'.*[101]

To find the right type of barges and other vessels that were needed for equipment and various other purposes, R.S. Kerr toured a number of ports where war surplus ships were moored. In June 1947 he bought two Yard-Fighter barges, a Landing Ship Tank and three Air-Rescue vessels. Under supervision of G.B. Parks, a shipbuilding engineer specially engaged for this project, the YF barges were made to house equipment as well as personnel. The LST was to be used as a supply ship (but would eventually house equipment and personnel instead of one of the YF barges), and the Air-Rescue vessels would ferry personnel to and from the drilling locations.[102]

All necessary equipment for Block 28 was ready just before the crucial date of 12 September. At this location light equipment was used. This was the result of Kerr-McGee's hopes being mainly placed in Block 32, 17 km offshore, whereas Block 28 was considered more of a contractual obligation. On 9 September, the well in Block 28 was spudded, and one day later operations in Block 32 could start. After one week of drilling, heavy gales forced the crew to leave the platforms. On 19 September work could be resumed, and on 4 October Kerr-McGee struck oil in Block 32. The well was completed on 14 November.[103]

The discovery of oil in the Gulf of Mexico turned out to be the start of interesting developments. The rapidly growing American post war economy showed an enormous need for energy. The Gulf of Mexico was regarded as a promising, but yet unconfirmed area. Kerr-McGee's finding showed that expectations had been realistic, and consequently led to unprecedented interest, speculation and activity.
A great variety of developments took place. Ownership of natural resources under the sea became a point of legal conflict between the states and the federal government. During the 1950s, oil companies went out to sea for seismic surveying in the Gulf in even bigger numbers than they had done between 1944 and 1947.

Kerr-McGee Corporation

In short, Kerr-McGee had started off the exploitation of a new and special area. The fact that it was Kerr-McGee, indicates that *finding* oil is much more important than *searching* for oil. Kerr-McGee *found* oil, using relatively simple and conceptually well-proven equipment. Magnolia and especially Superior, took far greater financial and technical risks, but years later their pioneering role was almost forgotten. By itself it is logical that the first finder of oil gets all the attention, because oil is what the oil industry is all about. The focusing on finding oil led to the remarkable reaction that, just because they had helped in finding the oil, the technical means used by Kerr-McGee were suddenly considered a revolutionary innovation. The years after 1947 saw a short but massive run for war surplus ships. Oil companies bought LSTs by the dozens and refitted them for offshore purposes. Superior's jacket approach for platform construction was almost taken for granted.[104]

A.T.F. Seale (sitting left) and D.A. McGee (sitting in the middle) are answering questions to the press on the site, right after Kerr-McGee's offshore oil discovery.

What is what in offshore

When in the spring of 1995, Shell and Greenpeace clashed over the disposal of the Brent Spar, many people and some journalists indignantly reffered to this floating tank as a 'drilling platform'. Apparently, understanding the different stages of finding and producing oil and bringing it to shore, and recognising the associated equipment in each stage, does not come naturally. This block offers a brief explanation, with some account to history.

Offshore activities, from searching for hydrocarbons to producing and transporting them to shore, are part of the so called *upstream* activities. From the moment oil is brought into a refinery until the final product flows into a car, a heater, a chemical factory or whatsoever, activities are called *downstream*. The same distinction between upstream and downstream applies to gas, where downstream comprises treatment in a gas plant in preparation for injection into distribution pipelines, or conversion into liquid natural gas (LNG) for storage, or distribution by ships.
The word 'offshore' in the oil and gas industry refers to upstream activities out at sea. However in the early days, drilling in lakes and near shore from piers was sometimes also called offshore.

Upstream activities can be divided into looking for oil or gas, actually finding it, getting it to the surface and moving it to shore. These stages are comprised under the terms *seismic surveying, exploration and production drilling, production and transportation*.

In most cases, especially on water, oil and gas deposits are not visible. Not always though: in the early days of the oil industry exploration was often done in areas where oil or gas came to the surface by itself, like in Summerland and Lake Caddo.
In those days some people, famous if they were lucky enough, specialised in studying the surface and pinpointing locations were oil was likely to be found. In the 1920s they were more and more replaced by specialists of another kind: geologists, practising *seismic investigation* of the subsea soil structure. This kind of investigation, or 'looking beneath the surface' developed into a professional industry. For the purpose of offshore seismic surveys, *seismic vessels* are used, which are mostly small to medium size ships, equipped with floating cables containing *hydrophones*, a sort of aquatic

microphones. These cables are called *streamers* and the hydrophones are used to pick up the reflections or echoes which follow a strong sound pulse in the water, triggered from the vessel. Originally, explosives were used, but on modern vessels the pulse is created by an air gun. The time delay between the detonation and the arrival of its reflection on any subsea soil layer tells something about the depth of that layer, provided the travel speed of sound is known. The geologist talks about *horizons* rather than layers. If more than one streamer is used, the seismic profile can be made *3-dimensional*, which provides highly enhanced information on the structure of the sediments. With the results of these surveys geologists draw a map, from which they can read sub-surface areas where oil or gas might be trapped.

When the presence of oil or gas is thought possible on the basis of seismic investigation, drilling is needed. The most obvious reason to drill is to hit the trapped oil or gas. In the early oil industry, this was the sole reason and the result of drilling was either a dry well or a *production well*. In later years oil companies started to realize that their could be more reasons for drilling.

First of all the presence of oil, indicated as a possibility by the geologists, is never sure. Secondly, there even could be misunderstanding on how deep horizons actually are. Therefore the oil industry used drilling also to verify indications and to establish the actual depth of the horizon to provide more geological information. In the 1960s it started to do this on a large scale. During drilling, cores can be taken, which was done mostly in shallow drilling. The combined information of geology, cores and seismic provides much more insight in the probability of the presence of a prospect than seismic alone.

In the third place, and only if oil or gas was found, it became common first to test the pressure/volume/-time relation of the hydrocarbon flow, in order to determine productivity of the well and the magnitude of the reservoir.

A never ending problem is caused by the fact that only after drilling one knows reasonably well where one should have drilled. Therefore, finally, *delineation wells* are often drilled to determine the contour of a reservoir, again in order to estimate its size and to locate the best spots for production and injection wells.

Drilling requires a drilling *rig,* which in turn needs a platform carrying the rig and usually also all other equipment and stores needed for drilling. This platform is a *drilling platform*. When stores, power plant etc. are not placed on the platform but on a floating barge or ship (the tender) moored to it, we talk about a *tender assisted drilling platform* which clearly can be smaller and lighter than a fully equipped drilling platform.

As was already mentioned, one is not certain of the presence of oil or gas during exploration drilling, even if seismic results look positive. For this reason oil men where looking for concepts to save money and avoid large investments in drilling platforms. In the 1950s tender assisted drilling platforms became common, and the latter half of that decade saw the development of *mobile drilling units (MODU)* for exploration drilling. A MODU is an integrated unit, carrying a complete drilling rig with all necessary auxiliaries, stores and accommodation. As the name says, it is mobile and can be towed or sailed from one drilling site to another. Also delineation wells are normally drilled by a MODU, but for the production wells two options exist: using a MODU or first building the *production platform* and drilling from it.

MODU's have been built in many shapes. The main categories are bottom supported (*submersibles, jack-ups* and a few *arctic caissons*), and floating (*ships* and *semi-submersibles*). The oldest concept in offshore drilling with mobile units is the submersible, essentially a barge sunk to the bottom of shallow waters. The second and most popular offshore drilling rig is the jack-up platform. About 300 are in existence today, with water depth capacities ranging from very shallow to about 120 m in the severe environment of the North Sea. The water depth limitation of the jack-ups explains why floaters started to be used for drilling. Since ships are subject to substantial motions in heavy seas, a more stable floater was sought and found in the semi-submersible.

The name of the game is not exploration, but production. *Production platforms* are omnipresent offshore. The most common type is the *jacket* platform, consisting of a steel structure which is placed on and piled into the seabed and extends to above the highest wave crests, and platform decks on top of the jacket. On the decks the necessary equipment is placed: wellheads, manifolds, separators, pumps, compressors, water treatment etc. Accommodation facilities may be on the same or on a separate jacket. To simplify installation and hook-up at sea, the equipment and facilities are often packed in *modules* which may weigh from several hundreds to many thousands of tons. These modules are completely prefabricated and tested onshore, after which they are transported and lifted onto the jacket deck(s) by heavy offshore cranes. The tallest jacket ever built supports Shell's Bullwinkle platform in the Gulf of Mexico, 492 m tall, standing in 412m water depth. The platform jacket and its piles consist of 54300 tons of steel.

A typical North Sea variant to the steel jacket platform is the concrete production platform. These are *gravity structures*, that is: structures which because of their immense weight and large footprint remain stable on the sea floor and do not need to be nailed down with piles. Within their substructures, gravity platforms can store crude if this is required. The size and mass of these gravity structures challenges the imagination: the tallest one is the Troll gas production platform, 430m high from seabed to the tip of the flare boom. Its structure, equipment and ballast weigh well over a million tons.

To build large gravity platforms, one needs deep water such as typically available in Norwegian fjords. In comparison to the weight of the substructure, the topsides are light. It is therefore common to place the production decks on top before the gravity platform is towed out to sea for installation.

The cost of these large jacket and gravity platforms for deep water is enormous. For the Troll project a number of $ 4.8 billion has been published. In search for less expensive solutions, the industry has developed several lines of thinking. One line covers the use of bottom-*hinged* or *compliant* platforms, to avoid the need for a wide basis on the seabed and thereby reduce the weight. Vertical stability is derived from either flotation elements or *stays* (also called *guys*). Another line is the use of floating platforms while still allowing the use of more or less conventional well completion techniques and surface wellheads by fully suppressing the heave motion by a vertical anchoring system: the *tension leg platform* or *TLP*. Still another option is the use of a floater type which by nature has virtually zero

heave response: the floating *spar*. The best known spar, as a matter of fact, was not a production platform, but a storage and offloading facility for the Brent field.

'Normal' offshore floaters like ships or semi-submersibles were for a long time not regarded as fit for production purposes. Ultimately, however, they have been accepted, and heave is allowed for by replacing the rigid well risers by *flexible hoses*. This step requires that the wellhead with safety valves is placed on the seabed instead of on the production platform deck. A last option to be mentioned is to try and bring the separation of oil, gas and water subsea, so that well fluids can be transported over large distances without passing through equipment on a platform deck above water. This approach is still in its infancy.

The produced well liquids need to be brought to shore. A pipeline is the first option, but if this is technically impossible or commercially undesirable, then oil can also be carried by *shuttle tankers*. A rather unique unit in this respect is BP's production ship Seillean, which is capable to first produce oil as a floating production platform, then detach itself from the well when its storage tanks are full and take the crude ashore. Normally shuttle tankers take their load from a *storage facility* in the field, often at a considerable and safe distance from the production platform. The Brent Spar was such a floating oil storage facility. An increasingly popular unit is the tanker-based *FPSO* (floating production, storage and offloading vessel), which combines the storage function with production. In other scenario's the shuttle tanker takes its load from dedicated storage ships, directly from the producing platform (e.g. the early production phase at the Ekofisk field in the North Sea) or from a special *loading buoy* or *loading tower* which is connected to the production facility with a flow line. Loading buoys and loading towers have in common that the tanker can weathervane around them, to minimise mooring forces.

To build, install and maintain offshore structures and pipelines, the contractors world-wide have developed many specialised ships, cranes and other equipment. The most visible ones are *pipe lay barges* and heavy lift *crane vessels*, but not less important are the many hundreds of smaller vessels: supply boats, anchor handling ships, tugs, crew boats, diving support ships, pipe carriers etc. Offshore operations also make use of equipment which is not typically offshore in itself, but nevertheless indispensable. The most obvious example of such equipment is the helicopter. Without it, personnel could not arrive on or leave platforms so easily. The importance of the helicopter may also be illustrated by the fact, that not only platforms are fitted with landing decks for helicopters, but that also vessels like laying barges, crane ships, mobile drilling units and diving support ships are carrying a helideck.

Chapter 2

Offshore expansion in the Gulf of Mexico
The period 1947-1959

1. Exploration and production

'The discovery of Kerr-McGee's Ship Shoal-Block 32, as a shallow productive piercement-type salt dome marks the first successful venture in the Gulf of Mexico. At the end of the year [1947] it was a one well field and its full potentialities were unknown due to lack of additional development.'[1]

In the three months of 1947 that remained after Kerr-McGee's striking oil, the field was not explored any further. This had not been planned anyway, as Kerr-McGee had concentrated on drilling two wells that involved some risk because of the short time. Preparations for the development of Block 32 were made in 1948. 'It is planned to attempt drilling directional wells from the same platform from which the discovery well was drilled', and 'several methods of moving the oil are now under consideration', A.F.T. Seale wrote in World Oil in May 1948.[2]
It was not uncommon in the American oil industry as a whole to take a field into production only some time after its actual discovery. When building an exploration platform, Magnolia and Superior took into account its future role when the field would actually be in production. This 'foresight' was mainly due to the cost of offshore operations.[3] Kerr-McGee's 'minimum-platform' approach cannot be fully explained from the company's financial position or its lack of experience in offshore activities. The matter of its great hurry remains, as does the question why companies are so focused on drilling wells. We come across this single minded attention in literature but also in the develop-ment of technology in this period.[4] Drilling techniques

developed relatively fast into advanced concepts, whereas techniques to control wells and to create an efficient and complete exploitation were only developed much later.
In the 1950s and 1960s, the offshore sector showed a similar discrepancy between drilling and production techniques. To understand this phenomenon, we must go back to the development of the American pre-war oil industry.

The wildcatter
Until the mid-1920s there was a chronical oil shortage in the United States. The expanding American economy and a wider use of oil and oil-based products created a booming demand for oil, which could not be met by the young oil industry. It is not surprising that in this period absolute priority was given to finding oil. The sector gave newcomers a chance who by sinking wells more or less at random in unexplored areas, hoped for success and their share of the expanding market. This was the time of the so-called wildcatters, whipped up by analysts who quantified the quality of areas through success rates and joining colleagues who made an area prospective by even a minor success.
By 1925 supply began to exceed demand, which led to an altogether different situation on the market. This situation was to get stronger until the outbreak of World War II. The falling prices led to a slump in the industry, in which especially the smaller adventurers were hit. Strangely enough, exploration activities did not suffer, in some areas they even were more numerous than ever before. As has been explained in Chapter 1, the reason for this development lay in new

Detail of Kerr McGee's jack-up rig 62.

geophysical technology and drilling techniques. The individual companies tried to survive by stepping up their exploration activities in order to outdo competitors. This led to a concentration movement, in which big firms got even bigger and small ones disappeared. But this does not in itself account for the *continuing* high number of *drilling activities*. It seems logical that firms with rich reserves would have opted for better methods of exploitation, but they preferred to increase drilling. This particular development can be explained by looking at the role of American government.

Free enterprise and its limitations

From the start of the oil industry in the second half of the nineteenth century, there had been dispute over the ownership of oil reserves. Characteristic of the American tradition, but entirely different from opinions elsewhere in the world, oil reserves were regarded as owned by the party who owned the soil above. However, this clear principle immediately caused trouble, as oil reserves generally do not conform to registered boundaries. As a consequence, the owner of a plot of land that held oil, could not help winning oil or gas which flowed from underneath his neighbour's plot to his well. In 1899 a Pennsylvanian court was asked to solve a situation of this type. Landowners sued their neighbours for 'stealing gas' because they had sunk wells on the edge of their property. The judges simply concluded *'Only go and do likewise'*, which legalised sinking 'offset wells'.

As a result, it became normal to drill as many wells as possible on one's own land, in order to produce as much oil in the shortest possible time, i.e., faster than one's neighbour. The principle of free enterprise, private ownership and legislation led to soil perforation or overdrilling, which badly affected the useful pressure exercised on a field by gas caps. In the end, production of these fields was far less than would have been possible. Further, the idea that resident oil and gas might fall into the hands of neighbouring landowners was the ultimate stimulus to get the stuff to the surface, regardless of any real demand.[5]

Conservation

This situation led to an explosive growth of American oil production, but also to a large quantity of oil that could not be extracted through the existing technical means, field pressure being a condition for production. With the growing importance of oil and mounting public irritation over the jungle of derricks and the reputedly greedy and indifferent operators, American government began to worry. Already before World War I a number of states took measures to change the situation.[6] But the principles of free enterprise and private property were left untouched, and the focus was on the so-called *waste*, the negative side effects. It was production, not exploration that needed regulation. With demand rising, the need for reserves grew. It was thought that unrestrained and technically irresponsible production could be controlled by conservation of these reserves, and unrestricted drilling would increase the total of these reserves. Taking the technology of the moment as fixed, wells were rated according to their maximum rate of efficiency flow, the so-called discovery allowables. The aggregate discovery allowables of all wells made up the total capacity of each state. A market analysis led to a percentage of this total capacity that could be produced, so individual wells had to stay within this percentage of their discovery allowables.[7]

Initially the conservation laws were not a success. Companies did not feel like complying with these rules in a situation where demand was excessive. They considered the laws as a breach of free enterprise. Although production could be controlled through the refineries, the authorities lacked knowledge and experience to enforce the law. In fact, the conservation laws did not stop overdrilling, but even were a stimulus. It became important to collect discovery allowables, as many and as high as possible. Growth in the oil industry became in part based on a maximum number of holes with a high success rate. In that situation, extra money was not made through efficient exploitation.[8]

This stimulus to explore was even reinforced by additional regulations and tax facilities. In Texas, wells were exempt from 'percentage proration' during the

Brown & Root

Early platform erection required skill and daring of the offshore workers, who often had to do their job without protection or sophisticated equipment.

first two years, because it was thought that production in this period could not be used to establish a proper rate of efficiency flow. Tax facilities made drilling, successful or not, into an interesting means to reduce taxation. This *'drilling up to one's tax'* also offered interesting opportunities for people outside the oil industry, who were willing to invest extra capital for exploration purposes.[9]

The American authorities had created a system that stimulated exploration. With the growing number of companies that got involved and the larger area that had been surveyed, the system induced innovations in exploration technology.

Rotary drilling, for instance, was a technique that speeded up drilling and which made much deeper layers accessible.

Directional drilling, intentional or not, was a 'method' that enabled to drill under a neighbouring parcel without being noticed. However, drilling of non-vertical holes was not allowed, and authorities used to check wells on being vertical. So-called well spacing paragraphs annex to the conservation laws stated the maximum number of wells on a certain area, which in later years led to the development of sinking more wells on one location and intentional directional drilling as a legitimate technique.[10]

Oil prices

The surplus of oil and oil reserves that came to exist by the mid-1920s changed the conservation laws into a system which the oil producers began to appreciate. Although they had never been intended as such, and the authorities had not even in times of surplus presented them in these terms, the conservation laws became price regulating instruments that could keep oil prices at a sufficiently high level by controlling supply.[11]

Conservation led to a somewhat problematic situation for the large, integrated companies. Conservation was realised through the instrument of rateable take, i.e. the refineries were forced to get oil from all wells that were linked to them by pipelines. Every month, production of individual wells was fixed, and refineries were not allowed to process more than a fixed quantity. The refining companies could not give priority to oil produced by their own wells, which would have been commercially more interesting. Processing other companies' oil restricted earnings to downstream activities. Perhaps for that reason the integrated oil companies imported an increasing amount of foreign oil for their American refineries. The term 'cheap oil' to indicate this foreign oil refers perhaps mainly to the fact that, after all, this oil was produced abroad by these same firms.[12]

A production site in the Gulf of Mexico in 1953. In the foreground, there is a typical well completion of the time, with a production platform in the background. This platform serviced five wells. The piling around the well was used to secure the drilling barge which drilled the well.

The situation of the American oil supply after World War II was, on one side, influenced by a growing consumption, but on the other side there was an immense reserve that developed into a stabilising factor on the international oil market. Besides, exploration and production of oil world wide was mainly an American affair. Apart from Shell and BP, all major oil companies were American; the United States had a large number of medium-sized firms operating on the home market. Although oil had by then been recognized as a major political factor, governments let oil supply be a matter of privately owned companies, that also formed a strong network in which the biggest companies set the price. There existed a gentlemen's consensus among these firms, which earned them the nickname *'The Seven Sisters'* in the 1970s. The American home oil reserve played an important role in forming the oil price. A committee of wise men from the Texas Railroad Commission[13], who since 1919 were charged

with execution of the conservation laws, played a dominant role in fixing the monthly proration. Texan oil reserves made up a fair part of the US oil reserve and consequently acted as a stabilising factor in which both surplus and shortages could easily be levelled out, although this would be a disadvantage to the independents, who were oriented towards the US home market.[14]

Offshore

During the postwar years, concentration remained on exploration. The number of drilled metres continued to rise, but this was mainly due to the increasing depth of wells. The number of wells fell slightly, whereas the number of successful drillings decreased dramatically.[15] The boom of great findings on land seemed over and the most promising areas had been given out. There were but two exceptions: the Gulf of Mexico and, later, the Californian coast.

The Gulf of Mexico developed rapidly, and the initial grand expectations became more than true. Development in the Gulf went along similar lines as the on land developments before the war. Conservation laws regulated production and created stimuli for exploration. The state of Louisiana even offered significantly higher discovery allowables for offshore wells than for onshore wells, to compensate for higher investments. In the Gulf, too, the focus was on creating reserves rather than production. Exploration was developed quickly, but production technology stayed behind. *'The present status of offshore technology reflects substantially greater water-depth capability for exploration than for exploitation'*, the National Petroleum Council, the representing body of the oil and gas industry that advised the Department of the Interior, concluded in 1969.[16]

2. The tidelands controversy and federal oil

Conservation as a form of government interference became acceptable to the industry after World War II because of its protective aspects. It created a separation of exploration and the situation on the oil market.

Growing faster than competitors had to be based on collecting as many reserves as possible by finding as much as possible. Shell called this the *'fight for new production'* and *'the struggle to obtain new territory'*.[17] In particular the big independents saw good opportunities for this strategy in the Louisiana swamps, that were made attractive by high discovery allowables. But the largest integrated firms concentrated more and more on activities outside the US.

Crisis, conservation and high allowables can explain the behaviour of the oil companies and their special

Producing oil in the Main Pass area of the Mississippi Delta in the Gulf of Mexico, in the 1960's. The platforms were relatively small.

Shell International - Photographic Services London

focus on exploration during the 1920s and 1930s. But for the following years, we have to look for other factors. The Gulf of Mexico became a very important area, although the start was slow, which cannot just be explained by a lack of technology. Besides, the Gulf was the playground of the major independents, the biggest companies entering at a later stage, and even then the Gulf was not of prime importance to them. The environment in which offshore was developed deserves closer attention.

World War II changed the function of reserves, from a price regulating instrument into an instrument of war. American reserves became part of national security and an important aspect in winning the war. But in spite of a continuing high level of exploration, reserves failed to grow. *'The Bonanza days of oil discovery, for the most part, belong to history'*, the Petroleum Administration for War reported in 1943.[18]
The American federal government faced a new problem. Supplying allied troops with oil products took vast proportions, so the need for oil reserves in America rose correspondingly. *'If there should be a World War III it would have to be fought with someone else's petroleum, because the United States wouldn't have it'*, H. Ickes, Secretary of Interior, wrote.[19]
This statement sparked off the idea with the federal government that it should, for reasons of national security, control American oil companies in their dealings with foreign, i.e. Arab oil. In order to create a policy, talks were held with Great Britain, and an agreement was reached by the end of the war. However, this plan was never implemented, as many politicians lost interest after the war, and it was generally thought that the Middle East would be a reserve that could hardly be secured in case of a new war.[20]
After 1945 several alternatives for the original plan were presented. Large oil imports in time of peace might save home reserves to build up a reserve for use in periods of conflict. An ambitious plan was proposed to develop a technology to make synthetic fuels. The most realistic idea seemed, however, to start using a hitherto unwanted byproduct of oil production, gas.[21]
The United States, represented by its federal govern-

ment, kept worrying about its oil reserves and its dependence on oil. The government looked for instruments to influence the oil industry in order to secure oil supply and oil reserves. New international relations, the Cold War and an unprecedented economic growth after the war reinforced the government's desire.

The federal government looked for 'oil of its own', and found it offshore.[22] Coastal areas off California and, especially, Louisiana had been interesting already before the war. Exploration activities had moved seaward and in 1944 oil companies had started large scale seismic surveys in the Gulf of Mexico. Louisiana was ready to grant concessions in parts of the Gulf of Mexico, partly outside the three-mile zone.[23] But if ownership within this zone, that belonged to the United States, was unclear, it was even more so regarding the area outside. Louisiana considered large parts of the Gulf simply as belonging to its territory and granted concessions on hundreds of thousands of acres after 1945. But before that, conflicts had already arisen with neighbouring states and the federal government.[24]
In 1945 President Harry S. Truman came up with a *Proclamation on the Continental Shelf*, in which he stated that:

'Having concern for the urgency of conserving and prudently utilizing its natural resources, the Government of the United States regards the natural resources of the subsoil and sea bed of the continental shelf beneath the high seas but contiguous to the coasts to the United States as appertaining to the United States, subject to its jurisdiction and control [ ].'[25]

Intended as a point of view in an expected international discussion on the ownership of the continental shelf, the proclamation also contained an indirect federal claim on the areas that had been declared American property. However, with the complete lack of any legal background to this claim the states did not consider it an obstacle to their own policy.[26]
A first conflict arose in 1947 between the federal

authorities and California. In May both parties met before the Supreme Court. The federal government argued that *'the mineral resources in question might very well become the subject of an international controversy'* and that *'it is the federal government that must engage in commerce and live in peace with the world.'*[27] California appealed on its constitution, that had been approved by Congress when it became one of the United States, in which California *'had set her boundaries at a point three miles from shore.'*[28]

On 23 June 1947 the Supreme Court reached its verdict. The federal government obtained *'paramount rights in and power over'* the three mile zone. The question of federal ownership of mineral resources was answered positively in October. It took until 1965 until a decision was taken in the matter of drawing up a coast line and fixing a three mile zone in three bays, one of them the Santa Barbara Channel.[29]

Ickes, Secretary of the Interior, was content with the Supreme Court's decision, as he assumed the California verdict was a precedent that would solve the tidelands controversy once and for all. However, Texas and Louisiana did not feel bound by the decision and continued to grant concessions in 1947 and 1948. Many of the areas given out were beyond the three mile zone, as Louisiana had, in 1938, decided to extend the zone for another 24 nautical miles, arguing that 'a modern gun shoots further than in the days when the three mile zone was established'. Even when the United States v. California case was still before the court, Texas moved its zone to what it perceived to be the edge of the continental shelf, which at some places was more than 100 miles offshore.[30]

The federal government began cases against Louisiana and Texas as well, and both states referred to the arrangements made at the time of their joining the United States. Although in either case these arguments were not accepted by the Supreme Court, the *tidelands controversy* had turned into an important and sensitive political issue, and had stalled leasing beyond the three miles zone. In 1950 the Court decided in the Texas and Louisiana cases, but at the 1952 presidential elections the matter was still present.[31] Harry S. Truman had taken a clear stand by declaring the entire offshore area a matter of U.S. security. The

new president Dwight D. Eisenhower, who during his campaign had promised to lift the offshore moratorium, supported the position of the two states, and in 1953 he tried to put an end to the discussion through legislation. Two Acts divided the continental waters in two. The area within the three mile zone was given to the states, the rest fell to the federation. Only Texas and Louisiana held a special position, allowing for a circa 8 mile zone off the coast. By the Submerged Lands Act the states were given possession over the sea areas along the coast that would later be known as the Continental Shelf. The federation's property rights were settled in the Outer Continental Shelf Lands Act.[32] The Outer Continental Shelf was much larger, and especially in the Gulf of Mexico, it became the most important area. In this way the federal government obtained 'oil of its own', but six years had passed since the first discovery of oil in the Gulf. During that period, concessionaries were rather cautious in their activities as they were not sure of the future legal situation. Immediately after the passing of the 1953 Acts, exploration and production soared.

3. Offshore expansion in the Gulf of Mexico

Between 1947 and 1953, the relatively simple and cheap concept launched by Kerr-McGee in 1947 was generally accepted as the way to explore for offshore oil. Independents bought large numbers of war surplus LSTs, and the tender-platform combination became the standard method for drilling in the Gulf. Some new ideas were developed, but they hardly ever left the experimental or even drawing board stage. Probably 90 percent of all wells drilled between 1947 and 1953 were done from tender-platform combinations.[33] This combination allowed the platform to be small, which reduced the cost of building and installation and kept the structure's technical requirements low. YF and LST barges were the most popular tenders because of their low cost, and the fact that they could be used time and again. However, they were far from ideal to operate with. *'The LST was narrow (30 ft. inside the wing tanks) and chopped into many compartments. Hatches were too narrow and ladders too steep. The keel line was trimmed upward instead of downward, and the pilot house was too low for good visibility.'* [34]

With the new situation that arose in 1953, after passing of the Lands Acts, the tender-platform concept lost its stronghold. In 1954 the federal government granted its first concessions in the Gulf. In the following years the number of concessions grew steadily. [35] The oil companies recognized the Gulf as an interesting area where risks were 'limited' to nature's looms and the stage of technological development. In a short time the Gulf developed into an oil province of prime importance, where both independents and majors were active.

The stable prospects of Gulf operations were inductive to large investments for the development of offshore installations. Platform-tender combinations were replaced by larger platforms and new types of tenders, specially designed for their task. New ideas were elaborated, as well as already existing concepts on paper that had never matured. Suddenly, a huge variety of hardware came into being, in which we still may observe a strict separation of exploration and production installations, even stricter than it had ever been before. In the lake and swamp areas, structures usually served both drilling and production, and with the platform-tender combination, the platform used to be left behind as the foundation for the production installation. The new mobile drilling equipment, how-

ever, was specifically designed for exploration, and once the drilling was done, nothing but a capped wellhead remained at the location.

Two important reasons can be found to explain this strict separation between exploration and production: Sinking a well does not always produce results. Even though in the 1950s success rates in the Gulf were higher than on land, many holes were dry. They produced some interesting information about the geological structure but as a location they had no function. Building a multi purpose structure would be financially irresponsible because of the investments required. The most sensible thing would be the building of structures specifically equipped for drilling purposes.

Conservation policy urged oil companies to obtain as many discovery allowables as possible in a very short time, which implied a large number of wells to be drilled. Production would follow in due course, provided that drilling was successful at least on some locations. Operators therefore preferred drilling equipment to be available at short notice, which requirement was a stimulus to the development of specialised machinery and contractors.

Mobile drilling equipment

'For drilling in water more than 500 or 600 ft. deep rigid foundations become costly and floating foundations must be used.' This statement was made by H.E. Gross

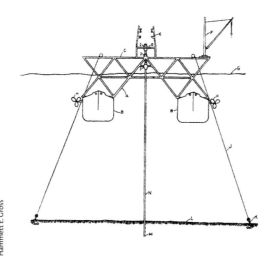

Hammett E. Gross

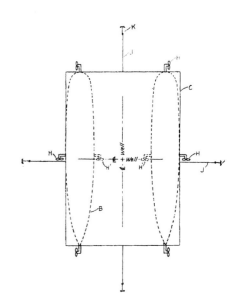

at the annual meeting of the American Institute of Mining and Metallurgical Engineers as early as 1946.[36] Gross hinted at the use of platforms at a depth which no one had in mind at that stage, and he suggested that floating platforms be used. Such a drilling platform should be *'sufficiently above sea level to be safely above any storm waves'*, and it should be built on an *'open type substructure supported on hulls, which [ ] are submerged sufficiently to escape wave action in storms'*.[37] It would take 15 years before Gross' suggestion was developed into the semi- submersible. From this presentation we may draw some conclusions. Apparently, some people involved held high hopes of offshore technology development. Gross did not restrict his ideas to straightforward equipment, he conceived a whole network of modern technology being set up around offshore operations. Helicopters, meteorology, radio, radar and landing craft would become relevant to activities in the Gulf of Mexico.[38] He also gave an amazingly complete set of requirements for future drilling installations:

'The conductor pipe, casing and drill pipe when in use must be under constant tension and not undulating with the waves. The derrick floor and drilling platform must maintain a constant level even when loading and unloading material, or welding casing or drill pipe on the bottom of the well, or when injecting into or removing quantities of liquids from the well and not rise and fall with the waves. The foundation must be open type in that part of the structure subject to action of wind and wave. The drilling platform must remain in a fixed position at all times and must have provided means for overcoming torsion imposed by the drilling operation. The foundation must handle all the loads amply for the drilling of the well or wells if several wells are drilled from one location, and must provide ample storage space for rotary mud and space for fresh water and crude oil to cover the needs of several days, at all times. It is understood that under all circumstances metacentric conditions must be such that the floating foundation can not overturn.'[39]

Gross described a sort of semi-submersible with storage facilities in the hulls, six propellers to counteract rotation and relieve anchorlines, anchoring by means of piles and taut cables, a hydraulic drilling table and an open steel substructure. But since drilling in 600 ft. of water was not yet on the agenda, Gross' paper ideas merely indicate that such concepts at that time were taken serious enough to be presented to the AIME and to be published as an article in *The Petroleum Engineer*. On hindsight Gross' concept was not feasible in several respects, but it was nevertheless a remarkable proposition.

The Submersible

J.T. Hayward was a researcher who, like Gross, thought of floating drilling equipment. Barnsdall, Callery and Hurt and the Seabord Oil Company asked him to look

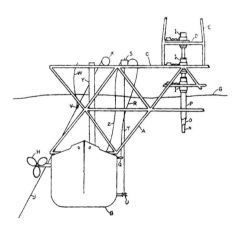

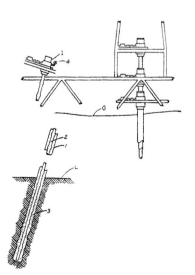

In 1945, H. Gross presented some thoughts of a 'semi-submersible' rig to the petroleum industry.

John Hayward's 'stabilised sea drill' exploring Breton Sound offshore Louisiana. The rig was the first submersible barge used offshore. It was built for Barnsdall, but later sold to Kerr-McGee, where it became part of Kerr-McGee's Transworld fleet. The rig was used for 20 years and drilled 138 wells. Submerging of this vessel was supported by two hydraulically adjustable hinged pontoons on each side of the rig. On the picture, the vessel is submerged. Both vessel and side pontoons rest on the sea bed.

into the possibilities of drilling at sea in a way that would be less costly than by means of a platform-tender combination. Hayward saw opportunities for modified submersibles. The installations as were used in South Louisiana performed well in shallow, inland waters where wind and waves played hardly any role. Their main problem was to sink them, because then they were unstable until they settled on the bottom. This problem would be even larger out in the open sea, where the water was deeper. Greater water depth would also imply a larger spacing between the platform deck and the barge, which affected the installation's stability when towed towards any location.

All this made Hayward's proposals debatable at least,

but the three cooperating principals decided in 1948 that time was pressing, so Hayward was ordered to build the contraption. In 1949 the submersible 'Breton Rig 20' was ready.[40]

The design derived its special proporties from two stabiliser pontoons, mounted flexibly on either side of the vessel. When the barge was sunk and disappeared under water, these tanks remained in the waterline and provided the stability and floating capacity that was needed. Once the vessel had settled on the bottom, the pontoons which could be moved in position by hydraulic jacks were sunk as well.[41]

Or, as explained by D.A. McGee in 1949:
'The drilling equipment for this operation is carried on the 'stabilized sea drill', which has been described as a floating oil foundation. The piles are attached at their base to a large barge which, when flooded, rests on the ocean floor. Stability is provided by two large adjustable 'outrigger' pontoons on each side of the structure.'[42]
Breton Rig 20 performed well, and in 1949 six wells were drilled. Installing and refloating the submersible took little time, which proved the value of the idea. Although results were convincing, other operators were not inclined to use it as well. Those working in the Gulf of Mexico had opted for the Kerr-McGee tender-platform combination and, for the duration of the tidelands controversy, they were not willing to invest in new technological concepts. Besides, in 1949, the year that Breton Rig 20 was launched, Louisiana and Texas stopped giving out new concessions. Although the submersible functioned well, Barnsdall's offshore activities were very disappointing and the firm quitted. In November 1950 Breton Rig 20 was sold in a package deal with a number of licences in Breton Sound, along the Mississippi delta. The lot was bought by Kerr-McGee. Kerr-McGee had just made a contract with Sun Oil Company to drill 13 wells in shallow water off the Texas coast, and the company was looking for a cheap method to work by. The new owners, who renamed the rig Rig 40, were not very impressed by its capacity. T. Kerr, one of the managers, called Hayward's unit one *'that could drill in twelve to fourteen feet of water if you hold your breath and that even that was a gamble because of wave action.'*[43]

Once the tidelands controversy had come to an end, more companies showed interest in the submersible concept. In ten years time several variations on the theme were launched. They mainly differed in size and in the type of stabilizers, two aspects that were closely related. Operations in deeper water became unavoidable with the awarding of new concessions further out to sea, and this led to larger units. The stabilising problem developed accordingly. Hayward's pontoons had moving parts, but these became a source of technical uneasiness. In 1954 and 1955 Kerr-McGee built two more rigs of the Hayward-type, but those were the last. In spite of an accident in 1957, when a damaged pontoon caused Rig 40 to lean over some 30 degrees, this first generation was to remain in operation until the 1970s.[44]

A former Marine Superintendent of Kerr-McGee, A.J. Laborde found Murphy Oil and a number of private investors prepared to venture on an improved version of Rig 40 in which design he had been involved. Ocean Drilling and Exploration Company (ODECO) was formed in 1953 an placed a building order with Alexander Shipyard in New Orleans. Instead of vertically moving stabilising tanks, hinged tanks were attached to one end of the rig. By taking on ballast, the tanks dragged down one end of the submersible, until it touched the bottom. Then water was let into the ballast tanks at the other end of the submersible. During this sinking process, instability could not occur as the submersible was never entirely under water without touching ground. The original intention had been to submerge without tilting. However due to weight increases during construction, the stability provided by the columns proved insufficient and the hinging tanks were added.

The unit was named Mr. Charlie, after the father of Charles Murphy Jr., president of Murphy Oil, who held a 50% stake in ODECO. Its first well in 1954 was for Shell in a water depth of 12 m. It served until 1990, and was then turned into a museum at Morgan City.

In 1954 a second, and last, submersible was built according to this principle. Both, Mr. Charlie and American Tidelands 101, were changed into submersibles with fixed pontoons soon after launching,

Ocean Drilling and Exploration Company's Mr. Charlie.

American Tidelands 101.

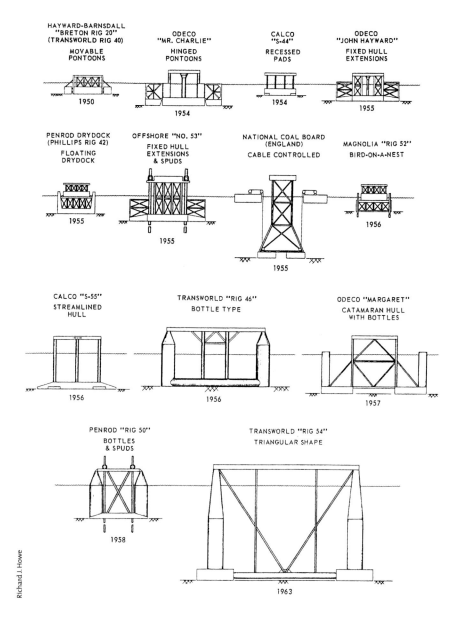

Richard J. Howe

*These drawings by R.J. Howe
show the development of
submersible drilling rigs. The
scale of all drawings is
approximately equal. Howe's
drawings are added as an
illustration of rig
development, and also in
recognition of his contribution to offshore history
writing.*

but the method of sinking was not altered.

The year 1954 also saw the development of rigs that
were fitted with legs. These were lowered to the
bottom before sinking and during the actual sinking
they assured stability and correct positioning.
S44, owned by the California Company, was the first
of seven built to this principle.

The general tendency with all new types of submersibles was to avoid moving parts, which turned out
to be susceptible to failure, and to increase depth of
operations. It was tried to solve the problem by using a
dry dock, but this was not a success due to wind and
wave action on the dock's large surface. The same
problems were met during experiments with a fixed
template under water, on which a submersible could
be sunk. This so-called bird-on-the-nest principle was
realized in 1956 by Magnolia.[45]

The most eye-catching submersibles in the 1950s were
of the 'bottle type'. This idea was developed by
P.A. Wolff, who had come to Kerr-McGee after working
for Barnsdall, where, like A.J. Laborde, he had been
involved with the design of Breton Rig 20. To Kerr-
McGee Wolff suggested a structure with four columns,
or bottles, placed far apart and linked at the bottom by
an open structure of tubulars, with the platform
connecting the top ends. The bottle-type submersible
had no moving parts, and Wolff thought the four
bottles would give enough stability. The first version of
this type was launched in 1956 as Rig 46, followed by
Rig 47 later in the year. Measuring 242 x 202 ft. and
some 100 ft. high, Rig 46 was very large. In fact it was
twice as high as, and had six times the platform
surface of Hayward's Breton Rig 20. The company had
paid less than half a million dollars to buy Haywards
submersible in 1950, but in 1962 Kerr-McGee built
Rig 54, a bottle-type submersible, at a cost of $ 6.25
million. This one, the last and largest ever, could drill
in 175 ft. of water and was based on three bottles
standing in a triangle, 388 ft. apart. The platform had a
surface of nearly 65,000 sqft.[46]

Between 1954 and 1958 a total of more than thirty
submersibles were built.[47] The operators had the
structures built by shipyards, which to a greater or
lesser extent were also involved in the design. The

Kerr-McGee Corporation

most important constructors were Alexander, builder of Breton Rig 20, and contracting with ODECO and others; Ingalls, working for Kerr-McGee, and Levingston, who was a contractor for Penrod Drilling and others.

The Jackup Platform

Offshore drilling was booming business. The submersibles were just part of the story. In this section we will turn to units of an entirely different type, that were built in even greater numbers, and were also used in other areas than the Gulf of Mexico.

'It is only five years since drilling on a large scale began in the Gulf of Mexico, yet by mid-1957 there were over a hundred deepwater units - including more than 30 mobile ones - in operation there alone, while drilling at sea is going on in many other parts of the world: off the Pacific coast of the U.S., in the Caribbean (Lake Maracaibo and the Gulf of Paria), in the Persian Gulf and in the Far East off British Borneo.'[48]

Drilling rigs existed in large numbers, and hardly two were identical. New installations drew heavily on their

The Transworld Rig 46, designed by P. Wolff, and built in 1956, was a bottle type submersible. The bottles and lower hulls controlled the rig stability during submerging and raising. The bottle-stabilising concept eliminated the need for moving parts. This type of submersible would later be used for conversion into the first semi-submersible.

Kerr-McGee Corporation

'To reach open water from the shipyard, Kerr McGee's Transworld Rig 54, had to be towed down the Mississippi River and pass under two bridges. [ ] If completed at the shipyard, the structure would be too tall to pass under the first bridge. [ ] The fit (under the first bridge) was so tight that lookouts on the rig's deck wrote their names on the bridge's supporting girders.' Stated by Paul Wolff in an interview (D.G. Baker, 1980).

The Offshore Company's No 51 was the first mobile jackup drilling unit. It utilised DeLong type jacking systems. Its number of legs originally was 10, but shortly after its commissioning, a helideck and two more legs were added.

predecessors, but incorporated the latest know-how in offshore operations. *'Yet so rapid is the rate of change and progress in this new sphere that mobile platforms termed revolutionary only a year ago, may already be considered conventional.'*[49]

The tendency was to adapt and improve on existing concepts. Some basic concepts were known for many years before engineers recognized their actual potential. We saw Kerr-McGee's platform-tender combination been described in T.F. Rowland's patent of 1869 and used on Lake Maracaibo.[50] Hayward's submersible was derived from drilling barges in the Louisiana swamps. Gross had suggested the semi-submersible in 1946, but it was built for the first time in 1962. The type of mobile unit which this section will deal with, originated outside the oil and gas industry, and had even been patented in 1869.

During the 1940s, in areas that combined the lacking of heavy industrial facilities and a problematic access by water, so-called DeLong docks, or Jackups, were in use. These docks, invented by L.B. DeLong, consisted of a pontoon and a number of tubular legs that could move up and down through cut-outs in the pontoon. With the legs drawn up, the docks were towed to a location, where the legs were lowered. When they stood firmly on the bottom, the pontoon climbed up along the legs until it was above the water.

DeLong docks were also used by the US Army in World War II after the invasion of Normandy, because Rotterdam and the entrance to Antwerpen were not yet liberated.

In 1950 Magnolia started to convert a DeLong dock into an offshore platform to serve as production equipment. Three years later, this platform was ready. The Offshore Company was the second user of DeLong docks. It acquired a dock in 1954, which McDermott had built and adapted for Humble Oil Company. The Offshore Company, a joint venture of McDermott and some private investors, had plans that differed from those of Magnolia. The platform was intended to be a mobile unit for drilling wells at various locations. It originally had 10 legs, each 6 ft. diameter and 160 ft. long. The Offshore Company added a helipad and two

Mr. Gus, owned by the Glasscock Drilling Company, was the first jackup to reach the 100 feet mark. Originally it consisted of two separate platforms - one for drilling and one for accommodation and supplies -, which were later joined to overcome problems of relative positioning. Of the 6 legs of each original platform, 4 were jacked into the seabed and two were used to adjust the spacing between work deck and lower barge.

Zapata Off-Shore Company was the first owner of a LeTourneau jackup, the Scorpion.

extra legs to carry this extra weight. The 'self elevating' platform could rise 40 ft. above the water. Drilling was done over one side, through a so-called side drilling slot.[51]

Installing a DeLong dock held some risks as long as the platform had not reached a height where the waves could not touch it. More than once, legs were seriously damaged and had even broken when waves lifted the vessel when it was just coming out of the water. A notorious unit in use since 1954 was named Mr. Gus, owned by the C.G. Glasscock Drilling Company. It was designed by the Bethlehem Steel Company, and combined submersible characteristics with DeLong's jackup principle. Mr. Gus consisted of a barge and a platform supported by four legs that could move through the barge and the platform. At the location the legs were lowered and then the barge was sunk to the bottom, using the legs as guideposts. Originally, Mr. Gus consisted of two such rigs that could be installed separately and were connected by a footbridge. The idea was to use both parts at different

locations, one for drilling, the other as a service platform. However, this turned out to be an illusion. At the first location, one of the platforms listed heavily during installation, causing one, and later a second leg to break. Bethlehem concluded that the trouble originated from the use of two small platforms instead of a single larger one. Mr. Gus was rebuilt as one single platform with stronger legs. It served for several years and then it capsized in 1957 off Padre Island. In 1956 and 1957 Bethlehem built successors to Mr. Gus for Glasscock and Penrod. A variation on Bethlehem's principle was Stormdrill III, owned by Storm Drilling Company. Here, a mat was used instead of a barge and the legs' lower ends were rigidly connected to the mat. Of this mat-type jackup some ten were built in the 1950s and 1960s.[52]

A third jackup concept was developed in 1953 by R.G. LeTourneau, former entrepreneur in earthmoving equipment. He set out from DeLong's self-elevating principle, but added some drastic modifications. He reduced the number of legs to three, which resulted in a triangular platform. The closed, caisson like legs were replaced by open steel structures or truss-type legs, along which the platform was moved by electrically powered rack and pinion drives instead of DeLong's pneumatic boots and hydraulic slips. Two years after his first ideas, LeTourneau managed to draw the attention of the Zapata Off-Shore Company, a young offshore contractor. In December 1955, when the first rig was almost ready, the two made up a contract. After completion in March 1956 the jackup was launched as Scorpion. This was LeTourneau's first step towards a successful career as a jackup builder. His principle was generally accepted, and a large variety of LeTourneau jackups and derivatives would be built. In 1963 the Dixilyn Corporation began to use a jackup with three inclined legs. This was meant to make the platform more stable, but the structure required a very complicated system of jacks and adjustable jacking systems as with the rising of the platform, the angle of the legs changes.[53]

The jackup, and in particular the three legged, rack and pinion design, developed into the most popular of all mobile drilling unit types, in spite of its water depth limitation. In the fifties, this limit was a mere 200 ft, but even so it made the jackup a strong and ultimately superior competitor of the submersible.

The Template Structure

The interesting aspect of both submersibles and jackups was that they could be used more than once without special effort. This made them very well suited to exploration purposes. Production facilities on a well site had to meet other requirements. The general production facilities were not designed to be re-used, as wells were supposed to produce for many years. An installation was to stay where it was for the rest of its (technical) life, so the emphasis was on durability, especially resistance to corrosion, safety against the onslaught of waves, current and wind, and the capacity of being self-supporting. The installations

Schematic of the installation of a platform jacket or template.

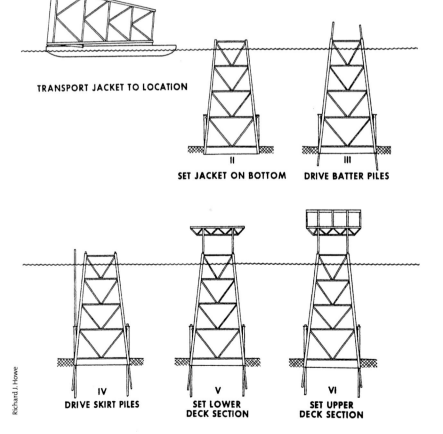

Richard J. Howe

TRANSPORT JACKET TO LOCATION

II
SET JACKET ON BOTTOM

III
DRIVE BATTER PILES

IV
DRIVE SKIRT PILES

V
SET LOWER
DECK SECTION

VI
SET UPPER
DECK SECTION

should be part of a transport network to bring the products ashore.

Fixed platforms were the obvious answer to many of the requirements. Immediately after World War II, ideas and experiments with fixed platforms had contributed to new ways. Superior's platform, using prefabricated jackets, was of great importance. It was intended for exploration and production, but the production stage was reached only in 1948. By that time, however, Kerr-McGee had pointed the way to other operators with its tender-platform combination. The general approach became that of relatively small platforms, which could be extended if required, and most drilling equipment installed on a tender. During the platform-tender period the method of building these small platforms changed. Operators quickly came to prefer prefabricated jackets over assembling a configuration of piles at sea. The development of fixed steel jacket structures was based on the search for the cheapest possible compromise between prefabrication and assembly at sea. The development of fixed production platforms was therefore determined to a large degree by development in installation methods and installation equipment. In Chapter 5 the influence of heavy lift capacity on the design and size of fixed platforms will be discussed.

Superior had elaborated a relatively simple and safe procedure to bring jackets to the location and install them. The jackets were built on land, shipped to the location on barges and then placed on the right spot by a 75 ton floating crane. After that, piles were put through the jacket's vertical members and driven into the bottom.

This way of handling did not change much after 1947. The arrival of a 150 ton crane, specifically built for offshore operations, enabled the building of jackets from larger and heavier tubulars, which allowed for simpler bracings.

The development of fixed platforms between 1947 and 1959 in the Gulf of Mexico was more gradual and less hectic than that of drilling units. This was caused by the relative calm that characterized the placing of production installations, as compared with the

Shell International - Photographic Services London

Shell International - Photographic Services London

Jackets were commonly lifted into their position. As jackets became larger, and therefore heavier, contractors started to use two crane barges instead of one. The picture shows a twin barge lift of a jacket in 1964.

Jackets which were too heavy for lifting could be launched from a barge.

Shell International - Photographic Services London

J. Ray McDermott

After pile driving, the decks were mated with the stubs of the jacket.

Another twin barge lift of a jacket. Picture was taken in 1959.

turbulent exploration activities. In those years a steady increase in activity can be seen, which continues after 1959. The increase in exploration activities after 1953 resulted in a need for platforms capable of standing in deeper water. The new concession areas were deeper than before, and the oil found there, at greater depth, demanded larger fixed production platforms.

In 1953 a crane with 250 tons lifting capacity was built, but soon it was impossible even for this 'giant' to install entirely prefabricated platforms. As a solution, the larger platforms were built in parts, and these parts were put together at the location. The jackets became much taller, too, which led to a modification in the installation procedure. In the mid-1950s it became normal practise to launch complete prefabricated jackets, and place them in a horizontal attitude on a barge before towing them to the location, where they were placed upright.

Another development was to fit the jackets with floaters on one side, on which they could float horizontally towards their location. At the location, the floaters took on ballast so that the jackets turned up and sank to their position on the bottom.

In 1959 not one but two 250 ton cranes, each on its own barge, were jointly used to lift larger jackets.[54]

Floating pipeline factories

Transportation of oil and gas is an important part of the chain of activities between well and customer, as was made brilliantly clear by J.D. Rockefeller. With offshore production, an extra factor comes into play: the hydrocarbons have first of all to be brought on shore, before they can enter into existing refining, transportation and trading systems. The link between an offshore oil well and a shore-based refinery was either a pipeline or a shuttle system, or a combination of both. The shuttle system would typically be based on tankships, the floating equivalent of the road and rail tankers used onshore. In the early Gulf of Mexico developments, which were in shallow waters relatively close to the coast, pipelines offered the more economical alternative. Over time, the pipeline network grew into high density, which in turn made it commercially attractive to develop small fields and tie them back to existing pipelines. Given the small yields per well in the shallow Gulf of Mexico, this was no undue luxury.

If an offshore well produced gas, there was no alternative to a pipeline for transporting the product. Pipelaying technology was well developed on land. Standard lengths of pipe (one joint = 40 feet or 12 m) were stringed out along a right-of-way and welded together, before they were lowered in a trench where necessary or just left above ground. Pipe wall thickness design was based on internal pressures with corrosion allowance and other margins.

A first step into the marine environment was a 40 km long crossing of Lake Pontchartrain, near New Orleans, in 1941. The first 16 km of offshore pipe were laid in 1951 in the Cameron gas field by Brown & Root.

Offshore, pipelaying started to be based on the same technology, except that the welding train did not travel along stringed-out pipe, but was concentrated at a single spot. In the shoreline shallows and marshes, pipes could be assembled on a shore-based yard and the line pushed or pulled into position. For longer offshore lines this was not possible: all welding and further activities were concentrated on a flat top barge, which would be moved along the intended pipe route and leave the fabricated pipe behind. To let the pipe be lowered to the seabed, it had to be weighted, since its structural weight was usually less than its buoyancy. The standard approach to this was applying a concrete coating to the pipe joints. When the bare pipe ends were welded together, the intersections had to be doped and coated as well, after the welds had been checked for quality. These activities determined the lay-out of a lay barge: a line-up station, several welding stations for the first weld (the stringer bead) and one or several filler welds, an X-ray station for inspection, and a doping and coating station.

The remaining particular of offshore pipelaying was the launching of the pipe from the deck of the barge to the seabed. In shallow waters a straight or curved extension of the assembly line was used as a launchway. The first time this method was applied, was on a pipeline laid by Brown & Root in 15 m deep water with their barge Dredge Booth off Louisiana in 1954. It had four work stations within its 57 m length.

Small as it was, it became the great grandfather of all later laybarges.

With pipelaying moving to deeper water, the launching concept appeared insufficient. Launchways were followed by stingers (straight or curved) which were rigidly or hinge attached to the stern of the lay barge. The deeper the water, the longer the stinger had to be, until in the mid 1960s tensioners were added to the standard equipment of lay barges. The tensioner prevents the pipe from kinking over the free end of the stinger, as well as from buckling due to strong curvature near the lay-down point on the seabed. It allowed to limit support of the pipe to a relatively short distance behind the lay barge and opened the way to lay pipe in increasing water depths.

The same contractors who had established themselves in the construction and installation of production platforms, provided pipelaying services. The lay barge was often equipped with a heavy crane, so that installation jobs could be combined with pipe laying. During these early years, the laying market was

X ray and protective coating stations on an offshore pipelaying barge.

J. Ray McDermott

Lay barges 22 and 23 (picture shows one of them), built in 1969, were the first centre-ramp lay barges and the largest barges built solely for pipelaying duties.

dominated by Brown & Root. The logistics of pipe laying required tugs to set and reset the anchors of the laybarge, and pipe supply vessels to feed new pipe joints to the spread. In the normally quiet waters of the Gulf of Mexico, this straightforward approach proved to be adequate and efficient.

For small diameter pipes, in particular flowlines, an alternative was using a reel barge. One of the very early examples of this technique had been the 80 miles Pluto fuel pipeline laid across the Channel after the invasion of Normandy in World War II. By using this technique, the time of pipelaying was drastically reduced, at the cost of prefabricating the required length of pipe on shore and spooling it onto a reel. Other conceivable methods, such as lowering the pipe by a multitude of slings on a lowering barge (comparable to using side booms on land) did not persist.

A one-off experiment with aluminum pipelines was conducted by Superior Oil Company in Lake Maracaibo during 1957, in view of the high corrosiveness of the water in the lake.[55]

Supply

With the increasing number of activities in the Gulf of Mexico came the need to transport people and materials to and from offshore platforms, supply pipe to pipelaying barges etc.. In the early days fishing boats had been chartered for such purposes, but the need for more specialised ships was quickly felt. Surplus Navy LST barges were used, but they appeared clumsy an underpowered for the purpose. In 1954 a brother of A.J. Laborde - the founder of ODECO, and superintendant on Barnsdall's Breton Rig 20 - took charge of a new company, Tidewater Marine Services Inc. which aimed at providing supply boats to the industry. Its first ship, the Ebb Tide, was a substantial improvement over the LST and became the example for many more to follow. Its lay-out, with bow wheelhouse and a long flat aft deck proved so well fit for purpose, that it has never been changed in principle.

The increasing need for supply activities and the development of specialised offshore supply boats made the supply business into an important part of offshore services.

4. Stabilising growth

The Gulf of Mexico experienced an intense but shortlived boom in exploration. As early as 1959 this period drew to an end.

This was partly due to the role foreign, especially Arab oil had come to play in the American oil supply. All over the world, oil was found, and originally many poorer countries could easily be tempted to grant very profitable concessions. Mainly the largest oil companies obtained these concessions, and with few exceptions, notably BP and Shell, these companies were American.

After World War II, the European economies recovered with the support of American dollars, and they became important buyers of Arab oil, which they paid in dollars as the dollar had become the international currency after the 1944 Bretton Woods Conference. Oil prices were controlled by the oil companies and related to American market prices. The majors saw their revenues increase, together with their power. But they also became more dependent on oil reserves outside the United States.

The Federal government welcomed the oil imports because they meant a reduced demand on its home reserves, which were considered an essential aspect of national security. Conservation policy, although originally intended to reduce wasting practise, became an instrument to support national security and to stabilise an affluent international oil market. Both the American government and the major oil companies benefited from its effects. But the American people paid more for its oil than the international market situation required. And the independents that concentrated on the home market, were less and less happy with the situation. Especially in Texas, the Railroad Commission was inclined to reduce monthly prorations ever more. This had made a geologist ask his senator in 1949 whether he could do something for *us independent oil suckers on that foreign oil that has destroyed the market*.[56]

But none of the successive American presidents felt like giving the prosperity of the independents a higher priority than national security based on oil imports - from which other American firms reaped fruits as well.

Something must be wrong with the reasoning of the people who would like to cut off our foreign trade for the benefit of the oil crowd', President Truman told a member of Congress.[57]

The growing lobby of independents was counteracted by another development, that placed even more emphasis on of national security in front. An increasing quantity of oil was imported from former European colonies, which by now had become known as developing countries. There, the struggle for power between the United States and the Soviet Union was at its fiercest. Especially the oil producing developing countries had to be 'kept within the family of the democratic nations', or at least far from the 'tentacles of the Soviets'. Free trade was considered one of the instruments to realise this aim, and, logically, import restrictions would produce contrary effects and thus affect American national security. Nevertheless, pressure on import policy continued to grow. In 1955, Congress forced the adoption of a National Security Amendment, enabling the President to control imports when the American economy needed such measures. President Eisenhower was unwilling to restrict oil imports, but he partly gave in to Congress by making an appeal to the oil industry for self imposed restrictions.

The fear that the oil producing countries, like the Arab states, would be driven from the American sphere of influence, was not without reason. There were developments in that direction indeed. In particular the frustration over the small compensation these countries received for their oil, inspired many governments to nationalise their oil reserves. The very first country to do so had been Mexico in 1938. Iran followed in 1951, but when its leader Mossadeq was overthrown, with American support, the oil companies managed to restore the old order in 1953.

In 1956, Egypt nationalised the Suez Canal and even closed it as an answer to French and British provocations. This led to military actions by France and Britain, and an oil crisis seemed unavoidable. The Suez Canal was of prime importance to Western oil supplies, as virtually all Arab oil passed through it. Now, tankers were forced to take the long route around the African continent. Egypt realised the Suez Canal was a very

powerful weapon. Europe feared petrol scarcity and some countries organised car-free Sundays.
One month after the closure of the Canal, Western governments and oil companies agreed on a plan to rearrange oil transport and use the American national oil reserve as an international reserve. This so-called Oil Lift was a success. Europe's oil supply was hardly touched by the Egyptian measures, although for a very short time oil prices soared. In April 1957, Egypt gave up the blockade after an agreement had been reached over its controlling rights, and under pressure of the oil producing Arab countries. Together with a relatively warm winter in Europe, the Oil Lift had saved Europe from bigger trouble. Besides, the European nations were not as completely dependent on oil supply as they would be some years later. Once the Suez crisis was over, oil prices on the international market dropped dramatically, because everyone had seen proof of the immense oil reserves in the United States. There appeared to be enough to keep two complete continents going for several months.[58]

Meanwhile, the offshore industry in the Gulf of Mexico experienced great days. This was caused by a complicated situation on the American oil market. The Federal government insisted on the home reserves to be left intact and on restoration of the good relations with oil producing developing countries. Increasing oil imports were the most likely way to go by. The Texas Railroad Commission and other authorities involved in the conservation policy, agreed that imports were an important element in the American oil supply, so the conservation laws were carried out strictly. This kept domestic oil prices relatively high, and American oil importers found a broad margin of profit on their imported Arab oil. The independents working in the United States aimed at more discovery allowables to compensate the low proration percentages. This incited them to explore the Gulf of Mexico, being an almost untouched and perhaps the nation's last oil province. So the boom that followed in the Gulf was caused by the need for discovery allowables rather than by a high oil price. Nevertheless had prices been lower, i.e. more in accordance with the world market, and proration at the same level, offshore operations

would not have been a very interesting option. The aftermath of the Suez crisis, therefore, could have led to a crisis in the Gulf of Mexico as well if the American market had responded normally to world prices. The independents warned that in the long run, the difference between the world market and American price levels would lead to a price erosion that could not be compensated by an increased production. This appeal for a change of policy was understood by President Eisenhower, who in 1957 announced a *'system of more explicit voluntary controls'*. But this did not silence those who demanded real import bans, and whose influence in Congress and in the Senate was growing. The independents could count on the support of influential members, like Texan Speaker of the House, S. Rayburn, who considered Texas and oil as two sides of the same coin. Other outstanding supporters were Lyndon B. Johnson, also from Texas, who raised funds for the Democrats in Texas, and Senator R. Kerr, who was the founder of Kerr-McGee. Fearing Congress to take over the political initiative, Eisenhower decided in March 1959 to reduce imports through fixed quotas.[59]

Import reduction meant an even better protection of oil prices, but also the need for an increasing internal production. Between 1959 and 1968, the price of oil on the American market rose by just 4 cts. a barrel. In comparison with other countries, the price was high, which meant that offshore production remained profitable, and American production during this period went up by nearly 30%.[60] There was no price effect to be felt of new wells being taken into production, or old wells being reopened. Proration policy weakened, and the need for exploration activities faded away. Six years after the end of the tidelands controversy, the companies shifted their attention from exploration to production. The offshore drilling contractors had to find new areas to employ their expensive installations.

During a twelve-year period, 1947-1959, of expanding offshore exploration in the Gulf of Mexico, a specialised offshore industry had developed. In this sector, the ultimately decisive actor was the federal government, who reacted to international events and national interests. Within the lines set out by legislation and markets, others looked for locations and technologies to explore them.

Firms like Bethlehem, Alexander, Ingalls and LeTourneau for mobile units, and Brown & Root and J. Ray McDermott for fixed units, built the installations to enable offshore operations. More and more, these shipbuilding and engineering companies became involved in developing new types of hardware. The builders of fixed platforms also had large fleets of support vessels to install the platforms. Another, and central group was that of the operators offshore.

Initially this consisted mainly of the larger inland oriented independents and a number of offshore drilling contractors working for the oil companies. Only when offshore activities really got under way, the majors began to move. An exception is Shell, who was active outside the Gulf of Mexico for some time already. It started offshore in the Lake of Maracaibo, had operations going in several parts of the world, became involved in the Gulf of Mexico and then became an innovator in California by introducing a number of the most important offshore drilling concepts: drilling vessels, semi-submersibles and dynamic positioning systems.

Jackup platforms

The earliest reference to a jackup platform is in the description of a US patent application filed by Samuel Lewis in 1869. It took 85 years before the first mobile unit for offshore oilwell drilling was built following the jackup principle. This unit, named DeLong McDermott No. 1, could be elevated above water by means of pneumatically operated jacks arranged around 10 tubular legs. Soon after it entered service, it was acquired by the Offshore Company which added, amongst others, a helicopter deck and 2 legs.

Apart from the legs and jacks, the platform strongly resembled a standard drilling barge. Several early jackups followed this same lay out, with a large numbers of legs. The record holder was The Offshore Company's rig No. 52 with 14 tubular legs. Leg stiffness and transparency to wave attack were improved in The Offshore Company's No. 54, which had 8 open truss legs. In this unit, the typical DeLong gripper jacks - which could conceivably slip on the smooth leg surface - were replaced by a hydraulically moved pin, positively engaged in holes in the leg corner members. Another direction chosen to provide positive engagement was by welding rings on the legs, to which the jacking forces could be applied.

In 1956, a design by LeTourneau reduced the number of legs to three, with the obvious advantage that the weight of the platform and equipment was more or less equally shared by the three legs. Another novelty in LeTourneau's design was the rack and pinion jacking system, which was electrically driven. The gearboxes of this system in the jacking structures of the platform have become a characteristic feature. The strength of the rack and pinion system was its continuous motion, as opposed to DeLong systems or similar hydraulic or pneumatic piston type jacks. This feature plays a role at the moment when the leg footings reach the seabed while the platform is still floating and rolling in the surface waves. The first unit of this type, Zapata's Scorpion, has had many followers of ever increasing size.

The standard jackup now typically consists of a triangular platform, three trusswork legs and a rack and pinion jacking system. Improvements over time were replacing the single row of pinions on a leg corner by dual opposed pinions (resulting in lighter bracing in the leg); standardising on triangular legs (lighter and more transparent than square ones); placing the drilling derrick on a large cantilever for maximum outboard reach; introducing rack chocks or fixation systems to improve the transfer of forces from hull to leg and to add to the overall structural stiffness. Through this evolution, the water depth capacity has grown from about 25 m in the Gulf of Mexico for the Scorpion to about 120 m in the North Sea for the largest units of the 1990s. The designs originally were proprietary to the builders, like Marathon LeTourneau, Bethlehem or CFEM. Later, design firms like Friede & Goldman or Marine Structure Consultants (MSC) took the lead for deep water, harsh environment units with such types as the L-780modVI or the CJ-62.Other types of jackups have also been developed. In soft sea beds the legs tend to penetrate deeply. Sometimes this can be solved by large footings or spud cans. Sometimes the solution is to fit a mat, to which three or four legs are rigidly connected. In such case the feature of independently moving legs is lost, but the fixation of the legs in the mat provides for a relatively light structure.

Remarkable units apart from the pioneering designs were two five legged platforms built by Gusto in the late 1960s; a few Marathon LeTourneau units with slanted legs which should improve water depth capability; and the Offshore Company's four legged self-propelled design which was equipped with posts to add or remove leg sections. An example of this class was the Gulftide, which was used temporarily as an early production platform at Ekofisk. Sometimes a jackup is not designed as a mobile unit, such as is the case with the Harding production jackup in the North Sea. The jacking systems then replace the use of offshore cranes for installation.

Some equally remarkable designs have not come further than the drawing board. In this category there has been a proposal for a unit for 180 m water depth (Gulf of Mexico conditions) with a mid depth intermediate platform. Such water depths, however, have remained the domain of the floaters.

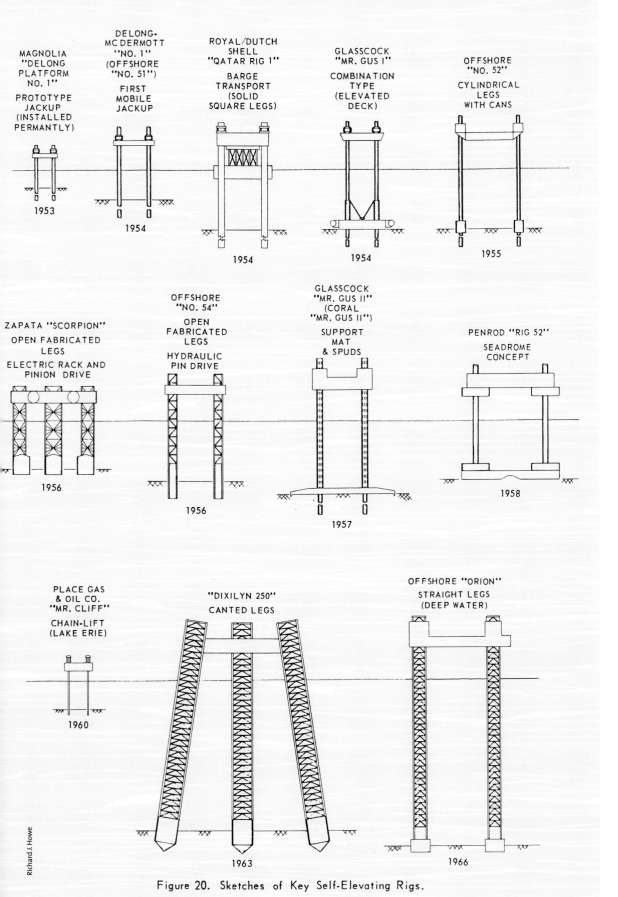

MAGNOLIA
"DELONG
PLATFORM
NO. 1"

PROTOTYPE
JACKUP
(INSTALLED
PERMANTLY)

1953

DELONG-
MCDERMOTT
"NO. 1"
(OFFSHORE
"NO. 51")

FIRST
MOBILE
JACKUP

1954

ROYAL/DUTCH
SHELL
"QATAR RIG 1"

BARGE
TRANSPORT
(SOLID
SQUARE LEGS)

1954

GLASSCOCK
"MR. GUS I"

COMBINATION
TYPE
(ELEVATED
DECK)

1954

OFFSHORE
"NO. 52"

CYLINDRICAL
LEGS
WITH CANS

1955

ZAPATA "SCORPION"

OPEN FABRICATED
LEGS

ELECTRIC RACK AND
PINION DRIVE

1956

OFFSHORE
"NO. 54"

OPEN
FABRICATED
LEGS

HYDRAULIC
PIN DRIVE

1956

GLASSCOCK
"MR. GUS II"
(CORAL
"MR. GUS II")

SUPPORT
MAT
& SPUDS

1957

PENROD "RIG 52"

SEADROME
CONCEPT

1958

PLACE GAS
& OIL CO.
"MR. CLIFF"

CHAIN-LIFT
(LAKE ERIE)

1960

"DIXILYN 250"
CANTED LEGS

1963

OFFSHORE "ORION"
STRAIGHT LEGS
(DEEP WATER)

1966

Richard J. Howe

Figure 20. Sketches of Key Self-Elevating Rigs.

Jackup development
according to R.J. Howe.

Jacket platforms

The most common support structure of the offshore industry is a steel space frame, most often called jacket. Above water, it carries a superstructure consisting of one or several decks for equipment used in production of oil and gas and all facilities which are needed to support and maintain the basic functions (power plant, accommodation for personnel, compressors, export pumps etc.). Often a drilling rig forms part of the equipment and then serves for first drilling and later maintaining the production wells. The production equipment and facilities are often called the topsides. The jacket is piled into the seabed, to avoid settlement, lateral displacements and overturning.

Another name for a jacket is template. This name derives from its function to lower the foundation piles through its hollow legs to guide them from the water surface to the seabed.

The idea of using a prefabricated template to provide a basis for a platform deck has since long been taken for granted. In 1947, however, it was a novelty, introduced by M. Willey of J. Ray McDermott. and embraced by Superior Oil Company. The basic motive to adopt this design was to save costly offshore time. An additional advantage which came up later was possible re-use. In 1955, for instance, Humble used salvaged template structures to economise on time and cost needed for a platform on a new site in the Gulf of Mexico. In any case, steel templates have quickly replaced wooden structures and installations of single, unguided piles for all but the smallest platforms.

The 1947 novelty used 6 templates to support a deck measuring 33 x 53 m in 6 m water depth. In 1955 the 100 feet (30 m) water depth mark was passed. By this time, jackets were much more 'transparent' than their early predecessors, thanks to the use of better materials and larger diameter members. Slowly water depth capacity increased, reaching 150 m in 1975. Jackets were now single template structures, built onshore, usually on their side, transported horizontally to the offshore location on a barge, launched on site and finally upended. The number of installed jacket platforms in the Gulf of Mexico increased steadily and reached some 1000 in 1963, 2000 in 1968 and over 4000 in 1996. In other shallow water offshore provinces of the world, the trend was the same. World-wide, over 6000 platforms of this type have been placed.

Design of a jacket structure is a matter of determining overall dimensions based on water depth and functional requirements, evaluating hydro-dynamic loads caused by currents and waves, determining scantlings of the space frame members, analysing stress concentrations in nodes and the associated risks for metal fatigue by unsteady loads, checking the risk of vibration of single braces or the complete structure, protecting against corrosion attack etc.. Appropriate data to define extreme current and wave conditions are sometimes difficult to obtain. Statistical information has helped to define the 50 or 100 years wave height, but more often than not statistics are based on observations during a relatively short period, and not quite reliable. Wind loads, and sometimes ice or earthquake risks also play a role.

Most horizontal loads are directly related to the diameters of legs and bracings, and therefore the design is a highly cyclical process. The design of the foundation piles is equally critical. The piles interact with the soil and its mechanical properties, and are required to transmit both vertical and lateral loads to the subsoil.

Two different ways of interaction between jacket or template and piles have been devised. One method was to drive piles through the template legs. The template itself served for lateral strength and stability. The decks were placed after pile driving and stood on top of the piles with short deck legs mated and welded to the piles. The other method was to equip the jacket base with short pile guides. Piles were driven through these guides by means of either pile followers or under-water hammers and were grouted to the guides. These jackets are often referred to as towers and their piles as skirt piles.

In 1969, the American Petroleum Institute published the first edition of Recommended Practice 2A, which has become the basic design guideline and standard for all steel offshore platforms.

The advent of fast computers and appropriate stress analysis programs has helped enormously to fine-tune the design and thereby increase the water depth capability of the concept. A proper description of wave kinematics is essential for the calculation of wave induced forces. Several models have been worked out, such as Stokes 5th order wave theory and Dean's stream function theory. Loads are derived from the kinematics with the Morison equation, which according to cynics is only the least inaccurate description of reality. Again, applying these tools became only practical with the introduction of the computer. The cumbersomeness of calculations and lack of computers in the early days has sometimes led to high factors of safety - or ignorance - and by consequence old structures often show an incredible longevity due to over-design.

The technology of building jackets had to follow the trend towards increasing water depths. Quality of welding and handling of the large space frames required highly skilled and specialised fabricators. In 1978 the ultimate seemed to have been reached by Shell's Cognac platform in 312 m water depth in the Gulf of Mexico, which was built and installed in three sections stacked vertically, one upon the other. However, ten years later Shell improved its own record with the Bullwinkle platform, standing in 412 m water depth also in the Gulf of Mexico. In the North Sea with its high productivity wells, water depth was smaller, but the topsides volume and weight was larger, leading to heavy support structures. Primarily in the Norwegian sector of the North Sea, concrete gravity platforms have taken the lead over jacket platforms.

The steel weight of a jacket or template is a function of water depth, environmental conditions and topsides load. The continually increasing size and weight tended to exceed the capacity of existing transportation and launch barges. Larger structures in the North Sea and some other areas were then only possible by adding special floatation tanks (e.g. BP's Forties jacket) or making the structure self-floating by increasing the diameter of the jacket legs (e.g. Shell's Brent, BP's Magnus, Shell's Maui A off New Zealand). At a later stage, large size transportation and launch barges became available, with Heerema's barge H851 as the ultimate. The H851 was specially designed and built to enable the Bullwinkle jacket to be transported and installed in one single piece in 1988. The increased capacity of the offshore cranes brought back the lift jackets where possible, which may be built lighter than an equivalent launch or float jacket.

A side step towards use of aluminium as the structural material (weight, and most importantly insensitivity to corrosion) remained restricted to application in Lake Maracaibo. In the 1980s the concept of 'slim jackets' for medium water depth was promoted. These were light enough to be lifted by a large crane, and could therefore avoid special structural provisions for launching and upending, making them light indeed. In the 30-50 m water depth range of the North Sea, some monopod platforms were placed, resembling the big 'Trading Bay' installed in Alaskan waters. The jacket platform with 3 to 8 main legs however remains the most common offshore platform to this day.

Chapter 3

Towards a professional and international offshore industry
American offshore in the 1960s

1. California

Import reductions and a successful conservation policy in the United States resulted in relatively high and stable prices and high proration percentages. In the Gulf of Mexico, the focus shifted from exploration to production.

The increased call on offshore production stimulated further innovation to bring down costs and increase profits. Prefabricated jackets made an important contribution to the realisation of this goal.

During the 1960s the Gulf of Mexico was characterised by a boom in production installations and the infrastructure they required. Shipping and shipbuilding experienced a golden era. There was a great demand for communications, and the Gulf became a post-war booming market for the professional radio industry. The helicopter, that had been so successful during the Korean War, found its first large scale civil use around the oil rigs. Divers experienced the offshore sector as a new but dangerous challenge. And the design, construction and installation of production platforms made a number of engineering firms develop into large, specialised offshore suppliers.

With the offshore activities taking place in ever deeper water, the need for expert knowledge increased. In the early years, offshore installations were built 'by brute strength'[1], but in the late 1950s and 1960s a more professional approach was wanted. Lower construction costs were required to counterbalance the overall rise in costs when rigs had to work in deeper water. This led to a more intense study of design, based on research, science and experiments. In this respect, the development of drill ships, semi-submersibles and dynamic positioning systems are interesting innovations, the more so because they took place in a specific environment. This environment consisted of three elements: cooperation, room for research and experiments, and a very directive society.

The development of these innovations started offshore California by a group of four companies working together under the name of CUSS.

Drill ships

In the 1948 Supreme Court verdict on the ownership of the Continental Shelf, the coast line at the Santa Barbara Channel was left undecided. The Lands Acts of 1953 said that the State of California owned the Continental Shelf up to three miles off the coast line, the area beyond that point belonged to the Federal authorities. Ten years later, the Californian coast line was formally fixed on the maps, and from that moment both California and the federal government could start giving out territory for oil winning purposes.[2]

Great expectation existed concerning the area in and around the Santa Barbara Channel. This bay, surrounded by the Californian mainland and some islands, is some ten miles wide. The official coast line made it part of both the Continental Shelf and the Outer Continental Shelf. California owned the Continental Shelf, and some four miles, on the Outer Continental Shelf, were federal property.

Before 1963, California had allowed operators to drill in areas that were expected to come under Californian state ownership. These attempts were subject to a special condition, viz., that they would not immediately discover oil. They merely had to serve geological and

Submarex, the experimental vessel converted from a Navy patrol craft by the CUSS Group, was the first ship based drilling unit. A cantilevered platform was built amidship to support the derrick outboard.

The second drill ship of the CUSS Group, used for experiments from 1954 to 1957, was a converted Yard Fighter barge. Its derrick, arranged over a moonpool on the centre line, was far heavier than the one of the Submarex. The CUSS I was later used for scientific drilling in the Mohole project.

geophysical purposes. When a potentially productive formation was detected, drilling had to be stopped before that formation was reached.[3]

The geological structure in the coastal area was complex because of the large number of fault lines, and the actual continental shelf was very narrow. *'Off California the ocean floor slopes steeply seaward, in contrast to the broad continental shelf formed by the gently sloping Gulf. In places the Pacific shelf - defined by the 600-ft. contour - is not more than a mile or two wide.'*[4] Techniques that were successfully used in the Gulf of Mexico, were impracticable here. This meant that drilling and core sampling as preliminary activities posed delicate technical problems.

Nevertheless, the oil companies showed intense interest as it was expected that in the end leases would be given out. They were ready to go and drill to increase their geological understanding of the area. As early as 1948, Continental, Union, Shell and Superior formed a study group *'to keep abreast of offshore drilling developments and to determine the direction that their research and experimentation should take.'*[5] This cooperation was exceptional, and it was the first of its kind within the offshore sector. Neither was it common in American on land exploration and production. Offshore was a young sector, where guts had produced impressive results. Apparently these oil companies thought that in the near future large and promising areas would become available where operating would be much more difficult than in the Gulf of Mexico. This prospect inspired systematic research and accumulation of knowledge in order to have the right equipment available when the time would come. Cooperation seemed the right strategy to follow.

The partnership between Continental, Union, Shell and Superior was called the CUSS group. It faced the challenge of developing concepts for drilling in deep water areas with unstable floors, like the continental shelf off California. Although Shell and Superior had experience in offshore operations, this type of problems was new to them as well, and the group as a whole lacked specialised know-how.

The CUSS group set out from the idea that for drilling off California the units must not be resting on the bottom. As a consequence, a floating unit became the option to be considered. Four questions guided further elaboration: *'(1) How do you hold a ship steady enough to drill in spite of tide and waves; (2) how do you re-enter a hole, change bits, and perform other necessary drilling operations; (3) how can a closed circuit, mud-circulating system be provided; and (4) how can blowout preventers be installed?'*[6]

In order to test solutions, the CUSS group bought a former Navy patrol craft in 1953. On this vessel, the Submarex, a cantilevered platform was built amidship. For one year Submarex was used to drill core holes off the Californian coast in an attempt to grasp the

problems related to re-entry, mud-circulation and blow-out preventers resting on the seabed. After a range of experiments and having completed drilling a total of some 300,000 ft., the CUSS group decided to procure a complete drilling vessel, CUSS I. For that purpose, a Navy surplus YF barge was bought in 1955. It took eighteen months and $ 700,000 to rebuild it. CUSS intended to carry out the first drilling trials in all secrecy. However, *'in the early days small boats with 'sight-seers' would circle for hours watching the operations through binoculars and photographing with telephoto lenses. Occasionally, the men aboard the CUSS would look back with their own binoculars and identify friends who worked for rival oil companies.'*[7]
In the years 1954-1957, CUSS was not the only one to experiment with the concept of a drilling vessel. Standard Oil of California, Richfield, and Humble, to mention a few, also refitted LSTs to that end, and these were in operation already before CUSS I began its work.[8] Neither was California the only place of action. In the Gulf of Mexico, Zapata Offshore Company converted a YF vessel into a drill barge, the Nola I, which drilled its first hole in 1959.

YF barges were large, strong and inexpensive, which made them very suitable for working offshore. In the CUSS I design a hexagonal aperture was cut in the hull, with a heavy derrick standing right above. As the barge had no motive power of its own, it had to be towed from one location to the next. Placing a derrick amidship had the advantage of minimal heave, and the choice for a very heavy derrick was based on the adaptations required for operating at sea and at great depth. Vertical guides were fitted inside the derrick to prevent the six-ton travelling block from swaying. The common practise of having a number of drilling pipes stacked in a vertical position in the derrick was rejected. CUSS I had a horizontal pipe storage near the derrick and the pipes were mechanically brought in a vertical position in the derrick, which contributed to a lower centre of gravity for better floating stability. CUSS I was kept in position by six lines, which were almost horizontally tied to six anchored buoys. Fore and aft winches pulled the lines tight to keep the vessel heading into the waves.

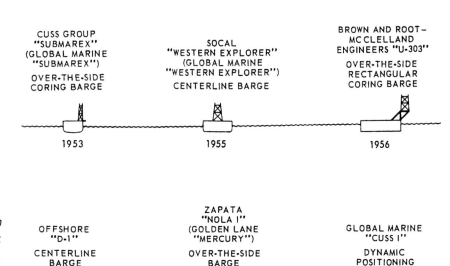

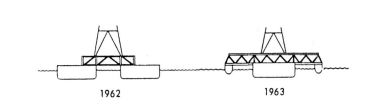

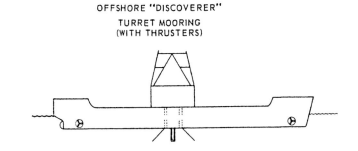

Richard J. Howe

Development of drill ships up to the advent of the large dynamically positioned vessels.

One of the necessary features of drilling from ships is the use of equipment on the seabed. CUSS used a kind of 'landing base', or 'birdcage'.[9] This was a steel frame with a blow-out preventer on top and a casing underneath, and it hung on steel cables above the vessels aperture, or 'moonpool'. The drilling procedure started by lowering drill pipe through the casing to the bottom of the sea. Then a hole was drilled for the casing and the birdcage was lowered and cemented in the bottom. The drill pipe was hoisted again and a long conductor pipe, the so-called riser, was fitted to the blow-out preventer. This riser, originally simply a $12^5/_8$ casing, was introduced to get rid of packing problems at the BOP. At this stage, the usual drilling could start. A major problem with more or less free floating drilling vessels is their vertical movement. This requires the drill bit to be connected to the rotary table through a telescopic structure, which conveys only the rotary movement and absorbs the vertical movement. Originally this was achieved by inserting a so called bumper-sub in the drill string, just above the bit. The riser was held taut by cables with counterweights over pulleys. Drilling collars or buckets filled with mud served as counter weights; hydraulic riser tensioners appeared later, and were followed by heave compensators for the complex drill string.
To inspect the subsea system, CUSS I used cameras that could be lowered by the birdcage cables.[10]

As indicated above, CUSS I was not the only existing drilling vessel, nor was it the first of its kind. Submarex was an experimental version, and a comparable vessel, La Ciencia, dated from the early 1950s as well. Brown & Root is known to have done geological surveys in the mid-1950s using two barges, each fitted with a small over the side rig. Standard Oil of California, Richfield and Humble built Western Explorer, SM 1, and Rincon, respectively, while CUSS I was still on the drawing boards. All these drilling vessels, CUSS I included, were meant to do surveys during the period that the property rights over the continental shelf were still not established. A first oil discovery was made in 1958 by the Offshore Company, working in the Gulf of Paria, off the coast of Trinidad, from a barge with a derrick in the centre.

For the history of offshore, CUSS I remains the most interesting example. It was built by and for the oil industry, but it also became the instrument for a scientific project, and in that capacity the concept's real potential was demonstrated. The introduction of the drill ship was a first step in removing water depth from the list of obstacles to offshore drilling.[11]

Drilling for science
In 1959, a unique interaction between an offshore company and the world of academic science was started. The so-called Mohole project was the outcome of a discussion among earth scientists that had started in the early twentieth century. In his report *The Great Earthquake of 1909* Zagreb University professor A. Mohorovicic launched a hypothesis on the inside structure of the earth. He had analysed seismic data of an earthquake in Croatia, in which he discovered not one but two waves. After various calculations, Mohorovicic postulated the existence of a crust or a change of matter at a certain depth. This became known as the Mohorovicic discontinuity, or Moho, and in the following years much geological research was done to test its existence. In that same period the idea was accepted that the earth's crust is at its thinnest underneath the oceans and very thick in mountain areas.
In 1956 an article appeared in Science, written by F.B. Estabrook who was working in the Basic Research Branch of the US Army. Estabrook suggested to drill through the crust and take a sample from the mantle beneath the crust. At a National Science Meeting geologist H. Hess and geophysicist W. Munk, both ambitious to do 'something big', came up with the same plan. Looking for the best place to foster this idea, they contacted the American Miscellaneous Society (AMSOC), a scientific association with usually ambitious schemes. AMSOC welcomed the plan and, after some preliminary research, presented it to the American scientific world in 1957. Fund raising started and in 1958 the support of the Academy of Science and others made the National Science Foundation grant 15 million dollar. The 'Mohole-project' was born.[12]

In an attempt to convince outsiders of the technical feasibility of the project, AMSOC had turned to the Union Oil Company in 1958. Union had become the owner of CUSS I when the CUSS group was disbanded after the core drilling experiments were over, and to exploit the vessel a subsidiary was set up, Global Marine Exploration Company. This firm was contracted by AMSOC in 1959 to act as an operator for the first phase of the Mohole-project, in which drilling trials had to reach the deepest possible level. Looking at the offshore sector, AMSOC had learned that CUSS I would probably be the most practical drilling tool for the experiment, far out on the ocean. For that job, the vessel needed further modification as positioning with mooring lines in very deep water was not thought possible.[13]

Now a situation developed which to the offshore industry was both new and attractive. Until then, technology was sometimes borrowed from other sectors to have rapid results in exploration and production of oil fields. But here offshore technology was being used in another sector. Apart from offering its still new technology, Union also brought its experience as an operator: oil drillers would drill for science. And after the contract, the modified drilling vessel was to serve the oil industry again. As we will see later, there would be even more spin off effects.

Refitting CUSS I involved the development and application of a dynamic positioning system. This system was based on four propeller drives fixed to the vessel's sides and enabling the unit to keep a fixed position without the use of anchors. Such steering propellers were in use already on ships that had to manoeuvre in small spaces. *'Although omnidirectional thrust propellers are not exactly in common use, they have been thoroughly tested under many kinds of situations'*, AMSOC's executive secretary W. Bascom added.[14] On CUSS I four Harbormaster propeller units were installed, units which look like the outboard motors of pleasure craft. The four Harbormasters were controlled semi-automatically. A joystick transferred an integrated steering signal, in which the individual steering signals were compiled by simple electro-magnetic means. A sonar system combined with a

number of underwater buoys enabled to make the vessel's position visible on a monitor, and the 'helmsman' used this information to handle a joystick.[15]

With the adapted CUSS I it became possible to drill in water of 3500 m, an incredible progression compared to the thirty or so metres which submersibles and jackups could manage. For the offshore world, this achievement was a nice asset to its trophy-cabinet, but it was rather useless so long as oil production at that depth was still an impossibility. But the enthusiasm among the Mohole group was great. *'We are asked whether Mohole can be drilled at all. With what we learned this year, we know it can be done'*, Bascom said when the trials were over.[16]

This optimism brought the idea on the AMSOC staff to build 'the ultimate drilling vessel'. By that time, in 1960, the Mohole project was known even among authorities in the highest federal and political circles, who attached great value to it. Some had already compared it with the man on the moon project, and it had received Cold War relevance because the Soviet Union had announced in 1957, before the start of Mohole, that they were already capable of drilling through the earth's crust. The funds made available to the Mohole project increased from $ 15 million in 1958, to $ 50 million in 1962, $ 100 million in 1965 and even $ 127 million in 1967.[17]

The plan to build a ship just for this project gave it vast dimensions, which led to a number of annoyed outsiders. When six contractors were invited to make a bid for the design of the new drilling vessel, AMSOC took six months to choose one. During this period in 1962 Bascom and his staff left the organisation to continue the job as an independent consulting firm.[18] The contract was obtained by Brown & Root, which raised much criticism in the Senate. Brown & Root's bid had not been the lowest, and the choice was regarded with suspicion. In spite of that, Brown & Root could start working and in 1963 they suggested to build a giant semi-submersible. It was to be a 279 by 234 ft. self-propelled colossus with an automatic dynamic positioning system. Both the Senate and Congress criticised this approach. Apart from this, a conflict arose with another semi-submersible constructor over the design, but the project seemed immune to all that. In January 1965 a location for a first drilling attempt was indicated, and in March industry was invited to submit a tender to the Brown & Root design. But then things stopped. Protest in Congress and the Senate had become much stronger, because of the ever increasing estimated cost but perhaps even more because of the dubious awarding of the contract to Brown & Root. Rumour had it that relations between Brown & Root and President Lyndon B. Johnson had influenced the decisions. Between $ 27 and $ 36 million had already been spent on the Mohole project, but the result seemed nothing more than an interesting drilling job for Global Marine and an even more interesting development project for Brown & Root. In August 1966, the Senate voted against the project and when President Johnson was not reelected in 1968, the last hopes evaporated. A semi-submersible resembling the Brown & Root design was built for the Offshore Company in 1971, but Mohole entered history as 'No Hole'.[19]

Drilling for science however, continued on a less ambitious scale with the dynamically positioned drill-ship Glomar Challenger. Around 1980, the National Science Foundation got support from the international scientific community.

The Santa Barbara blow-out

In 1963 and 1964 the federal government gave out the first areas along the North and Central coast of California. In the first lease sale of May 1963 Shell Oil, Socal, Humble and Superior acquired acreage with Shell taking by far the largest part. These licences caused resentment among the population, who feared that drilling for oil would lead to dangerous situations. It was not for the first time that people living on the Californian coast came at logger heads with the world of oil. Local memory was still full of images of jungles of derricks and piers, and concern over the influence on the natural environment was not wholly imaginary. This did not prevent the federal government from granting more concessions along the coast of Southern California, but these leases resulted in a nightmare: *'On January 28, 1969, an oil-production well being drilled on Union Oil Company's Platform A blew out around its casing, spilling up to 3 million gallons of oil into the Santa Barbara Channel. The spill eventually affected over 150 miles of coastline, and with national media coverage, its political effects were still even more widespread.'*[20]

Accidents with offshore installations were not everyday news, but not exceptional either. In July 1968, six months before the Santa Barbara blow-out, R.J. Howe in one of his articles on the development of Mobile Drilling Units, had referred to the dangers surrounding these installations. He counted thirty major accidents, eighteen of them in American waters. One third of the accidents with Mobile Drilling Units took place during the transfer to, or at the first location. Especially prototypes had a high accident rate, with jackups and semi-submersibles scoring high. Accidents of the kind described by Howe increased from less than 2% of the fleet annually before 1964 to 7% in 1965. Lloyd's, the largest insurance company for drilling units, took the consequences of these figures. Premiums went up and were recalculated, taking into account the location, the type of rig and the damage record of the operator.[21]

In 1993 E.P. Danenberger gave a presentation on accidents like the Santa Barbara blow-out. From 1971 to 1991 he counted nearly 90 blow-outs during drilling procedures in American federal waters. This seems a very modest number on a total of 21,436 wells. Not surprisingly, all blow-outs occurred in the Gulf of Mexico, since that is where more than 95% of all wells were drilled. Danenberger's conclusion is interesting where he states that the blow-outs after 1971 were not characterised by great losses of oil. This puts the Santa Barbara event in the position of an exception, but even so, its impact was exceptional. The incident had important consequences for the offshore activities off California, and to this day it is regarded as one of the sad milestones in offshore history.[22]

The Santa Barbara blow-out caused fierce reactions among the population. A few hours after it happened an action group was formed under the name of Get Oil Out, and it assumed a combative attitude towards further offshore operations. Actions and legal procedures by this group in 1969 and later were successful as offshore activities were made subject to restrictions. A referendum in California in 1972 led to the creation of a Coastal Commission. This Commission had to decide on the acceptability of various activities along the coast line, and it became a platform for a number of interest groups, like fishermen, landowners and environmentalists, who were opposed to offshore operations.

The blow-out inspired the development of a strong and well organised lobby whose influence was felt well beyond California. The accident seemed to emphasize already existing fears that had led to protests before that fatal day in January 1969. Before the Santa Barbara Channel area was leased, the State of California had been forced by public opinion to take measures to protect the coastline. Federal leases acted as a catalyst for the public discontent that had existed for a much longer time already. After the blow-out critics were provided with their prove that they did not have before: drilling for oil in the Santa Barbara Channel was dangerous and failures could seriously damage the environment.[23]

The massive protests were heard by the federal authorities, and it would last six years before new areas on the Outer Continental Shelf off California would be leased. But the effects of federal restraint in California were felt in the Gulf of Mexico, too, but there they meant a substantial increase in activities. For another, relatively new American offshore area, however, the consequence was a serious delay in its development. This area was Alaska.[24]

2. Alaska

In the 1950s and 1960s Alaska was regarded as the new offshore province, and expectations were high. It was not unlike California in that its natural environment was, on the one hand, a tremendous challenge for operators, and on the other hand a source for permanent concern among other groups in society. Strong protests were made to prevent nature being sacrificed and spoilt for the sake of profit. The most

famous action against oil winning in the area was aimed against the Trans Alaska Pipeline, and together with the reactions on the Santa Barbara blow-out, it resulted in a delayed exploitation. Only after the 1973 oil crisis, the situation would change.

Knowledge of the presence of oil reserves and exploitation in Alaska dated from the early years of the oil industry. 'Indications of petroleum have been found in five districts in Alaska [ ]. The oil seepages on Cook Inlet and Alaska Peninsula were apparently known during the period of Russian rule', G.C. Martin wrote in his Preliminary Report on Petroleum in Alaska (1921).[25] Apart from other places, intensive exploitation could be found on the western coast of Cook Inlet in the early twentieth century. In those years, a beginning Alaskan oil industry developed, with the Alaska Oil Company as one of its important firms. Activities were limited to on land drilling, with oil seepages as indicators. The main problem to overcome was transporting the oil. The coast had to be accessible from the sea and wagon-roads were needed to get the oil to the right places. A first attempt to drill offshore was made in 1957, East of Cook Inlet in the Swanson River on Kenai Peninsula. Five years later, three wells were sunk in Cook Inlet,

Watching for polar bears at a Beaufort Sea site.

followed by four more. Then a field was discovered. All this was done by platform-tender combinations during the summer months. The smaller platforms were unable to survive the cold season as the moving ice simply twisted and destroyed the steel structures. To exploit the newly found field, in 1964 Shell, Socal and Richfield built a platform that was intended as a permanent production installation. In 1968, Cook Inlet was the basis of a total of fourteen fixed platforms. From these platforms, pipes were laid to tanker loading terminals on the east and west coast.[26]

The Cook Inlet platforms had to meet high standards. The extremely heavy conditions were the primary problem. *'Extreme tides and low winter temperatures influence engineering and operating considerations to a greater degree in the Upper Cook Inlet area than heretofore experienced in other areas of offshore oilfield*

development. The tides create the swift currents; the low winter temperatures create the ice cover on the Inlet. Individually and in combination they pose new and difficult problems for which solutions were necessary before efficient exploitation of the petroleum reserves could proceed', wrote Shell staff member B.L. Goepfert in 1969.[27] J. Ray McDermott's J.B. Daigle gives a good impression of the consequences of these heavy conditions in his description of one of the first platforms: *'Since it was recognized that when the ice approached a platform in Cook Inlet, the two front legs would initially break up the floe and, in effect, shield the remaining legs from the full force of the ice, a reduced load criteria for two legs was used. In spite of this reduction, the lateral wind, current, and ice force acting on the [ ] platform in Cook Inlet was from three to four times as great as for the wave and wind force on a self-contained platform in the Gulf of Mexico.'*[28] In an attempt to get an indication for technical specifications to be drawn up for a platform, the oil companies placed testing poles near the first, smaller (tender)platforms. Use was also made of strain transducers on the diagonals of platforms, in order to understand the load on the structures. Many of these experiments failed, but a number of successful measurements in the winter of 1963 led to a list of fundamental design criteria. An important item was the conclusion that the platforms in Cook Inlet had to stand on a foundation of the smallest possible number of cylindrical legs. Pictures from the 1960s indeed show three types of platform being used: with one, three and four legs. Other important criteria concerned the foundation in the seabed, that had to resist the forces exercised by the icefloe, and methods to protect the foundation against moving ice and corrosion.[29]

By the end of the 1960s, the development of Cook Inlet lost its pace as a result of the Santa Barbara blow-out. The discussion on the exploitation of oil and gas in Alaska dragged on for some six years, and concentrated on the project of a Trans Alaska Pipeline, to substitute oil transport by tankers. Only after the 1973 oil crisis, new opportunities would come to resume large scale offshore activities in Alaska.[30]

Ice imposes severe forces on the substructure of an Arctic platform. This platform was built in Cook Inlet, Alaska.

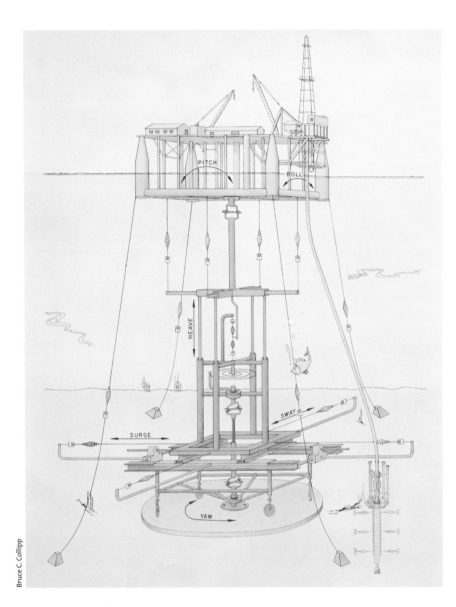

Bruce C. Collipp

Designing a semi-submersible is one thing, explaining the principle another. Inventor B.G. Collipp used this drawing to explain to his colleagues and superiors how a semi remains steady in waves. People tend to think that partly submerging the vessel gives the semi its stability. That in fact natural periods of motion of the mass-spring system are the key to the working principle, is not always grasped.

3. Offshore and know-how

By the time of the 1973 oil crisis, the offshore industry had developed from a nascent into a rather mature industrial sector. Structure became visible, and a number of companies concentrated on typical offshore related activities. Institutionalisation in the 1960s took place through specific forums discussing expert knowledge and presenting the sector's views to the authorities. Various new technological concepts were being developed, each in relation to clearly defined tasks.

This section deals with innovations in the offshore sector that can be regarded as characteristic for the development between 1960 and 1970.

Drilling with semi-submersible vessels and without anchors

The major, and obvious difference between fixed and mobile platforms is that the latter have to move from one place to the next, so they must be seaworthy during transportation. Therefore, the design of mobile platforms involves knowledge of shipbuilding and shipping in general. The implication of naval architects and marine engineers assisting in the design phase holds for submersibles and jackups, but even more for drill ships and semi-submersibles which remain afloat also during operations.

As it happened, naval architects and marine engineers were extremely rare among operators and rig builders at the start of the offshore era. The first individuals to appear on stage did not have much influence, as there was a tendency to get around marine construction problems in one way or another. Initially the offshore world preferred to convert existing ships or barges that could be obtained at low cost from war surplus depots. Of the first mobile rigs, the design and construction of the 'marine' part was left to a shipyard, and when that work was done, an offshore contractor was charged with the installation of equipment. This was anything but an integrated concept.

The notion that building fixed and mobile platforms required marine engineering specialists, slowly dawned on the offshore industry and its suppliers. The leading idea that *'we shouldn't be hiring people*

Shell International - Photographic Services London

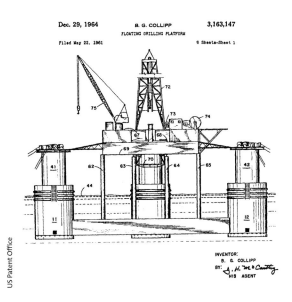

US Patent Office

who don't know our business' was gradually replaced
by *'we hired one, because our competitors hired one.'*[31]
New concepts and purpose built floating installations
were developed only after a small number of naval
architects and marine engineers had obtained
influential positions within the offshore companies.
This is most evident for the technological evolution of
dynamic positioning, semi-submersibles and subsea
wellheads.

Inventor and patent holder of the semi-submersible
was B.G. Collipp, one of the rare naval architects in the
business. When still at MIT, Collipp had become
interested in stability and movement of rigs. After
his graduation Collipp began to work for Shell Oil
Company in 1954, which made him familiar with
Shell's activities in the CUSS group and the resulting
experiments with Submarex and CUSS I. When the
CUSS trials were over in 1958, the group disbanded and
the vessel was left to Union.[32] But Shell continued
along the road that had been entered. Collipp found
inspiration in a University of California research
project on the *'concept that a device could be built with
natural periods outside the periods of the waves and so
substantially reduce pitch and roll'*. This might lead to a
floating drilling platform that, in the words of Collipp,
'would be almost immune to wave action'.[33] A range of
experiments preceded the building of the first complete unit. One of them was a *'donut shaped drill barge*

*which proved not sufficiently stable. Then came Trident
which had 40 ft. stabilizing columns at the corner of a
200-ft. equilateral triangular deck with most of the rig's
mass located under water.'*[34] After these experiments,
Shell decided to realise this concept through modification of a bottle-type submersible. It was launched as
Bluewater No. 1 in 1961.[35] Together with Howe, Collipp
published some possible names for the concept, but
the Coast Guard made Bluewater No. 1 enter its files
as a semi-submersible.[36]

In the following years, Collipp's rig was copied in a
number of variations, and the principle turned into a
useful instrument for drilling in rough waters.
Bluewater No. 1 itself did not live long enough to see
this success as it capsized in the Gulf of Mexico during
hurricane Hilda in 1964.[37]

Shell's next step was the construction of a drill ship. In
1962, a small ship called Eureka was built by SEDCO for
Shell to continue the development line started with
CUSS I. It had two azimuthing propeller units to keep
the ship automatically in position. Eureka did not
become famous in the offshore world, as Shell
managed to keep trials secret. Later drill ships that
SEDCO would build for Shell were all based on Eureka.
SEDCO 445, launched in 1971, was one of the first
entirely automatic dynamically positioned drill ships.[38]
Another line of development was managed by French
companies and institutes, in particular CFP and IFP. In
the mid 1960s IFP experimented with a counterpart of

*The first semisubmersible,
Bluewater I, moored in a
pattern of buoys in the Gulf
of Mexico. The mooring
arrangement was described
in one of Collipp's patents.*

*One of the illustrations in
B.G. Collipp's US patent
3163147 (1961) showing his
floating drilling platform.*

Eureka, the pioneering experimental drill ship which utilised dynamic positioning. Shell went a long way to keep its experiments secret.

The Sedco 445 was built by Sedco for Shell to make the step from experiment to full scale exploration drilling.

the Eureka, the Terebel. Capitalizing on this experience, CFP had the Pelican designed and built in the same year as the SEDCO 445. It became the prototype of a successful series of dynamically positioned drill ships, built between 1971 an 1985 by IHC Gusto and its licensees.

Subsea wellheads and offshore diving

When it is possible to drill with parts of the equipment installed on the seabed, it seems but a small step to have production facilities down there as well. The situation in the Gulf of Mexico was to a certain extent quite inviting to develop subsea production equipment. Leases had been given out in ever deeper areas. The rapid evolution of drilling rigs enabled exploration in those areas, but the capacity of production platforms lagged behind. The financial aspect was an important obstacle, too. Investments rose exponentially with the increasing depth of the water. All this turned the attention to ways of production that could do without a large number of giant platforms. The same problem had been felt offshore California as soon as the first federal leases had been given out in 1963. In that region, the danger of earthquakes and the uncompromising public opinion were additional arguments against fixed platforms.[39]

The first subsea completion was installed by Shell in the Gulf of Mexico in 1961. It sat in West Cameron Block 192, in a water depth of 17 m, well within reach of divers, and was a test case for application in deeper water. After 17 years the Christmas tree was recovered, and appeared to be still in good condition.[40]

The use of subsea production equipment has great consequences for the traditional concept of offshore operations. Before World War II, on Lake Maracaibo, a platform stood above just one well. After the war, it became common practise to have more wells linked to one platform through directional drilling. This enlarged the area covered by a production platform, but wells in the same field that were slightly farther away, still needed a platform of their own. The use of subsea production units made a platform's coverage much larger, but it also changed the role of the plat-

IHC

The drill ship Pelican during tests of the dynamic positioning system. The ship was built by Somaser for CFP and worked several seasons offshore Labrador.

form into a collecting station with a number of production satellites scattered over the bottom. A configuration of that kind was built for the Conception and Molino fields off California in the early 1960s. In the Conception field the platform was linked to twenty subsea units in rather shallow water. The Molino Christmas trees were designed for intervention by a special robot, to prepare for deep water application, even though at Molino the water was shallow and the trees within reach of divers. Only after 1970, the first subsea units were used at great depth. In the early stages, shallow water had the advantage of inspection and repair by divers.[41]

All early systems consisted of a subsea tree exposed to the surrounding seawater, so-called wet trees. Most were equipped for Through Flow Line (TFL) well servicing, a system easily recognised by the looped flow line connections. The TFL technique has not persisted in modern systems, but the wet trees have become the standard. Development of dry trees, placed in either atmospheric or pressurised habitats for human intervention in a 'shirt sleeve' environment started in the late 1960s and aimed at the use of standard oilfield trees. The specialised wet trees however have shown to be reliable, maintainable and ultimately less expensive. They were used as single

units or as groups, mounted in a template which also contained the manifold to control the flows.

The position of Shell and the million dollar school of offshore technology

Among the oil companies working offshore internationally and on a large scale before 1960, Shell was exceptional. It was not only non-American, but Shell also presented itself as an innovator, as we have demonstrated in the preceding sections. The company could be found everywhere outside the Gulf of Mexico: Lake Maracaibo, off the Californian coast, in Cook Inlet, off British Borneo and Brunei, in the Gulf of Paria, off Nigeria and in the Persian Gulf near Qatar. In these areas, developments were not substantially different from the history related above, but on the whole, Shell built up a large experience in offshore operations under various conditions.

The offshore operations in the Persian Gulf were mainly characterised by the larger size of the production installations when compared to those in the Gulf of Mexico. Natural conditions were quite good and during the 1950s and 1960s, Shell gradually obtained a firm footing there.[42]

In the Seria field, along the coast of British Borneo, Shell had started in 1936 by drilling some wells from

Shell International - Photographic Services London

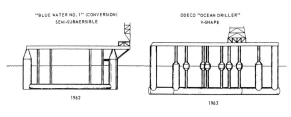

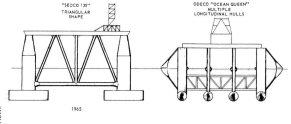

Richard J. Howe

Men seem to be tiny, standing on lower hulls getting shape. The picture shows the building site of the Sedco drilling rig 700 in 1972.

Semi-submersibles.

wooden platforms near the beach. In 1946, the company suggested the use of steel structures similar to those in Lake Maracaibo for the Seria field. However, the waves and problematic accessibility of the platforms by tender made Shell turn away from the idea. One year later, a contractor was approached with the plan to build a concrete foundation carrying Bailey bridging, but this did not materialise either. Only in 1952 a real platform was built and installed. It was a template or jacket, similar to the one owned by Superior in the Gulf of Mexico some years earlier, and similar to structures built by Shell in Lake Maracaibo. An outstanding feature was the one mile long cableway between the platform and the shore, a detail absorbing 60% of the total investments. Helicopters appearing as a means of transport by the mid-1950s The cableway was made redundant in 1965. The low level of exploration in the Gulf of Mexico caused some operators to tow their mobile drilling units to Brunei. In 1959 a jackup appeared in the area, and in 1963 a drilling vessel.[43]

Having collected much experience in various corners of the world, including the CUSS operation, Shell held a special position in the otherwise young and still rather

unstructured offshore sector. Shell had become the main contributor to the development of offshore technology. Although its results were kept secret, rumours could be heard on what these developments were all about.

In 1963, Shell took a remarkable initiative. It organised a three-week course for colleagues and contractors. The theme was floating drilling and underwater well completions, which may be regarded as a worthy conclusion of a research project that had started with CUSS and culminated in Bluewater and Eureka. Twenty years later, D.M. Taylor gave a summary of what was presented:

'The technology and equipment Shell had developed was almost overwhelming. It involved more than 160 patents - granted or applied for - and it included such basic innovations as the semi-submersible drilling rig, a dynamic positioning system for floating vessels, a sea floor wellhead and guide base, a mooring system for drilling rigs, remotely controlled blowout preventers, an underwater manipulator, today called a Remotely Operated Vehicle (ROV), that could operate connectors and override valves at the seafloor, through flowline (TFL) well service and maintenance system and

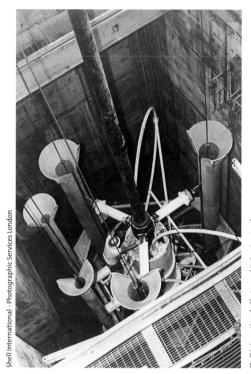

Shell International - Photographic Services London

Shell International - Photographic Services London

Shell International - Photographic Services London

instrumentation and control systems that could make underwater drilling and production feasible.'[44]

Shell seemed to give away its expertise for $ 100,000 per participant and for stimulating the offshore sector as a whole. Reactions were favourable, indeed, with, e.g., Humble (a subsidiary of ESSO) sending ten and Mobil twelve participants. A first step towards an institutionalised knowledge industry was made.[45] But Shell's course served a special goal. The initiative for the course was not taken by Public Relations or Research & Development, but by Patents & Licensing. Shell used the course to get rid of rumours and to make clear its (patented) knowledge, and to subsequently sell it through proper licensing. Shell's million dollar school thus demonstrated the basics of the patent system. Patents give innovators the right of ownership of an invention, in return for making its contents public and giving opportunities to others for further developments.

The offshore sector expands

The expansion of offshore operations led to the rise of a special sector of industry, first in the United States, but soon also in other countries, in particular in

France. It became structured around clusters of firms specialising in certain fields, and within each of these fields two or three companies usually assumed a leading role. Only a few companies were active in more than one subsector.

Operating offshore gradually became a term covering an increasing set of separate and more or less defined specialisms. A common division was that of geological and geophysical surveys, exploration, production, infrastructure, and support. Geological and geophysical surveys refer to all activities needed to chart possible deposits of oil and gas. Exploration is the drilling for oil and gas and the construction work related to drilling, whereas completion is the next stage, in which a well is made ready for exploitation. Production implies building and installing platforms and equipment. The facilities needed to bring the products ashore are called infrastructure, and they consists of pipelines, storage terminals, transhipment terminals, and even tankers. Support is the term used to indicate all transport of personnel and materials. During the 1950s and 1960s, all these activities were increasingly performed by different (sub)contractors. The oil companies holding a concession acted as principals, and often a number of oil companies

Guide wire template being prepared for lowering to the seabed.

An under-water blow-out preventer.

A wet subsea christmas tree for a well in the Gulf of Mexico. The pipe loop is typical for through the flowline pumping of tools (TFL).

*Back to the classroom: the
Shell million dollar school of
offshore technology
assembled engineers of
many oil companies.*

Shell International - Photographic Services London

combined their interests in exploiting one lease together. The operations outside the actual production sphere were left to others. Contrary to the 1940s, it later became rare that an oil company would take responsibility for the construction of installations. Generally, they were merely concerned with the strategic development of know-how.

In this way, an industrial sector grew around oil production consisting of shipyards, engineering firms, seismic surveyors, pipelaying firms, derrick ship operators, tugs, air transporters, consulting engineers etc.. This manifested itself as local industrial clusters, concentrated in Houston, New Orleans and Los Angeles.

Contracting and subcontracting was regarded as the common way of operating, which was remarkable as, during the 1960s, other industrial sectors became strong believers in far reaching vertical integration. Even on shore activities of the oil companies had never relied so extensively on subcontracting.

Some activities, like the design and building of drilling rigs, combined a range of traditional disciplines. Other than petroleum engineering and petroleum geology, which are specifically oil oriented, these were marine engineering, civil engineering, and mechanical engineering. Each of them contributed parts of its expertise to form a new body of knowledge called offshore technology. In spite of that, a separate offshore engineer has never developed. Technicians came from a specific discipline, and remained working along the lines of their original education without making a further move towards institutionalisation of an integrated new discipline.

Attempts to create such a new field were made by the end of the 1960s. In February 1966, a first international forum was held in Long Beach, California, under the name of Offshore Exploration Conference (OECon). It combined with an exhibition and set the tone for following organisations. After two OECconferences, the Society of Petroleum Engineers in cooperation with several other American technical societies took the initiative to announce a new, special conference solely devoted to offshore technology, the *Annual Offshore Technology Conference* (OTC), which was held for the first time in May 1969.[46] This conference would develop into a worldwide exchange of knowledge, however without any institutional effects in terms of offshore engineering as a discipline. The initiators took care to

The Jennifer project

Know-how generated in or for the offshore industry has found applications in other areas, such as structural analysis, oceanography, hydrodynamics or routing of ships. Offshore equipment by contrast has had little direct application outside of the offshore industry. The civil contracting world is using jack-up platforms for a variety of tasks (bridge construction, sewer outlet building, boring) but then, jack-up platforms are not really indigenous to the offshore world and civil jack-ups predate the offshore applications. The DeLong jacks were applied to self elevating jetties after the allied landing in Normandy. Military use of jack-up platforms was again considered around 1990, now as mobile launching pads for missiles. Small platforms have sometimes been used as targets for shooting exercises.

Bridge building in estuaries has borrowed different techniques from the drilling and installation contractors. An example is the crane vessel Svanen, designed and built for the Storebelt West bridge construction in Denmark in the early nineties and converted in 1994 for further work on a Canadian bridge project. More recently the offshore crane semi-submersible DB 102 has been used to erect the pylon of the new Erasmus bridge in Rotterdam.

No project involving offshore technology in another world can boggle the mind more than the saga of the Hughes Glomar Explorer. This 189 m long, 35 m wide ship was designed and built for the CIA in the early 1970s, for the single purpose of lifting a sunk Russian submarine from the deep waters (over 5000 m) near Hawaii, a project with code name Jennifer. The cover story, saying that the ship was intended for nodule mining, was not blown until the first - and last - lifting effort was about to start, and even then a lot of mystery remained. The eccentric millionaire Howard Hughes believed in the cause and provided the cover with his Summa Corporation. The budget for the project was over 200 million US dollars (1970). A dynamically positioned 'mining' ship was built by Sun Ship-builders, which contained an excessively large moonpool (60 x 22.5 m) with bottom covers, so that it looked more like a dry-dock than anything else. This dock was bridged with a heavy substructure at mid-length, which carried a derrick and pipe handling system, all placed on an oversized heave compensator supporting gimbals. In the deckhouse, the builder had to leave the major portion of one deck open for containers which were to be installed after delivery. These contained the acoustic instrumentation and control equipment for the operation. Under a separate contract, a large clamp, nicknamed Clementine, was built by Lockheed Ocean Systems, which would fit in the dry-dock. Even its loading on board was secretive. It was placed on the bottom of San Francisco Bay by means of a covered submersible dry-dock barge, denominated HMV-1, and then picked up by the ship. The gimballed and heave compensated derrick and pipe handling system served to lower this clamp over the Russian submarine.

How successful the expedition has been is a well kept secret. Once the cover was blown, the ship was without obvious further use until 1978, when it was selected for real deep ocean mining tests by the Ocean Minerals Company of Delaware. Nodule mining was tested by several consortia around 1980, and leaned heavily on offshore technology. Economic and legal aspects, however, put an early end to most of these developments, which techni-cally seemed quite feasible. Again the ship was laid up, but in 1996 it was remobilized for conversion into a deep water drill ship.

George Steinmetz/Transworld

Working offshore is tough and demanding. So, workers deserve some rest once in a while. This man uses his break to catch some sun on a helideck, somewhere in the Arabian Gulf.

keep a balance in the papers admitted from the various disciplines. The Offshore Technology Conference provided mostly the latest news in designs and developments, and not so much in-depth technology transfer. Its significance was and is in the first place being an international meeting ground for colleagues, competitors and old buddies in this new industry.

Other exhibitions and conferences have followed, such as the Offshore Northern Sea (ONS) in Stavanger and the Offshore Europe Conference in Aberdeen (both bi-annual events in even and odd years respectively) or the more scientifically oriented BOSS (Behaviour of Off-Shore Structures, every third year since 1976) but none have even come close to paralleling the OTC in size of the exhibition, number of attendants or diversity of papers.

After nearly 25 years the offshore sector had developed into an industry playing a small but significant role in oil production. Technical innovations made it possible to meet the challenge of working at sea. Research and modern methods of design had become accepted, and Shell's million dollar school of offshore technology was a pivotal event.

In its way Shell suggested to the offshore industry to give more attention to research and development, to execute research and development in the form of actual projects, and to organize these projects in partnership. The company had shown this concept with CUSS and later on in partnerships with individual entities, like IFP and Gusto.

In the seventies, Shell's concept was accepted and furthered. The industry created independently operating partnerships focused on R&D. An example was Subsea Equipment Associated Ltd. (SEAL). Also, individual companies started to work like 'brokers' in knowledge, trying to trigger joint industry projects. Organisations like MARIN in Europe and Deep Oil Technology in de United States are examples. These initiatives were remarkable, because the main line in industry was more towards vertical integrations and the creation of individual positions in knowledge, which were far away from movements toward cluster building which could be seen in de offshore industry.

George Steinmetz/Transworld

Work on rigs can be dangerous. Even with safety precautions one needs some daring to work on the riser of a semi-submersible.

Offshore Technology Conference Awards

Offshore technology grew as an interdisciplinary activity, involving engineers from different education, in particular civil engineering, mechanical engineering and naval architecture. The people involved exchanged ideas, views and small talk in their professional society meetings. A separate forum for offshore technology, however, did not exist during the first decades of the industry's growth.

In 1968 the Society of Petroleum Engineers (SPE) in co-operation with eight other professional societies took the initiative to organise a dedicated technical conference, the *Annual Offshore Technology Conference* (OTC). Starting in 1969, this event would take place annually in the early days of May in Houston, originally in a downtown convention hall, but after two years of rapidly growing participation, it was moved to the Astrohall, a livestock showground and convention centre next door to the famous Astrodome. It clearly responded to a need as shown by its astronomic growth. This was in part due to the need for a technical conference, and in part due to the exhibition which took place during the conference days. Very quickly, the exhibition took over as the main people attraction, and until today, the OTC is the main technical/commercial event in the offshore world.

Yet the OTC mostly provided the latest news on designs and developments, and not so much in-depth technology transfer. Its significance was and is in the first place being an international meeting ground for colleagues, competitors and old buddies in this new industry. The rapid growth of the commercial exhibition attracted literally every contractor and supplier from everywhere, who wanted to be seen as a serious offshore partner. During OTC days in the late 1970s all hotels in Houston were fully booked well in advance and so were international flights to its airport.

In the early years, while the US dominance was still clearly present, many new ideas and designs were displayed in the exhibition. With its growing size and internationalisation, the exhibitors tried to catch the attention of the audience by having their products and services highlighted by stunt men, magicians and most of all attractive girls, to such an extent that the organising committee had to request future exhibitors to restrict themselves more to the substance of their business. It probably was a typical attitude of an industry in which terms as bigger, newer, faster, better always strove for the first place. Exhibits at the OTC during its growing years were competing with each other in size, vigour, ingenuity and most of all visibility, which was hoped to provide a competitive edge. The general feeling was that you had to be there, and had to present a paper to be considered successful. When the increasing cost of participation and the decline of profits in the service industry stopped the growth of the OTC in 1983 (in 1984 the exhibition frequency was changed to bi-annual, but immediately after 1984 this idea was abandoned again), the 'phenomenon' OTC entered into a more stable course, still providing an important place to present new ideas or equipment, but no longer the absolute Mecca of the industry, where the visitor was buried under an avalanche of exuberant displays, company representatives, good-looking girls, gifts, tokens and brochures, followed by long evenings at the many courtesy parties in Houston hotels. The OTC had matured into what it was always intended to be: a professional meeting ground.

Related to the technology transfer at conferences is the setting of rules and regulations. ABS published their first Rules for Building and Classing Offshore Mobile Drilling Units in 1968 at the request of the industry's MODU operators committee. The later IMCO Rules for Mobile Offshore Drilling Units were based on these. In 1978, ABS started an offshore division and its requirements for structural integrity of platforms became the basis for governmental regulations for the US Outer Continental Shelf. Across the Atlantic, Lloyds Register and Det Norske Veritas developed their own rules for construction and classification of rigs and platforms. The Norwegian and British authorities published regulations in view of their concern for human safety. In November 1987, in an unusual initiative, Shell assembled the owners and designers of jack-up platforms, because of concerns about discrepancies in design and analysis methods. The result was a sort of self-ruling of the industry, which was published under the auspices of SNAME as a Guideline for Site Specific Assessment of Mobile Jack-Up Units, together with a Recommended Practice.

Year	Visitors x 1000	Award winning person	For	Award winning company	For
1969	4				
1970	12				
1971	11	J.A. Stratton (Ford Found.)	'Our Nation and the Sea'	Shell Oil	Many offshore innovations
1972	16	J.L. Goldman (F&G)	Pioneering MODU design	Humble Oil	NW passage SS Manhattan
1973	22	T.D. Barrow (Exxon)	Promotion of offshore affairs	Global Marine	Design Glomar Challenger
1974	34	W.M. Ewing (Marine Biomedical Institute - UT)	Geological/geophysical research		
1975	51	H.D. Hedberg (Gulf)	Geology/geophysics technology	Chicago Bridge	Sea floor oil storage units
1976	62	A. Lubinski (Amoco)	Technology & co-operative research	Texas A&M	Education & technology
1977	66	A.J. Laborde (Odeco)	Evolution of drilling rig technology	Phillips Petroleum	Concrete tank Ekofisk
1978	80	C.J. Lambertsen (University of Pennsylvania)	Hyperbaric physiology	IHC Holland	Innovative equipment
1979	79	G.M. Pavey (Seismic Eng.)	Advancing seismology equipment	Honeywell	Dynamic positioning
1980	90	R.C. Crooke (Global)	Glomar Challenger & Explorer	Exxon	Diverless subsea production
1981	100	L.S. St.Amant (LCCMR)	Coastal and estuarine environment	Gulf Universities & Research Consortium	Understanding the effects of offshore act. on environment
1982	108	F. Huntsinger (Vetco)	50 years innovator of equipment	Shell Oil	Cognac platform
1983	59	P.R. Vail (Exxon)	Geological/physical interpretation	Cameron Ironworks	Caisson subsea completion
1984	3	R.L. Geer (Shell)	Floating drilling & industry coop.	Exxon	Lena guyed tower
1985	56	H. Madlock (Earth Techn. Corp) & L. C. Reese (UT)	Research in offshore foundation	Conoco	Hutton TLP
1986	28	W.H. Mayne (Geosource)	Seismic data analysis	McClelland	Geotechnical engineering
1987	26	L.B. Curtis (Conoco)	Hutton TLP and other innovations	Scripps Institute	8 decades research and technology development
1988	26	W.H. Silcox (Chevron)	Pioneering platform & subsea eqt.	Norwegian Contractors	Concrete platforms
1989	26	B.H. Johansson (Canmar)	Arctic developments and vessels	Placid	Deep water floating prod.
1990	31	H. Allen (Cameron)	Offshore well control eqt.	Halliburton Geophysical Serv.	3D seismic marine survey
1991	34	H.G. Delauze (Comex)	Deep diving & ROV's	Heerema	Semisub twin crane vessels
1992	35	M.M. Backus (UT Austin)	Pioneering in 3D seismic	Petrobras	Deep water production techn.
1993	33	F.P. Dunn (Shell)	Outstanding leadership	Freeport-McMoRan	Mining + oil & gas prod.
1994	33	B. McClelland (McClelland)	Pioneering in soil mechanics	Brown & Root	Design & construction
1995	33	J.B. Weidler (Brown & Root)	World-wide structural engineering	Coflexip	Flexible steel pipe
1996	36	C.G. Langner (Shell)	Pipelay innovations	Conoco	Concrete TLP
1997	44	E.E. Horton (DOT)	TLP development	Amoco	Liuhua field project

Chapter 4

The North Sea
'Petroleum, for once, just where it can be used'[1]

'There is methane under the North Sea. British Petroleum's find of a show of natural gas with its first well in Block 48/6, about 40 miles east of the Humber estuary, is more encouraging than any of the companies prospecting on Britain's share of the Continental Shelf could have counted on as soon as this.'[2]

In 1964, BP was one of the few companies to get permission to drill in the North Sea. In May 1965 work started and in September the first find was reported in what became the West Sole field. Drilling took place with the Sea Gem, a construction barge owned by the Compagnie d'Exploration Pétrolière that had been rebuilt into a drilling unit. This jackup stood on ten cylindrical legs. It stood firmly when the first gas occurrence was found. It stood steady when a second deeper reservoir was hit in November. On the 9th of December drilling reached the target depth of 10000 ft and was suspended. Then, on 27 December, during preparations for the tow to a new location, the Sea Gem capsized and sank in the North Sea.[3] BP's pride of being the first to find gas offshore Western Europe was overshadowed by a hard confrontation with the risks of working offshore in this area.

BP found gas in the North Sea and became the 'Kerr-McGee' of a new offshore province. Like in the 1947 Kerr-McGee case BP's spectacular news led to speculations in newspaper reports which later turned out to be over-optimistic, and the follow up to this success was not as massive as was expected. The immediate euphoria also tended to obscure the long history leading up to the event.
This chapter is dedicated to the history of oil and gas

British Petroleum

Sea Gem was the first to find gas on the British part of the North Sea, but was tragically lost shortly after the discovery.

in Europe, back to the prewar years in Germany, The Netherlands and Great Britain, and ending just before the 1973 oil crisis.

1. Oil and gas in Western Europe

As early as the 1920s Germany produced oil from fields mainly in the Hannover region. In terms of quantity and profit, production was not very spectacular. After being elected in 1933, Hitler nationalised all oil and gas reserves, hoping to create a strategic reserve.
But Germany would never become a great producer. Between 1933 and 1945 Germany mainly had to rely on oil from Austria as the Hannover area did not fulfil initial expectations, in spite of great efforts. The adjacent territories occupied after 1940, like The Netherlands, were not of great help either as sabotage

Bob Fleumer Aerial Photography

Hydrocarbon carrying formations do not care where coastlines are. At Ameland (one of the Dutch Wadden Islands) one can observe the difference between a gas production site on land and offshore. On land, available space usually is not an issue, but offshore platforms are compact by definition.

and operator's go-slow policy frustrated developments thoroughly.[4] Moreover, there was not much oil there anyway.

In The Netherlands, the 1810 Mining Act had made the state the owner of all underground natural resources. The Dutch government gave a concession to the Bataafsche Petroleum Maatschappij to search and drill in nearly all Dutch provinces. The presence of oil in the ground was established, but it seemed that quantities were rather limited. A first find was reported near the German border, and in 1930 oil was found by sheer luck near The Hague. During an exhibition on oil winning in the Dutch East Indies, a drilling rig was built for promotional and educational purposes. After six weeks of demonstration drilling, traces of oil were found at a depth of 450 m.

The German occupation enabled German authorities to explore on both sides of the Dutch-German border, and in 1943 locations near Coevorden and Schoonebeek were found to contain commercial quantities of oil. After the war, exploration and production rights were given to a Shell-Esso joint venture, the Nederlandse Aardolie Maatschappij (NAM).[5]

In Great Britain the majority of concessions was obtained by the Anglo-Iranian Oil Company (which became BP). The 1934 Petroleum Production Act assigned all potential reserves to the Crown and regulated exploration and production. BP's efforts were not very rewarding. Gas was found in Yorkshire in 1937. Two years later, oil was located near Nottingham but, together with a series of later finds, this led to only a very moderate production which was virtually nothing compared to the huge quantities of BP's own oil in Iran.[6]

Western Europe did not appear very rich in oil, but then oil and gas were not considered vital sources of energy. Coal was much more important. As late as 1950, 70% of West Germany's energy was supplied by coal, whereas oil held just 5%. Great Britain and The Netherlands, being the seats of BP and Shell, came to a 13 and 24% oil share respectively, which could not be called a major part.[7]

After the war, governments extended the search for mineral resources to the bottom of the North Sea. In 1933 and 1938 Germany had already done some gravity surveys offshore. In 1948, results of a Dutch survey were added, and in 1951 and 1953 the US Navy assisted with three refraction measurements in the Dogger Bank area. A German survey between 1950 and 1956 led to a first activity, some 4 km off Cuxhaven. In 1957 a large scale geological survey started, financed by Nieder Saksen. Its results were published in 1962 and 1963.[8] During the 1950s the general impression was that the geological formations in which oil was found on land, continued underneath the North Sea. However, the oil companies showed little interest in these offshore surveys. They expected the reserves to be as modest as those on land, and the high cost of operations made exploration even less attractive. Elsewhere, oil could be found at only a fraction of the investments, which was a very rational argument for not engaging in any offshore gamble. A slow increase of oil consumption in Europe could be noticed, leading to growing imports, but this demand could easily be met by Middle East supplies.

Slochteren

Having lost most of their colonies, the Western European countries could be regarded as the world's have-nots where oil was concerned. For The Netherlands, the situation changed dramatically when on 22 July 1959 natural gas was found in Slochteren, in the province of Groningen. The NAM discovered a gas deposit at 3000 m depth, that later turned out to be the largest in the Western world.[9] *'New school book phrase: The Netherlands abound with mineral resources'*, and *'Too much gas already'* were the immediate newspaper headlines.[10] Indeed, the nation appeared to be richly compensated for the loss of most of its colonies, and an unmistakable euphoria pervaded the country.

The 1959 discovery, however, was in fact not the first one. In 1955, NAM had been searching for oil near Ten Boer, 10 km North-West of Slochteren. Instead of oil, they encountered traces of gas at 2800 m. Gas was not considered commercially interesting, so the hole was abandoned.[11]

The size of the Slochteren findings was recognized during the early 1960s, and this led to a reconside-

ration of the earlier results of North Sea prospecting. Would, perhaps, the North Sea be equally promising? Oil prices of the day made it not worthwhile to start drilling right away, but the area suddenly became strategically important. The United States had come to consider oil as a vital strategic reserve in the Cold War. The 1956 Suez crisis had threatened European oil supplies. Developments in the Middle East made it more and more difficult for the oil companies to secure their control over Arab oil. All this added to the value of North Sea gas, and perhaps oil reserves. Operators and independents, facing a surplus in drilling rigs after Eisenhower's import bans, turned their attention to the North Sea. There, they hoped for an opportunity to use their expensive rigs, which they often had leased for a number of years.

However, the governments were slow to react. In 1958 the United Nations had already initiated the partitioning of the North Sea, but ratification of the UN proposals by the North Sea countries and negotiations between the governments involved, took place only during the 1960s. The Danish government granted its entire area to a single company in a fifty year concession, which understandably did not incite the monopolist concessionary to great speed. Norway enjoyed a satisfying economical situation, and did not expect anything commercial from their deep North Sea. The Dutch were preoccupied by creating markets for their Slochteren gas, whereas Germany believed that its economic development profited best from the import of cheap foreign oil. Only the British government, fearing a growing balance of payments deficit and structural unemployment in Scotland, was in a hurry. It turned out that this eagerness would seriously frustrate policy.[12]

2. Governments and offshore

Partitioning the North Sea

Before any concessions could be given, the adjacent countries first had to agree on the division of the North Sea. The 1958 United Nations Convention on the Continental Shelf held in Geneva was the first step

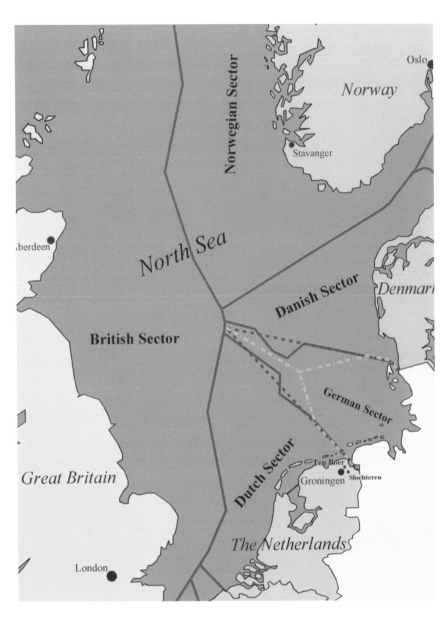

The division of the North Sea did not come about without arguments on fairness. The map shows the German claim in green, the Danish/Dutch claims in yellow, and the final division in red. Also Groningen City and the two villages, Ten Boer and Slochteren, where gas was discovered, are indicated.

towards an arrangement. The Convention offered a combination of two demarcation principles to guide negotiations on the actual allotment. The Continental Shelf was limited by the 200 m depth contour. The border between two nations in water less than 200 m deep was established by the median line between the coastlines of both countries. The North Sea countries, with the exception of Germany ratified the treaty in 1964.[13]

These principles left enough room for discussion on the reasonableness and fairness of any subdivision. Small islands far off a country's actual coast could disproportionately enlarge that country's claims on a part of the Shelf, whereas a strongly concave coast line, like the German coast, resulted in just a very small portion.

This implied that, in the original subdivision, Germany would have only a very minor part of the Continental Shelf. The German argument that the shape of its coast line did not reflect the nation's size and importance within Europe was brought for the International Court of Justice. In 1967 the Court sent the parties involved back to the negotiating table to reach an agreement based on an amended convention act.[14] Amendments had created the possibility to abandon the median line concept and draw an imaginary coast line seaward. In spite of Dutch and Danish preference for the original principle, Germany was granted a considerably larger part of the Continental Shelf in 1971.[15]

For the history of exploration, the discussion between Norway, Denmark and Great Britain was much more important. Along the Norwegian coast, a deep trench cuts into the North Sea. The question was whether this trench would be part of the Continental Shelf or not. In the positive case, the median line principle was to be applied, resulting in a considerable part of the North Sea to become Norwegian. If the trench was supposed to be the end of the Shelf, Norway's part would end just off its coast. In that case, Denmark and even more so Britain could claim property rights over a much larger area. Although the Norwegian position was not entirely hopeless, Britain and Denmark probably held stronger legal positions. However, they did not benefit from this advantage. Denmark being in conflict with Germany over the median line principle, decided to remain a strict follower of that concept and thus left ground to Norway. Britain was in a hurry to start exploration, but Norway was not. Moreover expectations for the Northern North Sea were low if not zero at all, whilst expectations in the Southern North Sea weren't high either. The Northern North Sea was deep and therefore expensive. As early as 1963 both countries agreed on a partitioning in which the trench was considered part, or a minor interruption of the Continental Shelf.[16]

The ultimate division of the Continental Shelf gave Great Britain the major share (46.7%). Norway obtained 25.1%, The Netherlands 10.7%, Denmark 8.8%, and Germany 6.8%. Great Britain, The Netherlands and Denmark saw their territory more than doubled. Norway had a per capita area of the North Sea that was 57 times as large as the German per capita area. But it was by no means evident that anyone would benefit from it.[17]

Government policy and offshore operations in the North Sea

It is only with hindsight that some authors have labeled government policy on offshore operations in various countries during the 1960s as a remarkable series of blunders based on ignorance. Such hindsight is strongly influenced by the enormous boom in offshore operations during the next decade, and it does not do justice to the historical situation. Nevertheless, the six year gap between the Slochteren discovery and Sea Gem's discovery requires explanation.

By the end of the 1950s the situation on the international oil market was very favourable to consumers. The ending of the Suez crisis in 1956 leading to even lower oil prices had emphasized this. The United States mainly used American oil, whereas the European countries relied on Arab oil, the price of which was controlled by the large oil companies. The US import restrictions of 1959 created something close to a surplus of Middle East oil for the European market. All this greatly reduced the importance of possible European oil reserves. Even a strategic role was not used as an argument for more intensive exploration,

Photo Sea Sky Martin

Photo Sea Sky Martin

Helicopters are essential for the logistics of most offshore operations. Many thousands of offshore workers worldwide are flying back and forth in shifts to keep activities going. Not every-

body realises that this commuting is one of the most risky aspects of offshore work. Helicopter passengers wear survival suits and need special training to be prepared for the worse.

A net on the helideck of a North Sea jackup provides for safe operations in this windy and wet environment. Helicopters can be attached to the net by hooks, to avoid being blown away.

Photo Sea Sky Martin

Nothing compares to working on the drill floor. The name these workers are known by is an accurate illustration of this. The picture shows 'roughnecks' handling – or rather footing – the tongs to unscrew the top of the drill string.

nor was there any serious reference to a trade balance that could be disturbed by excessive oil imports. The expanding economies of the 1950s and 1960s had enough dollars to spend.

Apart from that, none of the North Sea countries had a strong tradition in the petroleum industry. It was completely absent in Norway and Denmark, and in Germany the Allied powers initially had prohibited the rebuilding of German owned downstream facilities. The only oil processing industries were owned by foreign companies. Britain had BP, which was partly state owned, and Shell which was partly Dutch, but both companies operated abroad. The Netherlands had its own oil industry in 'its' Shell, but Rotterdam which became a mainport for European oil and the Slochteren gas shifted the focus of attention to marketing and trading of oil and gas, away from exploration and production. France, finally, held a special position, related to its declining Algerian oil position and its general industry policy.[18]

European governments, hardly involved in oil production, not worried about oil supply and oil prices, hardly experienced in oil politics, and finally enjoying limited dependency on oil, were in a different situation in comparison with the United States. Expectations for on land drilling were low, strategic reserves were not a political issue and since all resources belonged to the states, exploration couldn't start without governments moving first.

But, the oil companies were willing to explore the North Sea, although oil prices were still low. As a few oil companies got interested, others followed.

BP lost power in Iran and experienced slow progress in Alaska. They hoped for preferential treatment in the British North Sea. American independents suffered a slow down in exploration in the Gulf of Mexico. Drilling rigs, representing an enormous amount of (leased) capital, passed the time idle in American waters. Exploration activities in other areas would be very welcome.[19]

Germany

In post war Germany, oil supply was mainly in the hands of foreign companies. Initially the Allied powers

did not allow the Germans to build refineries or extract oil from coal. By the time the Allies left room for more autonomy, German politics were strongly dominated by liberals who welcomed foreign investment, so the already powerful position of the major oil companies was left untouched. Characteristic for the situation was that Texaco's take-over of Deutsche Erdöl AG in 1966 was welcomed by the federal government as an American investment in the German economy. German liberal federal policy was based on the belief that oil would be abundantly available and that especially the American oil companies would guarantee future supply. This point of view could not be affected by the opposition's argument, in 1955, that the combined foreign companies seemed to act like a monopolist. The government simply replied that these companies were ready to invest and that they guaranteed low prices.

Also the government did not have many opportunities to give to national enterprise. There was a legal restriction to the nation's oil stock, which should not exceed a 65 days stock in tanks.[20]

Photo Sea Sky Martin

Photo Sea Sky Martin

The top of the drill string, where it passes the rotary table, shows all essential functions: the hook for vertical handling, the hose and swivel to pump drilling mud down, and the rotary table and kelly to impart the rotating motion to the string and drilling bit downhole.

The drilling process and draw works are controlled from the drillmaster's cabin.

In the early 1950s a federal organization, Prakla, had carried out some geological surveys in the North Sea, but this had not triggered federal offshore ambitions. The private sector acted much faster, and shortly after 1959 a consortium of American oil companies and German mining related firms was established. This consortium asked the Oberbergamt (the mining authority of four Länder) for concessions to start drilling in the North Sea. Then the federal government stated that the North Sea belonged to federal juris-diction. Having established its competence, the federation charged the Oberbergamt with the granting of concessions in the North Sea anyway. This resulted in temporary arrangements in 1964, in order that the consortium could start operations. Drilling activities turned out to be disappointing, as only nitrogen was found.[21]

A few years later, new offshore activities developed. The Israeli-Arab conflict of 1967 and the growing share of oil in energy supply made the federal government change its policy. It decided to establish a state oil company, that should control the price and supply of oil and allow German firms to produce and process oil. This company, Deutsche Erdölversorgungsgesellschaft Deminex, started in 1969 as a consortium of seven German firms. In 1973 Deminex reported to have obtained concessions covering a total of 200 km², mainly offshore. Together with BP, it was to drill in the North Sea and, in cooperation with the Nigerian National Oil Company, off the coast of Nigeria.[22]

Norway

Expectations concerning the Norwegian shelf were anything but high. A large oil company's geologist even promised to drink all oil that would eventually be produced in the area. Neither the government, nor the companies showed great interest. Only Phillips Petroleum Company asked for a concession to drill a wildcat. The request was made in 1962, even before Norway and Great Britain had agreed on their shares of the Shelf. In 1963 Phillips and some other firms were allowed to do seismic surveys. This led to rather positive results, but the Norwegian government still remained unconvinced of the presence of oil and gas in the Northern part of the Shelf. Once the negotiations with Denmark and Britain had been concluded, drilling concessions were given in 1965. These covered the entire Southern part of the Norwegian Shelf, which was considered at least potentially interesting. Not many conditions were imposed, even participation of Norwegian industry was not included.[23]

The contracting companies concentrated in the southernmost corner. As was expected, the first drilling attempts were without success. Phillips nevertheless continued exploration as it was convinced that at least some blocks would contain oil. Some others seriously thought of pulling out. When in 1969 Phillips finally struck oil the mood changed completely, not only within the oil industry, but also in the Norwegian government and among the Norwegian public.

'We have survived the astonishment of discovering oil here. We never dreamt of it', Norway's Minister of Industry, Mr. Rostoft declared in 1971.[24]

From that moment the policy changed. Some described the years that followed as a period of go-slow policy with a heavy nationalist smell. Perhaps regretting its earlier spontaneous massive handing out of concessions, the government decided to take its time to develop a consistent offshore policy. Within Norwegian political circles there was a good deal less disagreement than, e.g., in Britain. Setting up a Norwegian oil industry was considered important, and the economy should not be frustrated by uncontrolled growth. Government intervention was a very useful tool to do the job properly. In order to keep developments on the Continental Shelf at the right, controllable pace, and allow Norwegian industry to react accordingly, foreign companies were invited to operate in combination with Norwegian firms, in order to let the latter learn the job. Therefore, the Labour government proposed the establishment of a state oil company that had to take part in offshore activities. This led to the birth of Statoil, based in Stavanger, in 1972. In the following years, Statoil was to act as the main carrier of Norwegian offshore policy, which in its turn came to be a constant and active instrument for economic development.[25]

The Netherlands

Dutch policy was entirely different, and to a certain extent hard to label. Abroad it was generally considered liberal, whereas Dutch firms complained of a lack of policy. It was not until 1969 that rules were fixed for the giving out of concessions, and only in 1974 the Dutch government presented a policy in which stimulating offshore activities was mentioned explicitly. Meanwhile licensing rounds were held in 1968, 1970 and 1972.[26]

As has been said, The Netherlands were overwhelmed by the 1959 discovery of gas in Groningen. When the extent of the deposits became clear, in 1962, the government decided that this treasure must be developed. In good Dutch trading tradition all attention went to marketing and selling the gas. Production was left to the Shell-Esso joint venture NAM, and the required investment and technological developments in which Dutch industry might participate were not made part of government policy. Main aspects of policy were securing a government take and creating a large home market. Bringing gas to the market was done by a new organisation, Gasunie, in which the state, the NAM and DSM participated. DSM, formerly De Staatsmijnen, was a state owned company which controlled most coal mining in the South of the country. When the mines were closed in the 1960s, DSM was transformed into a large chemical concern.[27]

It was a basic issue of the Dutch gas policy to have as much gas produced as possible. This idea still prevailed after the oil crisis. Immediate profits for the state by the gas sales were considered more important than a reduction of oil imports. Oil imports were profitable for the national economy as well, as a large part of the oil consumed in Europe was shipped via Rotterdam, where it was refined. Little by little, the government became dependent on gas sales, and decisions to increase production and allow for additional drilling were inspired by the needs of the national budget. As long as the gas deposits seemed inexhaustible, as was thought in the 1960s, there was no need to go and look elsewhere for new fields.[28]

Whereas governments in other countries intervened to create a strong national offshore industry, Dutch firms

Bob Fleumer Aerial Photography

When oil or gas is encountered, the potential production rate is tested by the exploration rig, in this case the jackup Neddrill 3. During testing, the production is flared. Note the size of the structure indicated by the man on the left.

received hardly any attention. Industry was just not on the politicians' mind. The Dutch government opted to not impose measures for protecting or favouring Dutch offshore industry. Instead it endeavoured to convince other countries of the advantage of free trade. *'Deliberately not pursuing a protectionist policy is in itself pursuing a policy'*, the director-general of the Ministry of Economic Affairs declared in 1984.[29]

In short, Dutch industry had to fight for a position in the North Sea offshore world by its own strength. Initially firms were successful because of a quick reaction to opportunities, but later some firms came to lag behind foreign competitors, supported by their respective governments.[30]

Although The Netherlands started to give concessions only by the end of the 1960s, drilling was carried out already before that time. The 1810 Mining Act allowed anyone to explore the earth, but reserves had to be proven, before licensing procedures could be started.[31]

Denmark

Denmark had already seen drilling rigs on its territory as early as 1936, when the American wildcatter F. Ravlin was given a concession for salt mining. With his Danish-American Prospecting Company (Dapco) Ravlin claimed to have found salt. When this salt turned out to be common salt that had been bought at a local grocer, Dapco was already in the hands of Gulf. After some time, Gulf sold Dapco and its concession to Esso, but Esso gave up its rights in 1959.[32]

The Danish A.P. Møller Group then offered to take over the concession, together with the rights on the Danish shelf. Møller argued that he couldn't imagine worse conditions than those which had been imposed on Gulf and Esso. The government's reaction was favourable, as in 1962 Møller was granted the sole right for exploration and production of oil and gas under the Danish Shelf and Jutland and the other islands. In this way, the government hoped to have secured the

Photo Sea Sky Martin

The jackup 'Dan King' is towed to its next location. The essence of mobile drilling equipment is mobility. Most MODU's, like this jackup platform, are to be towed by tugs or transported by specialised submersible barges. The wet ocean tow (by tugs) used to be the most risky episode in a jackup's life and has almost completely been substituted by dry tow (on a barge).

nation's offshore interests in the hands of a Danish firm, so a fair share of the future profits was expected to flow to the Danish treasury.

To exploit his fifty-year concession, Møller set up a consortium in which Shell, Gulf, Texaco and Socal participated. The government's conditions were very mild: a royalty was asked, and for the rest the consortium had to start production of one type of hydrocarbon (oil or gas) within a year, and production of the other one within the five following years. In an earlier version, the contract had insisted on 'commercial' production, but that adjective was deleted shortly afterwards. Oil and gas production was to be exempt from taxation, and Møller received substantial 'tax compensation'.[33]

France

In the international oil business, France is more associated with the service company started around 1920 by the Schlumberger brothers, than with oil reserves. France was not one of the lucky nations with an immense continental shelf. The country's main oil interests were in its former colony Algeria, but on the whole, France's position as an oil producing country was dwindling. In order to get a hold on the Algerian reserves, the Government activated state oil companies in the 1960s.[34]

Within France itself activities started in the early fifties, triggered by the large but difficult gas reservoir near Lac. An oil field was found in 1952 near Bordeaux by Esso. The French believed this field would extend into the Gulf of Biscay.

Seeking energy independence, the French government used this opportunity to organize offshore research and development intended to lead to an independent offshore industry, like it tried in other sectors (such as nuclear, aircraft an motorcar industry). France already had a strong tradition of state industries, and the government had large interests in a number of sectors, in order to create a technologically leading position. The French never found oil in their Gulf, but in the process they more or less accidentally became prepared for North Sea and West Africa offshore. France managed to create leading companies in all aspects of offshore technology, in some cases as early as in the 1960s. Examples are Technip for engineering, C.G. Doris for platforms, Comex for diving, Neptune for drilling and Coflexip for flexible pipes. Some of these - like Technip and Coflexip - were offsprings of the Institute Français du Pétrole (IFP), itself a non-profit organisation focused on research and development. Innovation policy in specific areas would greatly contribute to the position of French oil companies operating in the North Sea during the 1970s and 1980s.[35]

Great Britain

British policy concerning the North Sea is most complex and has been the subject of a large number of publications. During the 1960s Great Britain held a special position. It was the only North Sea country to press forward developments in the North Sea, and also the only economy that was conscious of a number of worrying trends. But Britain was also the only nation where fundamental differences of opinion existed between political parties on future policy in oil matters. Every new government was to initiate a drastic change of policy.

The early 1960s saw a Conservative government developing legislation for the exploitation of the continental shelf. In 1964 the first concession could be given out. The British were most worried by the idea that it might take a long time to get actual production of oil and gas started, as oil prices were low and offshore operations were expensive. It was feared that the oil companies would sit on their concessions, waiting for better times. Therefore, the concessions held stipulations to prevent such behaviour. This of course made exploration rights less attractive, but compensation was found in low pricing of the licences. In doing so, it was also hoped that the Arab countries would refrain from levying higher royalties and taxes. Some groups suggested that British oil companies should have first access to the North Sea, but the government feared that these companies were unable to comply with its requirements of speed and efficiency, so the idea was dropped.[36] The oil companies themselves were rather content with the way the government granted concessions.

The conservative government managed to get British offshore activities under way faster than any of the other North Sea countries. But when BP found the first gas, in 1965, a Labour government had taken over. This new government noticed that the Treasury hardly had a share in the success. And it was considered a shame that mainly American firms using American equipment operated in the North Sea. It was decided that these points were to be combined with a general policy to redress a growing deficit on the balance of payments and to prevent a threatening collapse of the Scottish shipbuilding industry.[37]

To start with, all offshore gas was to be sold to the British Gas Council, a state enterprise that was given the authority to fix the gas price. However, this was not a success. The first gas deposits that were found, were not as large as the Groningen field, and the price British Gas was willing to pay discouraged the operators. Only in 1985 British Gas would lose its monopoly. Forcing British Gas to pay prices, which gave oil companies the opportunity to explore new gasfields, became the new policy.[38]

The other frustrating fact for the government was that most engineering work for the first gas fields fell into the hands of the American firms of Brown & Root and J. Ray McDermott. As far as construction took place in Europe, mainly Dutch shipyards did the job. When in 1967 a second concession was granted, Labour firmly insisted on a greater British involvement. At least part of the work would have to be contracted to firms in Britain. But in spite of these stipulations, offshore operations on the British shelf continued to be carried out mainly by foreign companies and non-British contractors provided the equipment.[39]

The main British success was its fast first reaction to get offshore activities going. Continuing changes of policy after 1973 proved unable to secure the desired large share in the success for the state, industry and British society as a whole. Or, as a Dutch researcher put it in 1971: *'The British government proved to be a master in fishing behind the nets!'.*[40]

3. Activities between 1959 and 1973

Before the actual concessions were granted, large scale geological surveys in the North Sea took place in the early 1960s. Gravimetric and seismic surveys were done by several newly specialised firms, next to the larger oil companies' own teams. The surveys aimed at a comprehensive picture of the Continental Shelf and its potential oil and gas deposits. Based on that knowledge the oil companies made their bids on specific areas within a concession.

Seismic survey was the most important type of preliminary investigation. Nevertheless, it is usually not sufficient to rely on a single survey of a particular area, since results depend to a large extent on the interpretation of the raw data. During the 1960s, a vivid trade in the results of seismic surveys existed between interested oil companies.[41]

A great number of new techniques, like the use of tape recording and digital methods had strongly improved the reliability of the results of seismic surveys. In 1961, a digital system was used by the Geophysical Service for Mobil and Texaco, and two years later it was offered to other companies as well. Geophysical Service, which had started in 1931 as the first of its kind, was owned by Texas Instruments. It had seven teams working on the North Sea during the 1960s, doing about one third of all the seismic work in the area.[42]

The first wells were drilled 24 km off the Dutch coast at Kijkduin in 14 m water depth, between 1961 and 1963. NAM used a relatively small jackup named Triton, which Shell had built in 1961. Three wells were sunk, but none was successful. As the Dutch government was not inclined to take any legislative measures at short notice, the operations were not continued.[43]

In 1962 a consortium of companies in Germany announced drilling plans. It took some skirmishing between the Oberbergamt and the federal government before permission was given in 1964. The consortium contracted Reading & Bates to sink wells with their jackup Mr. Louie. The first attempt was a direct hit, as Mr. Louie struck a high pressure deposit of nitrogen, which resulted in a blow-out. In spite of this,

Exploration starts with seismic surveying. This seismic vessel trails six 'streamers' attached to outriggers, and two paravanes. The streamers contain hydrophones which record the echoes of sound waves emitted by an airgun on the ship.

Bob Fleumer Aerial Photography

Mr. Louie was able to continue its work, and two more wells were sunk, both dry holes. For the next ten years, no further attempts were made on the German shelf.[44]

In British waters, work started in December 1964. Amoseas, a joint venture of Socal and Texaco, chartered Mr. Cap, a seven year-old jackup built by Barnsdall. Gulf, too, started drilling, using Global Marine's new drilling vessel Glomar IV. As said before, BP was the first to be successful in British waters in September 1965, when its drilling unit Sea Gem found gas. At first, this rapid result was regarded as a proof of British decisiveness. Six days after the good news, the price was announced. Sea Gem had capsized, killing 13 of 23 people on board. But the British government did not issue additional safety measures and the search for gas continued. Four months after the tragedy, Shell and Esso found gas, as did Amoco one month later. Within a very short time, four gas deposits had been discovered, and offshore working in the North Sea could be said to have started.[45] However, reactions were anything but over-enthusiastic:

'Six more discoveries fast on the heels of BP's find removed any fears that the entire North Sea play might be a complete debacle. But jubilation gave way to new apprehension when Britain's Gas Council refused to offer producers what they felt was a fair price. The U.K. marketing hassle, Holland's failure to adopt acceptable rules for opening its waters, and dismal drilling results off Germany tended to cloud the picture as drillers passed the halfway mark of their third winter in the hostile North Sea.'[46]

Working in the North Sea was dangerous, indeed. The Gulf of Mexico had its occasional hurricanes, but the North Sea seemed to be stormy all the time. This put a heavy strain on the rigs, which had been built for Gulf of Mexico conditions, and some of them failed. *'Bad weather, for which the North Sea is notorious, affects every offshore operation: survey, diving, mooring, installation, pipelaying, and communications, and bad weather can develop rapidly with little warning. Over the sea as a whole there are fewer than 2% of calms throughout the year.'*[47] Apart from the bad weather,

George Steinmetz/Transworld

The results of a seismic survey are exposed on a glass screen. Two geophysicists are investigating the subsoil structure for potentially productive layers.

Bob Fleumer Aerial Photography

Bob Fleumer Aerial Photography

Separate platforms for the export risers, the wellheads, the living quarters and the production facilities. West Sole A installed in April 1967 in 27 m water depth.

The riser platform of this Leman F facility is supported by a lift jacket, the production deck was self floating and self elevating. After installation, the DeLong type jacking systems were removed. Amoco installed these platforms in 1975 in 19 m water depth.

there were more problems to face. Surface currents, trenches, but also a large number of cables crossing the North Sea could make pipelaying a frustratingly slow business. A special hazard was the presence of unexploded mines from World War II. Before a rig or platform could be installed, the location often had to be cleared of explosives first.[48]

At the start, there was virtually no specific knowledge concerning operations offshore Europe. American experience was rooted in other areas, and it appeared to be insufficient for the North Sea. The British gas finds challenged offshore engineers to develop appropriate technologies for the problems encountered in this specific area. As it was clear that straight-forward transfer of Gulf of Mexico concepts was inadequate, a European offshore industry developed in the late 1960s and 1970s which successfully concentrated on this local market of rigs and platforms. Originally France had a lead because of their early organised technology development. The Dutch and British industries followed suit, and ultimately outgrew the French thanks to their own North Sea sectors.

'The North Sea is [ ] in some respects taking on the role of a proving ground for new techniques, and in this aspect is undoubtedly working to the advantage of the emerging local industry. [It] has enabled European consulting design and contracting companies to compete on an equal footing with the traditional established (i.e., American) offshore companies', was Pendered and Taylor's conclusion in 1974.[49]

Striking oil

'It has been typical of the North Sea oil boom that a new field or discovery is almost instantly world-famous, often after only two or three wells have been completed. Then, except for those responsible for its development, interest quickly turns to a later find.'[50]

The most spectacular later find was that of oil, in Norwegian waters.
In 1962, Phillips had decided to join the North Sea offshore adventure in Norway. Seismic results in 1963 and 1964 made the company bid on some of the

278 blocks the Norwegian government had on offer. In 1967, Esso did the same.

For their operations, both firms used a semi-submersible. While the Ocean Viking for Phillips was still under construction in Norway, Esso's Ocean Explorer was damaged and Phillips ordered some changes in the Ocean Viking's design. A first test in shallow water led to some more adaptations.[51]

Then, Phillips was prepared for its task. But drilling went without satisfying discoveries for several months. In 1969, after several dry holes, Phillips was still left empty-handed. By that time, Amoco had also arrived on the Norwegian shelf, and Esso had just replaced Ocean Explorer by Glomar Grand Isle. Then came the moment for the Phillips management to act. *'Don't drill any more wells'* and *'Find interested companies who can sublease Ocean Viking'*, the head office summoned.[52] But there still was one well to drill before all five attempts planned in the concessions were completed. And this one was a success: Phillips found oil.

The discovery was made in a block numbered 2/4, which Phillips called the fifth block, or E. Earlier blocks had been given the names of fish, attached to the letter-indication of the block. Consequently, the E block became Echofish, a non-existing species, and in an attempt to translate it into Norwegian, the name was misspelt Ekofisk instead of Ekkofisk.[53]

Ekofisk was to become one of the most appealing fields in the North Sea. The next chapter will present its history as a special case study.

The oil find on the Norwegian shelf made other companies concentrate on the search for oil in British waters, and in due course they, too, met with success. Forties and Brent became Britain's largest fields. But the Ekofisk find also brought home a most disconcerting thought to the British government and public: unknowingly, in 1963 the government had not just given away a large part of the sea to their Norwegian counterparts, but also a vital source of income.

4. Innovations in the North Sea

Early activities in the North Sea depended heavily on American experience, but even more on American rigs. A large amount of equipment, being more or less idle in the Gulf of Mexico, was shipped to the North Sea. Soon it was discovered that this equipment didn't perform to expectations in the North Sea environment.

Innovation was required. Equipment had to be at least modified to North Sea conditions. This led to important changes in design of installations. The early years of the North Sea turned out to be extremely important in this respect, like also in the Gulf of Mexico the early years bred most of the new ideas. A further factor was the presence of what might be called technology clusters. In France, close contacts between the IFP, the oil companies and several contractors and industrial parties helped to create an innovative and productive environment for development of concepts. Likewise, in The Netherlands, the closeness of Shell, and some entrepreneurs like Heerema, De Groot and IHC Gusto who had focused on the offshore market, resulted in concentrated activity.

The semi-submersible drilling rig Ocean Viking drilling for oil in the Norwegian sector of the North Sea.

Phillips Petroleum Company Norway

Two SPM's ready for delivery show the size of even this small component.

Shuttle tanker Northia delivering oil from the Fulmar field to the Shell UK Anglesey terminal Single Point Mooring.

This section deals with some examples of technological concepts that were significantly influenced by North Sea operations.

Single Point Moorings

As early as 1959 the Dutch shipyard Gusto built a self-elevating drilling platform for Shell, called the Sea Shell. The cooperation between Gusto and Shell continued and resulted in a number of innovations including the Single Point Mooring or SPM. An SPM offered a solution to tanker loading or discharging offshore, where forces on a spread moored tanker frequently imposed limitations to operations. The SPM allowed a tanker to weathervane. Shell held a patent on the basic SPM, but a rather similar patent was granted to A.J. Schultz in New York.

The first SPM was produced by Gusto and delivered to Shell in 1959 for installation at Miri, Malaysia. In the same year the US firm Imodco supplied an SPM to the Swedish Navy at Dalaro, Sweden. By 1969, Gusto concentrated its commercial - and later all - SPM activities in SBM Inc and for many years Imodco and SBM were the main players and fierce competitors in this specialised sector. The important break-through into the offshore world was made around 1970, when two SPM's at the Ekofisk field enabled early production and export of oil by shuttle tankers. This application formed the overture towards new ideas in offshore production, ultimately resulting in the Floating Production, Storage and Offloading (FPSO) systems of the 1990s.

Most SPM's however found applications near locations where harbours were too small for the ever bigger tankers, where harbours were just non existent, or where governments didn't allow tankers to enter a harbour.[54]

Semi-submersibles

Semi-submersibles built for the Gulf of Mexico were to some extent derived from the last and largest submersibles, like Kerr-McGee's Transworld Rig 54. The semi-submersibles could be recognized by bottle-shaped columns interconnected by relatively light trusses.

In the North Sea environment these semis appeared

too light. Waves were much higher, requiring larger air gaps, and heavier anchoring systems placed a penalty on deckloads. Maintaining the stability of a semi with high airgap required wider spacing of the columns, and the heavier deckload asked for larger floaters and columns. Innovations in drilling equipment and the use of heavier and more mud circulation equipment contributed to the growth in size.

Early North Sea semi-submersibles, mostly built in European shipyards, tended to be of the catamaran type. The platforms were supported by two long submersible hulls and two to four columns on each of these two floaters, all interconnected by heavy bracing. North Sea semi-subs were equipped with heave

compensators to allow continuation of drilling during bad weather. Some companies experimented with different shapes. The most extreme probably was the Transworld 61 (1979), which was a hybrid between ship and semi, and contained jacking systems as well to transform from one type of rig into the other. It was used as a production unit for the Trilha field offshore Brazil from 1984 to 1989. A second unit of the same design, the Transocean III, perished in the North Sea during its first mission in 1974.

Semi-submersibles in the North Sea found there application in drilling, but also in pipelaying and lifting. In 1973, Hamilton Brothers decided to produce the small Argyll field in the British sector of the North

In a number of North Sea fields, oil is exported by shuttle tanker instead of a pipeline, sometimes as a temporary facility. Here, a tanker is moored to an articulated loading platform (ALP) at the Statfjord field.

Transworld rig 58, converted to the worlds first floating production platform in 1975, producing oil from the UK sector of the North Sea.

Transworld rig 61, was a hybrid structure: part jackup, part semi-submersible, and mostly ship during transport from one site to another.

Rotterdamse Droogdok Maatschappij

This photo was made in May 1966. The scene does not need comments.

Sea by means of subsea wellheads and a converted semi-submersible, the Transworld Rig 58. This system became a pioneer with many followers, in particular in Brazil. It is noteworthy, that the combination of three independent developments, viz. a semi-submersible floater, subsea wellhead trees and an SPM loading buoy made the Hamilton approach possible.

Subsea systems

Subsea wellheads had been tested off California and in the Gulf of Mexico. By 1972, a total of 72 systems had been supplied for water depths to about 100 m by five US firms. Four of them were used in the early production system at Ekofisk. All were essentially wet trees, modified from on-land application to be used under water. In the summer of 1972, Shell installed a first dry wellhead chamber produced by Lockheed Petroleum Services in the Gulf of Mexico, off Louisiana, in 115 m water depth. Instead of divers, 'normal' technicians could do maintenance and other work on the tree in this atmospheric chamber.

A European initiative towards a similar development was to form the SEAL group, backed by BP, CFP, Mobil, Westinghouse and a group of smaller companies. SEAL

set out to develop both atmospheric and wet systems with modular components. After a few years of limited success, the company disappeared from the scene, but the course towards under water technology was not to be changed anymore.[55]

Supply boats

The early operations in the southern North Sea were supported by supply boats over form the United States. Basicly they were all descendants of the Ebb Tide. It quickly transpired that Gulf of Mexico boats were too light for the North Sea environment. European shipowners saw their chance to participate in the offshore game, and started a development which resulted in extremely versatile and robust work horses for supplying the increasing number of platforms. Designs were modified for particular jobs such as towing, handling the anchors of semi-submersibles or pipelayers, and supplying pipe joints to the latter. The addition of bow thrusters, joystick control and dynamic positioning systems improved the performance near platforms. Size and load carrying capacity increased gradually, and with them the costs of these vessels.[56]

Chapter 5

The heydays of the North Sea
The period 1973-1985

In the early 1960s it was discovered that operating offshore in the North Sea could not be characterised as an attractive business. Wind, waves, moving sand and great depth made life real hard on the operators. The technology imported from the Gulf of Mexico appeared inappropriate for operations in the North Sea. Expectations were low and exploration was hardly rewarding in view of the oil prices on the world market. Only the proximity of important markets provided some motivation.

In the next decade the North Sea would nevertheless turn into the leading offshore area, a first rate strategic reserve and profit generator, and an ultimate testing ground for many things that were invented in offshore technology. This incredible transformation was the outcome of a range of events within and outside the oil industry. It led to many innovations in offshore technology, which cannot be properly described without first considering these backgrounds in society and economy.

The concentration of this Chapter on the North Sea does not mean that developments elsewhere were unimportant. The Gulf of Mexico remained active, and finds in the Bay of Campeche in the late 1970s were large. The Campos basin offshore Brazil appeared to be prolific, and at many other offshore areas around the world, activities soared. The North Sea however, became the main breeding ground for technology in this period.

1. Oil and the Western world

America, oil and the environmentalists

In the 1960s, America was a society in motion. This was literally true with a very central role for the automobile, but it also was true in a metaphorical way: rapidly increasing consumption, a never ending involvement in foreign adventures, an increasingly tense monetary situation and last but not least transformation of society itself.

The United States were a major power in the world, both politically and economically. They used to be reasonably well able to provide in their energy needs. However, as the 1960s progressed, these certitudes began to crack. Domestic oil production slowly started to become stagnant. Fewer and fewer new discoveries were made and at the same time the import restrictions depleted the existing domestic reserves at an increasing pace. In March 1971 the Texas Railroad Commission, for the first time in its existence, even allowed 'all-out production'.[1]

The economic situation of the United States gradually deteriorated, although there was no question of a depression. The Americans had come out of the second world war victoriously, and their economy proved capable to rebuild the world economy with American dollars. The dollar became the universal currency and the immense quantities of it needed for rebuilding the Western economies were initially covered by sufficient gold. When the European and Japanese economies really took off during the late 1950s, the increasing demand for dollars was met by monetary measures, which worked well as long as the world had confidence

Kerr-McGee Corporation

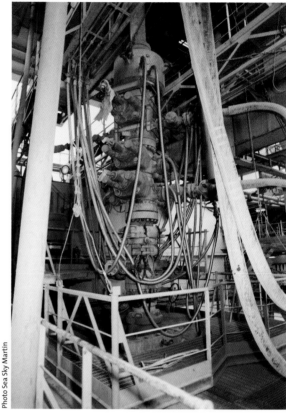

Photo Sea Sky Martin

In the 1960s, the offshore sector learned that the equipment used successfully in the Gulf of Mexico was not suitable for North Sea conditions. Transocean Nr 1, a jackup drilling rig built in 1964, was the first rig designed expressly for the severe environment of the North Sea.

The blow out preventer (BOP) stack is an essential tool for drilling.

in the US economy. Such confidence is bound to diminish in time, and in the 1960s the American economy as a whole also came under pressure due to increasing inflation of the dollar.[2]

In the sphere of international relations tension mounted, especially in the Middle East. Continuing conflicts between Israel and the Arab states had their effects on oil and on all the political aspects associated with it. The United States traditionally supported the Israeli side, but at the same time vast quantities of Arab oil were shipped to America. It was evident to the Americans, that this situation should sooner or later create problems. This was not seen equally clearly in Western Europe and Japan, also supporters of Israel, but more vulnerable because their dependence on Arab oil was much stronger.

And finally, the effects of public opinion on the issue of oil production versus the natural environment were felt by the industry, although in a sense there were two opposing effects. In the 1960s the industry and

environmentalists came at odds on issues like pollution. As far as environmentalists worried about the pollution from coal burning industries, they paved the way for 'cleaner' technologies like nuclear energy and oil burning power stations. In the mid 1960s, coal was finally banned from New York and other big cities. This helped the oil industry to reinforce its position in American society.[3]

The other aspect was the moratorium on offshore activities off California and the delays in Alaska enforced after the Santa Barbara blow-out in 1969. In an indirect way, the environmentalists contributed their bit to a reconsideration of the North Sea as a potentially profitable province, by discouraging exploration in the American waters.[4]

Majors, independents and new independents

The largest oil companies were in a position of increasing independence of the American market. These majors: Esso, Shell, BP, Socal, Texaco, Gulf and Mobil operated worldwide. Five of the seven were US based, but they too were mainly oriented towards the world market. Together, the seven virtually controlled most of the non-American oil as they fixed prices and acted as intermediaries between producer and consumer countries. These majors assured the oil supply of the consuming, i.e., Western nations, thus enabling their governments to separate oil from foreign policy.[5] This special position could only exist due to a very powerful position within the oil producing countries. The majors simply could dispose of the oil reserves and could tell the governments of the producing countries how much they were going to receive for their natural resources. The mechanism to this effect was the 'posted price' which was originally based on the market price (this relation was lost in the fifties) and which served to determine taxes and royalties. But little by little, this position was undermined.[6] There were several reasons for the majors losing control. Firstly, the oil producing countries became less charmed by foreign influence coming either from the Western or from the communist nations. Nationalisation of oil reserves and, in 1956, of the Suez Canal showed that there were means to restore the balance at least to a certain extent. The majors understood that their liberty in dealing with these oil reserves was not unlimited. Secondly, during the 1960s, the producing countries noticed that in spite of inflation of the dollar, the amount of dollars they received for their oil - the posted price - was not adjusted. Thirdly, the American import restrictions introduced in 1959 and stiffened later, led to a growing discontent of the producing countries. In the fourth place, two new groups of independents entered the market and weakened the position of the majors. One consisted of American firms like Phillips, Occidental, Getty and Stanolind, who tried to escape from the tightening American market by joining the majors abroad, and the other group was formed by new European firms, created by their respective governments in order to obtain a position of their own. The most notable examples are CFP and Elf in France, ENI in Italy and Deminex in Germany. Last, but not least, tensions between Israel and its Arab neighbours kept increasing and oil was dragged into the potential conflict.[7]

These five aspects together were the ingredients for a crisis in the powerful position of the majors and ultimately in the Western economy. A crucial factor in the course of events in the 1970s was OPEC, the organisation of petroleum exporting countries. OPEC was founded in 1960, and grew on the discontent of the 1960s, but it took years before its members managed to act collectively in a way that made the world realise there were also other interests than those of the Western economies.

The oil crisis
Clear signs in the 1960s and the early 1970s indicating a possible energy crisis, were not recognised in the Western world. The European nations thought that their energy supply was untouchable and energy prices would always be as low as they had been.[8] Warnings were received from oil companies, like Socal[9], oil experts like Adelman, Levy, and Akins[10], but also from scientists like Meadows and the Club of Rome[11], but these were all rejected as prophecies of doom.

Besides, the European nations were strongly divided and each had its reason to keep up a reassuring appearance. The Netherlands and Great Britain had their majors, Shell and BP. The Dutch gas deposits and Rotterdam as a trading and refining centre would only benefit from disruptions on the oil market, and the British with their North Sea gas and oil thought along the same lines. France had its own ways to take care of securing its oil interests by operating behind the screens, where it concentrated on creating a position less dependent upon the United States. Germany, still carrying its historical burden, could not permit an independent course by questioning the apparent confidence of the majors or by establishing relations with the Arab countries, which might be interpreted as insulting Israel. Moreover, all countries remembered how earlier crises in the Middle East, like the Suez crisis and the 1967 war, had been less dramatic in their consequences than expected. However, not everyone observed that the United States were rapidly losing their economic supremacy, which probably had been the most important mitigating factor during those previous events.[12]

The Superintendent.

George Steinmetz/Transworld

A first sign of threatening collapse was Colonel Khadaffi's take-over in Libya in 1970, which was soon followed by his announcement that the American oil companies had to hand over power and that posted prices must be adjusted. Having a clear view of the respective firms' position on the oil market, he picked Occidental as a first company that had to double posted prices. Occidental was an independent, and therefore an easy victim. In the past, the majors had demonstrated that they could simply move production from one area to another, whenever they were not satisfied with negotiations. This option was not available to Occidental, in part because the majors did not feel compelled to help this intruder on their

international market. Occidental therefore yielded quickly to Khadaffi's pressure.[13]

The most important effect of Khadaffi's action was that his display of power was interpreted by other OPEC members in the sence that they, too, were able to improve their situation. This put the majors in an entirely different negotiating position. At first, during negotiations in Tehran and Tripoli in 1971, it seemed that the old balance could be more or less restored.[14] But then, a new source of unrest arose when President Nixon abolished the Gold Standard later that year. This led to a devaluation of the dollar, and since oil was being paid in dollars, the OPEC members feared a serious reduction of income. A new round of talks with the oil companies was planned for 8 October 1973 in Vienna. Two days before the meeting the fourth Israeli-Arab war broke out, which overshadowed the negotiations. Something happened that all parties, i.e., the oil companies, the Western governments, but also OPEC representative and Saudi-Arabian oil minister Mr. Yamani, had hoped to prevent: the question of oil became openly related to politics.[15]

The oil companies and OPEC did not reach an agreement and the war continued. On 17 October, the OPEC members gathered in Kuwait and proclaimed unilaterally a 70% increase of posted prices, followed by gradually cutting off the oil supply. On president Nixon's decision of 19 October to support Israel with a military aid programme, the reaction was an oil embargo imposed on the United States.[16] A second embargo was aimed at The Netherlands, which had openly supported Israel. The choice for The Netherlands was also inspired by its position as a transit country for oil products. This made the embargo into a warning to the rest of Europe. Years later, it turned out that the Dutch government had been fully aware of the risks: before public support was given to the Israeli side, the government had asked Shell about the oil reserves stored in Rotterdam.[17]

Mr. M. Heikal, editor of the Al Ahram newspaper and for some time the Saudi foreign minister, admitted in 1975 that the effects of the embargo were limited: *'Every tanker captain was required to give a pledge that he would not discharge his cargo in any of the embargoed countries - that was all [ ]. Naturally, some captains gave the pledge and broke it, while others discharged their oil at, say, London, whence it was transferred in another tanker to Rotterdam.'*[18]

The events in the autumn of 1973 continued into 1974, and they became known as the first oil crisis. The Western world was hit hard, and the United States, Japan and Western Europe were about to face an economic crisis. *'Things will never be as they used to be'*, a European prime minister complained.[19]

But amidst all this misery, there was one light shining in the darkness. Suddenly prices on the spot market soared to unprecedented heights. Before the crisis, this market had been one of minor importance, where mainly surplus quantities were traded. Now it became the place for large volumes, where later even the Arab countries came to sell their products. North Sea oil reserves were made profitable by the high price and offshore activities in the North Sea did benefit tremendously from the situation, as illustrated by an immediate wave of investment in new drilling rigs. For commercial exploitation of North Sea oil a minimum price of $ 5 a barrel was thought to be required. In December 1973, the OPEC members had quadrupled the price of oil to $ 11.65 per barrel, and on the spot market the price even doubled that amount for a short time.[20]

After 1974, the crisis in the Western economies seemed impossible to neutralise. This was not only the result of the new situation on the oil market. The oil crisis as such had also unveiled a process of hidden inflation and an overstretched economy, which had caused the collapse of the monetary (dollar)system of Bretton Woods.

The immediate effects of the oil crisis were that governments took measures to economise on energy. European countries imposed speed limits on motorways, petrol was even rationed and car-free Sundays were enforced. In the longer run, the development of nuclear energy was stimulated together with innovating activities to produce domestic appliances with a lower energy consumption.[21]

The most important and most effective reaction to the rise of the oil price was made possible by the fact that all oil transactions were valued in US dollars. To compensate for the higher cost of fuel, many countries raised wages and this triggered inflation. The efforts to reduce energy consumption quickly faded away, with Japan as a favourable exception. Worse even, some countries gained enormously by the high cost of oil. Norway, Great Britain and The Netherlands could produce from their own reserves and were hardly interested in enforcing energy conservation, and even less in international cooperation to this effect. Norway and to an even greater extent Great Britain immediately began to stimulate the production of North Sea oil. The Netherlands adjusted gas prices to reflect the

Semisubmersibles

On March 21, 1958, Shell requested R.L. Wiegel at the Berkeley Campus of the University of California to conduct model tests in waves with an unusual floating vessel. The model, named Delta because of the resemblance of its plan view to this Greek letter, was the brainchild of Bruce Collipp and may have been inspired by the shape of some large submersibles then in use. It was, however, definitely not intended to sit on the seabed, but to float in a semi-submerged mode. The word 'semi-submersible' was later invented during explications to the Coast Guard. The Delta model test report mainly addressed mooring line forces, but also offered the observation that heave, roll and pitch were small. In a later design report by Collipp, the name Delta was replaced by Trident and the term semi-submersible was introduced.

Whatever the intention of these tests, the semi-submersible became the most typical vessel in the offshore industry, widely used for drilling in hostile seas, but also for pipe laying, heavy lifting, accommodation, work-over and maintenance. The 1961 prototype was a conversion for Shell of a submersible, Bluewater Rig No 1, originally built in 1957. The second semi-submersible for Shell was Bluewater 2, newly built in 1964 in San Francisco. In the crossed waves off Northern California and Oregon, it proved to be a much more efficient drilling vessel than the ships, which had performed reasonably well in the unidirectional swells off Southern California. Ironically, in 1979 the Bluewater 2 was converted into a submersible.

In the meantime ODECO had built a large V shaped unit, the Ocean Driller. Its first job in 1963 was for Texaco. Sedco followed with another semi-submersible design. By 1968, the list of semi-submersibles counted 23 units.
Their typical shape was defined by straight or bottle shaped columns, a deck on top of the bottles carrying drilling systems and crew quarters, and often cylindrical bodies connecting the bottles at their lower ends, like found on submersibles. Sedco replaced these structures by horizontal and slanted

bracings between the columns, in combination with large 'footing' pontoons under the columns. Theory caught up with practice and prescribed ratio's between waterline area, submerged volumes and floater shapes. Lower hulls or floaters were streamlined to decrease towing resistance, and sometimes propulsion units were added. Some companies preferred catamaran type, dual lower hulls, instead of multiple bodies or triangular shapes for lesser towing resistance.

In the mid 1970s the number of semi-submersibles jumped ahead: from 29 units in 1972 to 117 five years later. A second newbuilding wave took place in the early 1980s, bringing the total number to 187 in 1987. These were different designs, however. In 1971, Aker in Norway presented a design consisting of two, catamaran type floaters carrying four heavy corner columns and four smaller columns in between. The bracings connecting both floaters were arranged above the floater decks and served also to provide mid-support to the drilling deck. To some extent they looked like a Diamond M or a Sedco 700 design and there may have been some inspiration from ODECO's Ocean Viking, which was built by Aker in 1966. The special feature was that these designs were being offered by a group of shipyards and available to every interested contractor. The design proved a commercial success, starting from the first unit delivered in 1974, the Deep Sea Driller. The sinking of this unit in a heavy storm, a few years later, had no impact on the success.
Other 'independent' designs were also available, for instance Friede & Goldman's Pacesetter. GVA, the designers of the Gotaverke yard, entered the market with 4 column, catamaran type semi designs in the mid 1980s. In these, the drilling deck was no longer a single structural layer, but a box girder providing both enhanced stiffness and buoyancy in case of damage of a floater or column. GVA was neither the first nor the only proponent of this line of designs, which closed the gap between the civil engineering descent of most semi's and the naval architectural background of most builders. The designers of Sonat's Chris Chenery (1975) and its sister

Afortunada (later Neddrill 6) for instance had followed the same philosophy. In the mid 1980's, this line took over from the Aker H3 type. Most fourth and fifth generation units built in the 1980s were based on these principles: box type deck, 4 heavy columns, catamaran floaters and horizontal bracings only. The generation numbers were not always clearly defined, but certainly newer generations could handle deeper water and higher deck loads than the older ones. In the mid 1980s some real deep water units were proposed, which centred around handling of riser and drilling equipment: MSC's DSS-10000 and Friede & Goldman's Trendsetter. The Zane Barnes was built in 1986 to the latter design. The trend towards deeper water drilling however abruptly broke off when the oil price dropped in 1986.

Among the semi-submersibles, there are a few unique units. The Transworld Rig 61 was a cross breed between a ship and a semi-submersible, with some technology borrowed from jackups. The basic ship had two outriggers, in which columns could be lowered or raised with a jackup system. Its purpose was high versatility as a drilling unit, but it ended up as a production unit in Brazil. Also unique is the Troll Olje semi-submersible. It is the only semi so far built in concrete. The choice of this material contributed to its size: 101.5 x 101.5 x 65 m, with a displacement of 130000 tons.

The semisubmersible Sedco H anchored at transit draft.

Photo Sea Sky Martin

Neddrill 6 is a catamaran type semisubmersible drilling rig, originally designed in close conformity to the Mohole semi-submersible which was never built. Here, it is under tow by one tug which can just not be seen.

Shell International - Photographic Services London

The semisubmersible accommodation unit Treasure Finder had a three bed hospital, a team of paramedics and its own resident doctor. As happened more often, the unit was built as an Aker H3 type drilling semi, and later converted.

Hollandsche Staalbouw Maatschappij bv

The NAM F3-FB accommo-
dation module was built by
HSM in Schiedam, Holland, in
1993 in three parts: jacket,
substructure and topsides.

Hollandsche Staalbouw Maatschappij bv

Hollandsche Staalbouw Maatschappij bv

Hollandsche Staalbouw Maatschappij bv

oil price increase and tried to trade as much gas as possible while oil prices were at their high level.[22]

It didn't take long for the oil producing countries to react. Early 1979, a few months after Khomeini's take-over, Iran stopped production from its most important fields. The spot market turned into chaos, which led to a $ 34 per barrel price in May 1979. In 1980, a war broke out between Iran and Iraq, which contributed to another rise.[23] This kept the North Sea situation very profitable, although there still was no oil shortage. Oil buys greatly exceeded actual consumption. *'Tankers full of oil lay in Norwegian fjords waiting for even higher prices'.*[24] This second crisis seemed to confirm the power of the OPEC countries, but in fact they started to drift apart. Internal agreements on production levels were not followed, and oil was sold without OPEC's consent. Meanwhile, North Sea production grew very fast. In 1983, Great Britain alone produced more than Nigeria, Libya and Algeria together.[25] In a very short time, North Sea oil had become an important factor on the world oil market. When a slight fall

of prices occurred after 1983, a number of countries increased production to compensate losses. Saudi Arabia took on the role of swing producer, to maintain the balance of supply and demand, like Texas had done in the aftermath of the war. But after some time, Saudi Arabia was unable to maintain this course. In 1986 its new high level of production led to a sharp price fall. The prosperous years of North Sea oil were over.[26]

Between 1973 and 1986, many people experienced an economic slump, but others earned fortunes. The offshore industry, oil companies and a few govern-ments received incredible sums because of the market situation. As early as 1975, oil consumption started to rise again.[27] The oil companies earned gold with their offshore activities in the North Sea and saw their reserves increase in value.[28] The OPEC members, too, saw dollars coming in from everywhere. Or, as Mr. Yamani put it, *'It was like a flood after heavy showers: the water goes everywhere and you can't stop it. It was the same with dollars, we didn't know where to leave them.*[29]

2. Governments and North Sea offshore

The unexpected added value of North Sea reserves after the crisis of 1973 urged the surrounding states to review their oil and gas policies.

Norway stuck to its go-slow policy in order to create a Norwegian oil industry in a controlled development. The crisis seemed to confirm the correctness of this approach. Foreign companies were put under severe pressure. Statoil would take part for 50% in all activities, royalties reached a peak of 18%, and an off the top taxation after royalties and corporation tax of 25% was imposed. *'Companies say it is taking 90 per cent'*, The Economist reported in 1975 in an article with the meaningful title *'The Norwegians gave the oil companies hell - and then concessions'*.[30] Norwegian policy included a production limit, which was based on oil revenues that were needed for a controlled and healthy economic growth and no more. A further rise in oil prices and government takes would make the government even lower these limits. New finds increased Norway's reserves, but the government gave priority to the major fields.[31]

When the first offshore policy was formulated in the late 1960s, the Norwegian government had presented a scheme with ten points. It mentioned state participation through Statoil and the principle that all oil and gas reserves belonged to the state. Another relevant point was that all natural resources had to be brought on land in Norway. At the time, this ruled out the option of pipelines as a means of transport, as the potential oil fields were separated from the Norwegian coast by the deep trench. When the oil crisis fundamentally changed the North Sea situation, the government still was inclined only in special cases to accept other solutions. In this way it was hoped that the offshore sector would concentrate on the development of new pipelaying techniques.[32]

Foreign companies used to typify the Norwegian offshore policy as nationalistic and not very stimulating. Some even thought it communist in nature. Objective observation does not warrant these terms, certainly not in comparison with other countries'

Noordwinning K13-A platform operated by Pennzoil. The Noordwinning Group was one of the organisation formed to exploit the North Sea basin.

Photo Sea Sky Martin

policies. Also Germany, France, The Netherlands and Italy founded state owned companies to either sell their resources or participate in the operating oil companies. Even the UK had its national gas company, later joined by an oil company for both upstream and downstream activities.

Each country looked for opportunities to participate in those aspects of the bonanza, which were closest to their nature: trading for the Dutch, innovating for the French, or having their 'own' operators (Germany, Great Britain, France). The difference with Norway with its Statoil and its majority share in Hydro was Norway's successful policy to let the country share in and learn from the offshore activities. The Norwegian situation stimulated a 'go slow' or 'sit and wait' policy: its economy was strong, but small in comparison to the offshore potential. By going slow, Norway experienced a sensible and sustainable economic development.[33]

The Netherlands concentrated on its gas deposits even more than it had done before the crisis. Already after the Tehran agreement of 1971, the government had linked Gasunie prices directly to current oil prices, and in 1974 it proposed to increase the government take in some cases to at least 90%. A natural decline of productivity in Slochteren was expected from 1978 onwards, which led to a moderate pursuit of reduced consumption, but primarily incited the government to let Gasunie purchase non-Slochteren gas, for instance from small fields in the Dutch North Sea and from the Norwegian Ekofisk field. The policy as was followed in the 1960s to bring up the maximum quantity of gas in the shortest possible time, changed into a type of conservation policy. The Netherlands did not formulate an energy policy in which the offshore industry received special attention. The last memorandum on industrialisation dated from the late 1960s, and there the conclusion had been that industry as a whole was able to look after itself. When this policy was reviewed some years later, an active attitude towards industry was the result, but this time its emphasis was on social policy. As far as the offshore industry was concerned, the policy might be called liberal.[34]

Great Britain showed a much more complex develop-

Photo Sea Sky Martin

ment. The nation was caught unaware by the Tehran agreement and the oil crisis. In 1974 a Labour government was elected, and it tried to restructure offshore policy. The original liberal approach, which the oil companies had praised, was set aside, apart from the emphasis on rapid development. Looking at the national gas enterprise, but even more inspired by Norway's Statoil, Labour set up a state owned British National Oil Company (BNOC). The opposition regarded this as one more step towards all out socialism, whereas the government wanted to use it as a necessary means to generate more income from the North Sea, to direct oil to the British mainland and to serve as a starting point for a British petroleum

An impressive view of the travelling block.

industry and for downstream activities. The latter two arguments were mainly rooted in the oil shortages immediately after the crisis. Government had hoped to persuade Shell and BP to replenish the reserves of their country of origin first before supplying other nations, but these majors were not too happy with the idea. Now, Labour hoped to secure supplies in a future crisis through BNOC. The concessionaries who already operated in the North Sea were forced to sell half of their production to BNOC. They could buy back this oil on the condition that it would be refined in Great Britain. There was not much appreciation for this plan. The larger oil companies did not feel like reorganising their distribution and planning, and in this they were strongly supported by the Tory opposition. Those firms that did cooperate with the government, all had their own reasons to do so. Deminex hoped for new concessions, and Burmah Oil wanted to relieve its financial problems. In due course, Burmah was bought by

BNOC, which thus obtained a direct access to offshore oil.[35]

A few years after setting up BNOC, the British government went even further in its participation by having BNOC take a 51% share in leased out blocks. This allowed the firm to engage in offshore production and to use of half the production more easily.[36]

The next step for the government was to renegotiate the existing leases, but these attempts to regain what 'had been given away' by previous Tory governments met with little success.

All this produced anything but enthusiasm among operators. The roles of British Gas and BNOC, delays in offshore operations, a high inflation and notoriously wrongly estimated costs negatively affected the belief in the British offshore challenge, not only with the operators, but also with the financial world.[37]

In 1979, Mrs. Thatcher became Prime Minister, and she felt the need to diminish the role of BNOC drastically.

Amoco P15 undergoing maintenance of the accommodation platform and work-over on the wellhead platform. The Seafox 1 (foreground) is one of several dedicated North Sea maintenance jackups.

Production equipment

In essence, there is no difference between production onshore and offshore. In both cases, the purpose is to separate the mixture of oil, gas, water, sand and other contaminants - some of them highly corrosive - into its components and to prepare the oil and gas for transportation.

On fixed production platforms, the similarity goes very far, although the marine environment offshore sometimes requires use of special materials for structure, piping and vessels. A particular feature of an offshore production platform is its remoteness from an industrial infrastructure. If a valve or pump fails, its replacement will take more time and money than with an onshore plant. Therefore it became common practice to include redundancy in the design and first quality equipment in the procurement phase. The fact that this cost more was less important than the risk to have a complete offshore field being shut in because of a defective pump.

Most significant in offshore production was the real estate problem. On land, space was usually of no major concern. At sea, and certainly in deeper water, the cost per square metre of platform deck was very high. This resulted in tight packaging of the equipment, even of equipment and crew together.

On floating offshore production platforms, the situation was somewhat different, due to the wave induced oscillatory motions of such platforms. A separator which performed well on a fixed platform, might be impossible to operate on a rolling ship, if only because its level switches would trip. For years the uncertainty on how motion problems should be addressed put some kind of hold on floating production systems, in particular those on ships. On semi-submersibles and TLPs, the angular motions were limited or nearly zero, and people felt more confident that the motion problem could be coped with.

Of course, there have been more problems associated with floating production than sea motions only. A particular one is the need for a flexible riser to bring well fluids to the floating platform, be it semi-submersible or ship. With TLPs a fully flexible riser was not required; it was sufficient to include flexible joints at the ends of the riser or just rely on the flexibility of steel or titanium. The availability of Coflexip flexible high pressure hoses - soon followed by competitors - made possible a step forward towards floating production.

Over the years, the pressure on operators not to flare associated gas during production has increased. In most offshore areas in the world it has simply been forbidden since many years. A common solution is to re-inject the gas, if no infrastructure is available to bring it to shore. This calls for heavy compressors which take up considerable space on a platform and often consume a substantial part of the redundant gas as fuel to compress the remainder. Water injection pumps are also often present, but they are less specific to offshore production plants.

Although she was fundamentally opposed to state owned industry, BNOC was allowed to continue to possess, buy and sell oil. In this capacity, BNOC became a powerful organisation. Especially after the second oil crisis, BNOC had an important role in regulating the price of North Sea oil, and hence of world market prices. When prices reduced gradually after 1983, the company weighed heavily on the national budget. Oil was sold for a lower price than it had been bought for, and with the vast North Sea production, this trade caused vast losses. This production volume also was an argument for Mrs. Thatcher to say that Britain had become more or less self-sufficient.[38] So: *'She saw no security reason to maintain BNOC, and in the spring of 1985 she simply abolished it'*.[39]

Changes in the political balance regularly changed policies: *'the British development demonstrates that the offshore arrangements were not above political party struggle'*.[40]

3. Ekofisk

In 1965 BP had found gas on the British shelf, and soon more was found, so within a few years production installations and pipelines were put in place. Phillips discovered oil on the Southern Norwegian shelf in 1969, and this also was the start of a series of finds. The British rightly concluded that the 'Norwegian' fields would probably extend under their shelf, and they began leasing areas close to the Norwegian sector. Indeed, in the early 1970s, oil was also found in British waters.

North Sea oil had one major disadvantage: at the time it valued $ 3 a barrel at most. This made exploitation hardly profitable. The oil companies, after several years of experience in drilling in the North Sea, knew that this area required altogether more of the operators than the Gulf of Mexico. The exact nature of these new requirements was not quite clear because knowledge about the North Sea's surface whims and its bottom was far from complete. Nevertheless, it was obvious that operations in this area needed extra precautions and different structures, which simply meant higher investments.

In this atmosphere of doubt on the commercial future, the oil finds were taken into production. Nevertheless, due to the political and market developments after 1973, the fields turned into gold. In the wake of this commercial success, a new industrial infrastructure developed around the North Sea, and the oil companies and contractors increased their technical skills, sometimes forced by disasters.

As an example of the interacting elements involved in the development and production of a North Sea oil field, or complex of fields, the Norwegian Ekofisk field is analyzed in the following pages. Together with Forties and Brent in the British sector and Statfjord in the Norwegian sector, Ekofisk is regarded as one of the most important fields in the North Sea.

Ekofisk after its discovery

One of the leading thoughts after Phillips discovered Ekofisk, was to bring the field into production as fast as possible. This idea was inspired by the fact that Phillips had spent huge sums during the two preceding years on exploration drilling. In spite of the low oil price, the need was felt to start making money first. Selling the oil seemed no problem, thanks to the proximity of the markets.[41]

Phillips wanted to develop Ekofisk in stages. A first stage had to be the creation of a temporary production platform, which during the next stage could be replaced by permanent installations. In the following years, these installations might be expanded according to the situation. This splitting up in stages had some advantages. The temporary facilities allowed the company to start producing after a short time of preparations, and with limited investments. Major investments could wait until the Norwegian government had recovered from the sudden good news of the find and articulated its future policy on oil and gas. It was also a relevant fact that apart from Phillips, Amoco and Esso continued explorations in and around the area. More finds were made, but it still was unclear whether these were large deposits. The possibility of bringing these new fields together around an Ekofisk production base, was a thought in the background.

Another argument for being cautious at the start, was the acknowledged lack of experience in North Sea production. A 'test' production installation would be a sensible stage in the learning process.[42]

When the plans were developed on paper, it was evident that Ekofisk had the potential of becoming a very ambitious project. This perception was confirmed by further modifications that were added during the next period, when even greater ambitions emanated from the reports. Many have later wondered how all this fitted in with the low oil price of the moment. Did the plans just reflect the enthusiasm of the engineers? Or was there speculation that Ekofisk was to become the centre of a large number of very interesting fields nearby, for which an impressive production town at sea was a rational investment? Or was it felt that international relations in the near future would do away with low oil prices altogether? All these points appear to have been present at some moment. It was not for the first time that offshore plans were presented with an equally grand perspective. And as Ekofisk was far out at sea, far from every coast, it was logical to think of concentration and a large scale, integrated approach. As far as market predictions were concerned, tensions were evident and those who listened well, heard warnings of an approaching oil crisis.

Phillips' discovery attracted the attention of Amoco, who were already drilling for some time, and of Shell, who had plans to start exploration in a block further away. Amoco agreed with Phillips to drill a structure that covered Blocks 2/4 (Phillips) and 2/5 (Amoco). In August 1970, Amoco drilled its first well within this structure. Amoco called it Tor, and Phillips used the name Ergfisk for this attempt which resulted in the second oil find in Norwegian waters. Meanwhile, Phillips continued its exploration of Ekofisk. As a part of this scheme, there was a well drilled in what was considered to be the Western edge of the field. In November oil and gas were found, but it appeared that it did not belong to the Ekofisk deposits. In laboratory tests the oil had a different API-gravity, which led to the conclusion that Phillips had found another field. Nevertheless it was called West Ekofisk. Together with Cod, which was somewhat to the Northwest, where

Phillips had been exploring before the Ekofisk discovery, but at that time without commercially interesting results, there was a total of four fields. In 1973, three more finds could be added: Albuskjell, a gas field which Phillips and Shell discovered West of Block 2/4; Eldfisk, South of 2/4, which turned out to be the largest oil field next to Ekofisk; and Edda, a small field near Ekofisk and Eldfisk, which was declared commercially interesting because of its presence close to the large fields.[43]

Production developments

A staged development of Ekofisk[44] was begun in 1970. In Stage One it was planned to use a jackup as a production platform, linked to a number of subsea wellheads and loading buoys for tankers. It was decided to purchase the jackup Gulftide and convert it. Brown & Root was contracted for pipelaying between the wellheads and the platform location. As there were no specific rules for these activities, Phillips had to negotiate with the Norwegian authorities.[45]

Gulftide would only produce oil. Gas, coming from the

Phillips Petroleum Company Norway

The Ekofisk early production jackup Gulftide.

© Husmo Foto

View of the Ekofisk complex, the 'Grand Old Lady' of the Norwegian sector.

wells in considerable quantities, would be flared, since gas is hard to transport from a location at sea to the shore other than through pipelines. And at that moment, such pipelines were still non-existent. In July 1971, the first well was taken into production, the other three followed in September, October and February.[46]

Phillips had succeeded in extracting oil from the bottom of the North Sea in what nowadays could be called a fast track project. The water was deep and the waves so high that the design conditions after all appeared to be underestimated. Moreover, the reservoir was deep under ground and its pressure was high.[47]

While the first stage was underway, Phillips started preparations for Stage Two and tried to find a solution for the gas problem: who would buy it, and what about pipelines?[48] The Norwegian government had come to realise that its initial idea of bringing all gas and oil to the mainland, was not a real option. The pipelines would have to pass the deep trench off the coast, and recent proposals showed that laying them was possible, but maintenance and repair would be very difficult. New pipe concepts were presented, but apart from being not very convincing technologically, they were not financially sound in view of the market situation. It also became clear that Ekofisk's production would largely exceed the Norwegian need for gas and oil. A major part of the resources that would be landed on the Norwegian shore, would have to be shipped out again. In the long run, the use of oil tankers did not seem to be a solution as bad weather would prevent the loading of tankers in the field. Only an enormous storage tank at sea might give some relief but that was not regarded as realistic either.[49]

Finally, Phillips and the Norwegian authorities reached an agreement to move pipelines to laid to Teesside (Great Britain), and Emden (Germany). Norway was to be compensated through participation in the activities needed in building and operations.[50]

The concrete oil tank

The building of an oil storage tank was part of Stage Two. After some research, Phillips expressed its preference for concrete as construction material, and the French Compagnie Générale Doris was approached as the best qualified designer. In May 1971 a contract was made up. The building of the tank was left to F. Selmer and Høyer-Ellefsen, Norwegian firms with concrete structure building experience, who jointly formed Norwegian Contractors. Originally, the tank had to be ready by 1 August 1972. This schedule implied that in about one year's time, 120000 cubic metres of sand, 5000 tons of steel and 8000 breakwater elements had to be made into a concrete giant. The base of the tank was built in a special dry dock, from which it was towed early 1972 to start construction of the superstructure. Nine tanks surrounded by a casing of breakwater elements were built on top of the concrete base. Delays occurred as modifications and extras had to be taken care of. One of these was a double top deck to hold equipment and living quarters and serve as a helideck. This new plan was announced only in the summer of 1972, and on 21 June 1973 the tugs set off with the tank to Ekofisk. By that time it measured 215000 tons, being some 45 m in diameter and 100 m high. It was sunk to the bottom in 70 m deep water.[51]

Further developments

In the meantime, the plans were extended in relation to new finds around Ekofisk. Stage Three would make West Ekofisk, Cod and Tor part of the Ekofisk produc-

tion system, and the pipelines to Teesside and Emden were to be laid. Stage Four comprised the development of the other fields. During the 1970s, Ekofisk became an artificial town, made up of interconnected platforms, and it took thousands of people to build it. Platform construction was done mostly outside Norway, and installation was in the hands of foreign firms. In 1975, Phillips had a hotel platform built in the Ekofisk field to accommodate 268 people. One year later, the total number of people involved in the construction of the entire complex reached its maximum of 13000. They were ferried by helicopters, and in 1978 some 500000 passengers were transported through the air.[52]

The temporary operation of the Ekofisk jackup Gulftide was taken over by permanent platforms in 1975.[53] Shortly before the oil crisis broke out, the development of the other fields had begun, and between 1976 and 1979 the respective fields came in full production. By that time, oil prices were sky high, and Phillips could see profits rising, which was more than a slight compensation for two years of preparations and two years of frustration over unsuccessful drilling.

The rising profits appeared at risk when in the 1980s it became evident that seabed subsidence was too large to be ignored. In a major operation, by Technip and Hydraudyne, the platform decks were jacked up over 6 metres Also an outer wave breaking wall was placed around the concrete tank.

How prolific the Ekofisk area really was, appeared again in 1996, when the first of two new platforms was installed, which should produce to at least 2020, probably 2030.

Trouble

Just like many other sectors of industry, the offshore industry had its own record of setbacks and even disasters. There were delays in construction, financial and planning setbacks, failing experiments, and also accidents causing casualties. In the North Sea, experience was not different from the Gulf of Mexico. In 1965, Sea Gem had capsized, with 13 people getting killed. In February 1968, a semi-submersible, Ocean Prince, was destroyed by storm while being used in submersible mode. In 1969 the jackup Constellation

Bob Fleumer Aerial Photography

Bob Fleumer Aerial Photography

*The Ekofisk complex in its
stage 2 development. The
spacing between the flares is
about one kilometre.*

*The Ekofisk Central concrete
tank as built in the early
1970s. Bridges unite the
platforms to a city in the sea.*

sank during a storm and in 1974 the Transocean III
broke apart and sank. In November 1977 a helicopter
heading for Ekofisk fell into the sea, killing 12 people.
In that same year, a blow-out occurred at the Maersk
Explorer. In February 1982 the Ocean Ranger perished
with all 84 crew members on board during a storm off
Newfoundland.

In the period until 1974, more than sixty people died in
British waters alone. The numbers for 1975 and 1976
were 12 and 20, respectively.

All parties involved, oil companies, operators, divers,
helicopter firms, etc, knew there were risks associated
with offshore operations, but in the early years accidents seemed to happen less than expected. This
observation led to a general and comfortable feeling of
being in control.[54]

Some held different views, and the famous blow-out
and fire fighter Red Adair was one of those.
*'Whatever precautions are taken, there'll be a disaster
in the North Sea, sooner or later. There are no proper
facilities for coping with it. The thing is time, to get
trained personnel there. By then the well may have
caught fire - then it gets larger and larger, like a chain
reaction, from this well to the next well, to the next well.
The more wells you have, on any platform, the more
difficult it gets, because the heat will go to the next
[Christmas] tree. You get flames, leaks, and it just goes
on and on. [ ] At the moment, for a real blow out, you
don't have anything. Just a few little vessels, a thing that
will squirt water. [ ] Everything's sitting out there, wide
open, with nothing to protect it.'*
Red Adair said all this in a radio interview in April
1977.[55] Less than three weeks later, disaster struck,
indeed.

On 22 April 1977, a well belonging to the Ekofisk Bravo
platform was being inspected. The Christmas tree had
been removed, and a blow-out preventer was installed,
but before this was completed, mud came up, followed
by oil. Ekofisk had a blow-out. There were more than
one hundred men on the platform, and they all
jumped off. Oil gushed in great quantities over the
installation and into the sea. The difference with Red
Adair's scenario of doom was that no fires broke out.[56]
The oil companies directed all fireboats they had to

Ekofisk, and the Norwegian government banned all aircraft from the vicinity of the blow-out and ordered Phillips to cut off all production in the field. After 48 hours, Ekofisk Bravo sent 125 tons of oil per hour into the air. Red Adair was called in, and two of his staff, 'Boots' Hansen and Dick Hattenberg, arrived to take over command. Meanwhile, panic had spread rapidly and it was expected that the disaster would last for a long time.[57] *'When Hansen was asked in Stavanger whether it would take thirty-five days to control the blowout, he replied in suitable 'Red' tradition: 'Thirty-five days? I only work thirty-five days a year'.*[58] Six days later, when Red Adair had come to Norway himself, other remarks followed: *'It is just another blowout',* he reassuringly told the deeply concerned public, adding that *'you learn from mistakes. You will learn a lot from this one'.*[59]

The blow-out lasted for eight days, and six months later a Norwegian Commission of Inquiry estimated that 22,500 tons of oil and 60 million cubic metres of gas had been thrown into the air. The Commission's conclusions were direct and did not mask the truth. Apart from a human fault that had been the immediate cause of the blow-out, all persons in charge on and around the platform were to be blamed for what had happened.[60]

The Norwegian opposition did not need a report to ask the government, only six days after the accident, if the balance between the eagerness to develop oil and gas production and concern about safety regulations was not thoroughly disturbed. Only the other day the authorities had announced that oil clearing operations were impossible due to rough weather, and, on top of that, that the country was by no means equipped to deal with disasters of this size. The government felt no need to call off the offshore adventure, and it expressed its faith in new technological solutions that would prevent similar catastrophes. In the next few years, Norway focused on additional legislation to enforce safety measures, especially to prevent pollution.[61]

The British government decided to set up an offshore fire brigade, but most critics feared that such rather futile measures would be the best they could hope for.[62]

Phillips Petroleum Company Norway

On 22 April 1977, the well of the Ekofisk Bravo platform was inspected. The Christmas tree had been removed and the blow-out preventer was being installed, when mud came up, followed by oil. Ekofisk had a blow-out. On 30 April Red Adair, Boots Hansen and Dick Hattenberg shut off the well.

The Ekofisk complex subsided slowly. In the mid 1980s Phillips had the platforms jacked up over 6 metres and built a protective barrier around the tank.

One of the Ekofisk platforms' supporting legs is hydraulically jacked up.

© Husmo Foto

Serious accidents such as the Ekofisk blow-out had an impact on the public opinion at large, and sent negative signals to the general view on offshore activity. The oil industry was aware of the risks of offshore operations, but had to accept them to some extent as the risks of the trade. For the greater public, these risks were unknown, and often the first confrontation with the activity offshore. Authorities - in this particular case the Norwegian government - tried to contain risks by imposing stringent safety precautions, but their stakes in the offshore game were too high to avoid questioning of their independent position - again in particular the Norwegians were subject to this ambiguity.[63]

The Ekofisk blow-out was not to be the last ordeal. In 1980 another grave accident shook the public and the government alike and led to further sharpening of the rules. Adjacent to the Edda platform in the Ekofisk area, a semi-submersible was moored to serve as a

hotel and a safe haven for the crew working on the platform. This semi was the Alexander Kielland, a Norwegian unit built to the French Pentagone design. Because of heavy storm, the bridge connecting the Kielland to the Edda platform had been removed and the 'flotel' had been shifted on its mooring wires to a safe distance from the fixed platform. Without warning, one of the five columns supporting the deck of the Kielland broke away and in less than five minutes the loss of stability made the unit turn over 180 degrees. Hundred and twenty three people perished without chance of escape. Investigations later established that the event had been triggered by fatigue at a hull penetration which was made to retrofit a hydrophone.[64]

Bob Fleumer Aerial Photography

Bob Fleumer Aerial Photography

Bob Fleumer Aerial Photography

Shell International - Photographic Services London

The Brent Spar served as an oil storage and offloading facility in the Brent field. The Brent B platform is visible in the background.

The Brent field became one of the major producers in the British sector, and the quality of its oil made it a bench-mark for price setting. On Brent, four platforms were placed, of which only the Brent A had a steel jacket foundation. The platforms were installed between 1976 and 1981 in water depths of about 140 m. In the 1990s, the Brent complex under-went an extensive refurbish-ment to prepare for extend-ed lifetime.

Bob Fleumer Aerial Photography

BP's Forties platform 21/10 FB, installed in 1976 in 123 m water depth. Production and accommodation modules are piled up high.

The Frigg complex, operated by Elf, is the oldest example of a field right on the borderline between the Norwegian and the British sectors of the North Sea. It was installed between 1975 and 1978. Water depth is 104 m.

One of the platforms at Dan, the first Danish field.

Bob Fleumer Aerial Photography

Mærsk Olie og Gas AS

Bob Fleumer Aerial Photography

© Husmo Foto

Gullfaks C in 217 m water depth. An example of a large gravity platform, with a remarkable huge 'hotel'. The semi-submersible Polycastle houses additional workforce for hook-up and starting activities.

Statoil's Gullfaks B concrete platform receives some containers from a supply boat.

4. Platform installation in the North Sea

While the Ekofisk project was being carried out, oil finds in British waters were equally spectacular. Fields like Forties, Brent, and Piper, made Britain into an oil producing nation. This was experienced as an extra stimulus for the nascent offshore industrial sector: platform constructors, platform installation specialists, pipelayers and others found a place in the market. In this section, the focus will be on platform building and installation on location.

Rough weather, the deeper water, and an initially low oil price posed some difficult problems to the design engineers. Building and installation out at sea was more problematic, and hence more expensive. To save time and money, construction work was done on land as much as possible. Most platforms used in the North Sea during the 1970s were of steel. The concepts they were based on, were derived directly from those used in the Gulf of Mexico. However, the unpleasant nature of the North Sea urged the use of heavier structures and more robust production equipment. Secondly, the use of separate jacket platforms for drilling/production and accommodation, as sometimes applied in the Gulf of Mexico, was found impracticable in the North Sea: there was a tendency towards single jackets and larger superstructures. Finally, commercially rational production required the use of platforms that could accommodate the maximum number of wells. The resulting heavier jackets were more expensive to put in place because of the larger piles that had to be driven deep into the soil.

The North Sea, simply, was different from the Gulf of Mexico. Phillips' decision to go ahead with a jack-up for early production is to be seen against this background: there was still much to be learned.

The drive towards larger and heavier platforms was a challenge for builders of structures, but even more so for installation contractors. The heavier the lifts the installation contractor could handle, the more prefabrication on shore was possible. The design of platforms was thus strongly influenced by the available offshore crane capacity.

In the North Sea offshore sector, the role plaid by

suppliers and supporting technologies was crucial, perhaps even more so than elsewhere in the world. Without these innovating branches, the development of production would have been tempered due to obstacles such as the weather, water depth and the distance between offshore sites and land.

One of these specialists was the firm of Heerema. Its company history, showing the development of heavy lift technology, is characteristic of the interrelation of technology in the offshore sector. Besides, Heerema is an outstanding example of the rise of European firms next to the 'traditional' American specialist supporting industry.

Innovations in heavy lift crane vessels

In 1948, a construction and installation company was founded by the name of C.A. Constructora Heerema & Bomans. It was based in Venezuela, and very soon it held a strong position in Lake Maracaibo. Bomans left the partnership in 1950, and the company continued as C.A. Constructora Heerema, with P.S. Heerema (1908-1981), a Dutchman, as its single owner. Six years later, Heerema had great success with his own innovation, a prestressed concrete pile. His method to fabricate such piles was so efficient, that it has not significantly been changed until this very day. Looking for new opportunities, Heerema went to Canada and then, in 1961, to The Netherlands. In 1962, he set up a second firm in The Netherlands, Heerema Engineering Service. Speculating on the coming of some sort of activities in the North Sea in the near future, Heerema bought a tanker which he converted into a crane vessel. This was remarkable, as until that moment only barges had been used as a base for crane vessels. In 1964, the ship, Global Adventurer, with 300 tons crane capacity, was ready - but perspectives of a North Sea offshore paradise were still remote.[65]

There was a growing interest in seismic data, but nearly no country had even begun thinking of some sort of leasing policy. Drilling, as far as it was done, remained without results. Heerema had to look for work for his new vessel, and he contacted Brown & Root early 1964. They, too, were speculating on North Sea activities, and therefore in need of a stepping stone in Europe. Both firms quickly agreed to coope-

Bob Fleumer Aerial Photography

rate, and within a year Heerema's Global Adventurer was seen working for Mobil off the German coast. After that, the vessel was used to build a radio and television station off the Dutch coast. In the meantime, Heerema had bought another old tanker, as he wanted a second crane vessel. This action brought him in conflict with Brown & Root, whose managers did not believe in the concept of crane vessels, which they thought inferior or a threat to their traditional strategic preference for crane barges. Brown & Root bought out 57 year old Heerema on the agreement that he would not reenter the crane vessel market for three years. They thought these three years would be enough to stop Heerema starting in the offshore sector again.

But as soon as the three year period was over, Heerema continued his old policy, and again had another tanker converted. The result was the Challenger with a lifting capacity of no less than 800 tons, which was more than the combined lifting power of Brown & Root's five barges that still dominated the North Sea installation market. Even before the ship was ready, Heerema managed to secure a contract with Amoco to ship and install two drilling platforms, two production platforms, connecting bridges, and pipelines in the Gulf of Suez. The Challenger succeeded in getting this 7000 ton load to its location in one journey, and installation

Industrial estate offshore: Statfjord C, A and B with two tanker terminals, and in the distance Brent.

Heerema's Challenger preparing for its trip around Africa to the Gulf of Suez, loaded with 7000 tons of structures for the Amoco field to be installed.

Heerema

went equally well. This made Heerema obtain a new contract, this time for Amoco off the Trinidad coast. Convinced of its success, the company had a second ship-shaped crane vessel built in 1972, the Champion, with a 1000 tons lifting capacity. Two years later a third one followed: Thor was able to lift 2000 tons. Thor was the result of BP's expressed policy to install heavier structures in the Forties field. The confidence in Heerema's qualities was such that he was invited to bid on the project, next to Brown & Root and J. Ray McDermott. Heerema and Brown & Root got the job, for which Heerema used Thor and Brown & Root upgraded one of their barges to a 1200 ton capacity. Heerema's success so far had been the outcome of a strategy in which risks were accepted, both techno-logically and financially. Its leading position inspired others to venture along the same road. Soon after Thor, other firms also came up with 2000 ton crane vessels, like J. Ray McDermott, thereby outpacing its great competitor Brown & Root, and newcomers like Italian Micoperi and The Netherlands Offshore Company. Lifting capacities continued to increase during the

Heerema's fourth crane ship, the Odin, crane capacity 3000 short tons. This large capacity allowed Shell to install the Brent Alpha topsides.

Heerema

1970s, with American Hoist and IHC Gusto as competitors in designing and building. This, in turn, enabled design engineers to go for ever heavier modules, thereby inviting crane owners to develop even heavier equipment.

To counter the new rivals of Thor, Heerema needed a fourth craneship. In 1976, Odin was built with a capacity of 3000 tons. It allowed Shell to install the large topside of the Brent Alpha platform.

Concurrent with the increase of crane capacity was the development of ever larger steam-driven piling hammers between 1973 and 1980. In the same period the hydraulic hammer was developed, which opened the way to under-water pile driving. Foregoing the need for pile elongations to above water was an important cost reduction.

The firm of Heerema flourished, and it gradually changed into an organisation carried by experience and know-how, which was the basis of new ambitions. Heerema's close connection with a semi-submersible pipelay vessel design may have triggered him to build a semi-submersible crane vessel. In 1975 design studies were undertaken and Philishave inventor Alexandre Horowitz was asked to solve the problem of excessive listing of a semi-sub when a large crane unit slews. Also IHC Gusto assisted in this design process. Highly placed ballast tanks with large quick-emptying valves and similar tanks under the water line would jointly provide for immediate changes in displacement, stability and list when required. The final design incorporated a second crane of 1000 tons capacity, which was already upgraded to 2000 tons before construction. In 1977 the design was ready and during negotiations with shipbuilders Heerema decided to build two crane vessels instead of one as the offered price was relatively low. One year later, Balder and Hermod were launched from the Japanese yards of Mitsui. Both vessels were equipped with two cranes, capable of lifting 2000 and 3000 tons. They could reach locations without the help of tugs, and their operations could continue all year round.

The introduction of Balder and Hermod outdistanced Heerema's competitors completely. Not only did this

Heerema

The Conoco Hutton Tension Leg Platform moored between Heerema's Balder and Hermod.

Bob Fleumer Aerial Photography

The Challenger drives a pile by means of a steam hammer. Later high capacity hammers were mostly hydraulic.

Heerema

Bob Fleumer Aerial Photography

In preparation of a heavy lift, the slings are laid out and lifted over the hooks. Handling of the slings is an art in itself in view of their size. The place of action is the Gulf of Mexico and the deck is for the Bullwinkle platform.

Placing of the NAM F 15 deck, a regular view for the vessel's superintendent.

The Hermod lifting the topsides of Occidental's K12 platform.

Heerema

mean yet another increase of lifting capacity, it also implied a new type of service, which was aimed at permanent support and fast operations through the use of two cranes. Pile driving, for instance, now could be done in half the time needed so far. Heerema became the crucial factor on the installation market. Modules could be extended, installation schedules changed, and the number of contracts Heerema could fulfil in one year, was rising steadily. And so did the lifting capacity of the semi-submersibles. In 1986, after conversion, Hermod's capacity was upgraded to 5000 + 4000 tons, and Balder's to 3000 + 4000 tons.

Just before Heerema launched its vessels, another Dutch firm presented a semi-submersible crane vessel. This firm, The Netherlands Offshore Company, a consortium of the big Dutch dredging companies and owner of three ship shaped crane/pipelay vessels, built a semi-submersible crane vessel, the Narwhal, without a dynamic ballasting system and only one crane amidships, which could lift 2000 tons. Heerema tried to buy NOC, but failed to achieve this. He then started to buy large percentages of NOC's parent company shares on the stock market. His ultimate large holdings in most of these major Dutch contractors was found unacceptable, but contributed to the prosperity of the Heerema

Bob Fleumer Aerial Photography

The largest crane vessel of all was the Micoperi 7000, later taken over by Saipem and renamed Saipem 7000. It is capable of lifting 14000 tons. BP's Gyda platform in the Norwegian sector of the North Sea looks tiny in comparison.

HeereMac's DB 102 crane vessel installing a platform topside on the Danish Harald field in September 1996. Before Heerema and J.Ray McDermott joined forces in the heavy lift market, this vessel belonged to McDermott.

Group. Ultimately the NOC fleet was sold off and the Narwhal was obtained by McDermott who renamed it DB 101.

Shortly after Balder had entered service, the Santa Fe company accused Heerema of violating one of its semi-submersible patents.
This patent dated back to 1968, the time of building of Santa Fe's Choctaw, a 800/500 tons crane on a column stabilized catamaran and described as a semi-submersible vessel of elongated shape. As a matter of fact the Choctaw could only handle large loads when floating at shallow draft, as a catamaran. With the threat of a court case, Santa Fe had in 1976 succeeded to obtain royalty payments from Viking Jersey Eq Ltd., the then owner of the semi-submersible Viking Piper. Now Santa Fe believed to have a strong case against Heerema, and requested demolishing of Balder and Hermod plus 200 million dollars.
The accusation led to a law suit during the 1980s, but in 1985, both parties agreed on a financial settlement.

The following year saw the return of both McDermott and Micoperi, each with a semi-submersible of its own. DB 102 had a two times 6000 metric tons capacity, and M 7000 could lift two times 7000 metric tons. But by

Mærsk Olie og Gas AS

In 1989, Heerema and J.Ray McDermott joined forces and pooled their heavy lift semi-submersibles.

Bob Fleumer Aerial Photography

that time, the oil price had collapsed, and both competitors had great trouble to earn back their investments.

This more than doubling of the semi-submersible crane capacity was not followed by the hoped-for growth in the platform installation market, and put an end to competition in this field. To survive the crisis, Heerema and McDermott combined their installation activities in 1989, by the formation of a new company HeereMac, and Micoperi was later taken over by ENI's Saipem. The structural overcapacity, however, remained.[66]

5. Pipelaying

Large gas discoveries in the North Sea, like Leman and Frigg, required gas pipelines. But surface conditions and water depths in the North Sea created technical

difficulties and lots of time loss in pipe laying by the Gulf of Mexico methods. Brown & Root sought to solve this problem by increasing the size of the lay barge, but failed to achieve the desired result. Their introduction in 1971 of automatic welding further did not solve the basic problem of downtime caused by ship motions. Very early in the 1970s, the prospective need of 36 inch pipelines to be laid in the Northern North Sea and through the Norwegian trench triggered the initiative to build a semi-submersible lay barge, almost simultaneously with two companies: Semac, a combination of Shell-Nautilus and Esso with Zapata; and a consortium of European investors, contractors and IHC. Within IHC, the marine pipeline designer R.J. Brown provided the know-how of deep water pipe and stinger design. This combined with the naval architectural skills of its subsidiary IHC Gusto to provide an integral design package to the consortium members, who operated under the name Viking Jersey Eq Ltd.. By the end of 1972, a contract was signed with IHC Gusto in The Netherlands to build the Viking Piper, a semi larger than any one in existence and with a design deck load capacity of 10000 tons. Around that same time, the order for the slightly smaller Semac 1 was placed with Alabama Drydock & Shipbuilding Company. Both vessels came into operation in 1975 and neither proved to be the immediate success they were expected to be. After its first laying contract, which was delayed by severe problems with its 14 large mooring winches, the Viking Piper was laid up and ultimately sold to J. Ray McDermott, who rebaptised it the Laybarge LB 200. Semac I laid the 40 inch gas pipeline form Brent to the Shetlands for Shell and Esso, but pipelaying was not the core activity of its owners. In 1979 it was sold to Brown & Root.

Pipe laying nevertheless seemed an attractive activity. The new discoveries in the northern North Sea required long, large size pipes in relatively deep water. Several contractors developed specialized tools for the North Sea environment. In addition to Semac and Viking, also Saipem was active with their Castoro 6 - featuring a sloped fireline to reduce the required stinger length - and the French contractor ETPM with two ship shaped pipelayers. In The Netherlands, the major civil and dredging contractors stimulated by the success of Heerema jointly formed The Netherlands Offshore Combination, who owned several crane/pipe laying ships. For flowline laying, some companies reverted to reel systems, others to tow out of prefabricated flowline bundles. Although the flexible pipes fabricated by Coflexip were substantially more expensive than rigid steel pipes, they were occasionally used as flowlines because of the savings in mobilisation and use of pipe lay spreads. These flexibles could be laid by relatively small ships, which provided opportunities to a broad field of competitors. An additional feature was their easy recovery and re-usability.

Many of the pipelines in the North Sea had to be buried. This was a government requirement intended to protect the pipes from being damaged by fishery. Different concepts were developed to provide for post-lay burial, including jetting machines, large cutters

G.H.G. Lagers

IHC

18 May 1974 the first deck block of the Viking Piper – a semisubmersible pipe laying vessel – was placed. One of the authors was involved in the design and assembly of this vessel at IHC Gusto. His wife and son look on, together with a friend.

The semisubmersible pipelay barge Viking Piper (later renamed LB-200) during its first mission in the North Sea.

A novelty in pipelaying was the introduction of dynamic positioning. The result was high mobility of the layvessel and the capacity to work in deep water.

Allseas

and plows. Burying appeared to be a pain in the neck: it was difficult, expensive and not always successful. Moving sanddunes on the bottom of the North Sea could randomly cover or uncover the pipes. An alternative solution was offered by the idea to cover instead of bury the pipes. After some years, the pioneer in this activity, the Seaway Sandpiper jointly owned by Stolt Nielsen from Norway and Boskalis from Holland, was followed by a handful of competitors, when the method proved reliable. Norwegian quarries provided hundreds of thousands tons of stone, which were dumped on pipelines in the North Sea and elsewhere through a long pipe or socket suspended from the dumping vessel. These ships successfully borrowed the technique of dynamic positioning from the drilling industry, to control the position of the fall-pipe end straight over the pipeline. Even the 400 m water depth of the Strait of Gibraltar proved a feasible dumping ground for this method.

Water depth appeared to be no limitation for dumping, but for pipelaying it still was. Until in 1991, a short

stretch of pipe was laid by Heerema in 35 m water depth offshore New Zealand, in the Maui field, by applying the so-called J-lay method. In this method, the pipe joint assembly line is tilted to nearly vertical, so that the need for a stinger and the overbend are avoided. The J-lay method was slower than the conventional S-lay with its horizontal assembly line but the latter was more restricted in water depth/pipe size combinations, due to the need to tension the pipe horizontally and thereby keep the stinger limited in size. The required pipe tension in turn required a heavy mooring system, which is slow to handle and increasingly expensive in deep water. All factors combined, the J-lay method held the promise of a capacity for much deeper water than the S-lay method. However the deepest pipe laid so far, in 1640 m of water in 1996, was based on the S-lay method by the Lorelay.

In 1985 a new concept entered the pipe laying world. Edward Heerema, who had parted from Heerema three years after his father's death, started the offshore contracting firm Allseas and converted a bulkcarrier

The stinger for the DP pipelayer Solitaire during construction at the HSM yard in Schiedam.

Bob Fleumer Aerial Photography

The pipe reel ship Apache owned by Coflexip Stena Offshore was built in 1979.

into the first dynamically positioned pipe lay vessel. A further novelty was the enormous central pipe storage in the hull, which had a watertight door at the stern through which barges with pipe loads could enter into the ship. The Lorelay, as the vessel was named, quickly proved a success. Its limitation, however, was the maximum pipe size to be handled, 24 inch. Allseas grew fast on its first enterprise and introduced a much larger ship in 1997 to handle the largest pipe sizes foreseen at that time. In the meantime, the LB 200, Semac I and Castoro 6 had finally found their places in the market. Brown & Root UK joined forces with Saipem and formed EMC, and also McDermott and ETPM teamed up together.

6. The offshore sector

The years 1973-1985 showed a further boom in offshore oil and gas production. Hundreds of platforms crowded the North Sea. Most of these were of steel but especially the deeper parts of the Norwegian shelf saw the coming of concrete giants. Elsewhere in the world, offshore activities sprang up, and various 'older' areas were brought to life again.[67]
As far as the public became familiar with offshore

activities, this happened through oil companies. A large number of supplying and supporting companies operated in the shade of the oil companies. Together, oil companies and offshore firms made up a flourishing, internationally operating sector that was able to create capital artifacts, technologically advanced pieces of engineering of incredible size. The money to achieve all this was paid by a society that was thirsty for oil and gas, and prepared to pay almost any price to relieve its thirst.

In spite of the unmistakably crucial role of the offshore sector in the supply of oil and gas, not many outsiders were fully aware of this. Oil companies stood, so to speak, at the front door of a house filled with operators, suppliers, and the like. Governments negotiated with the oil companies, and the general public accused the oil companies of causing disaster. In this love-hatred relationship between society and oil companies, only a few people realised that behind the oil companies there was an extremely busy world called offshore industry.

In fact, the offshore sector consists of several worlds. In the centre of it all are the oil companies, which form the reason for the existence of all other players. They concentrate on producing and refining oil and selling its products. For all separate support activities, specialized firms have come into being. Seismic surveying, pipelaying and platform installation are fields of activity, where relatively few contracting companies operate and strong leaders can be found. Drilling, on the other hand, is performed by many contracting firms, grouped to some extent in specialists using jack-ups, semi-submersibles or ships. Designing and building production platforms is still another branch. Originally this trade was dominated by Brown & Root and J. Ray McDermott, who were typical steel builders. In the 1970s, many others joined this branch. Examples are Technip, Grootint, Heerema, Trafalgar House and McAlpine. A new branch originated in the Norwegian waters, where concrete platforms were erected. The major players here were Norwegian Contractors and Aker, who later merged. The superstructure of a platform, with its component parts and equipment had its own world of specialist suppliers.

As was the case with the drilling vessels during the 1950s and 1960s, it was the oil companies who were in charge of much of the designing of production platforms. Often, partnerships with contractors and consulting engineers were set up. Basic innovations were often contributed to oil companies. But, during the 1980s, innovation became also stimulated by the European Community, through several programs. As a second ring of firms around oil and gas production, there is a large group often indicated as jobbers. They worked for oil companies as well as contractors. And then there is the group of supporting specialists, like divers and helicopter companies. The network may even be extended into sectors that by nature have nothing to do with oil and gas, but are indispensable for the offshore sector as a whole. Suppliers of food, beds, furniture, and also photographers and model builders are some examples.

Reviewing the whole interacting system of activities, one comes to the conclusion that in this world of offshore and oil and gas production, vertical integration never became common practise. Remarkably enough, the 1990s see a host of fashionable expressions like co-makership, back to the core, and strategic alliances, which are supposed to act as eye-openers to modern international industry. The offshore industry has never acted otherwise. There is only one exception to this rule: far away from the multi-national offshore culture, and very successful in its own region, the Brazilian company Petrobras went its own way.

Petrobras

'For some reason Brazilians have had fears of large international oil companies', E.W. Owen observes in his book *Trek of the oil finders* (1975).

That reason is not hard to find. In the days that Brazil experienced internal resistance to foreign oil companies, these companies became active in other countries, like Venezuela, Mexico, and later, in the Middle East. For societies with strong ideas on national ownership of natural resources, the activities displayed by the Western oil companies came close to theft. And as these companies after World War II were often seen as representatives from American culture with its

Dockwise NV

J. Ray McDermott

Ocean tow of a jackup appeared to be risky. Submersible transport barges were introduced in 1979 and have since carried jackups, semi-submersibles and other large cargo items. Dockwise Super Servants 3 and 4 have a deck area of 3500 m2 and can load up to 14000 tons.

Fitting the two jacket sections of Esso's Hondo platform off Santa Barbara California in 1976.

unquestioning attitude of superiority, some nations were very reluctant to let them in. Owen adds that the Brazilians used to indicate the large international companies as *'trusts'*, which probably was not very far off the mark in the post-war era, but also may explain the fears.

Before 1930, foreign firms had been welcomed, and geologists had been allowed to make surveys of some scope. During the 1930s, the government restricted this freedom, and in 1938, before oil was actually found, the Conselho Nacional do Petróleo was established to bring exploration and production under government control. After World War II a strong movement in the army and among students and intellectuals tried to realise further nationalisation of oil reserves.

'O petróleo é nosso' was their slogan. This led to the formation, in 1953, of the state oil company Petróleos Brasileiros, or Petrobras.

Petrobras was given the mandate to supply Brazil with oil and, in relation to that task, establish self sufficient oil exploration and production. The basic assumption was that Brazil had rich oil reserves, and the first step was to explore and prove its existence. Esso's famous geologist W.K. Link was 'bought' for the project. Link was ordered *'to create and lead the best exploration team money could buy'*, and he was given the opportunity to start an operation of exceptional size. With Brazil's rather prejudiced conviction that the country was rich with oil, the operation could only produce disappointing results. In his own words, Link ended up as a public enemy, a saboteur and 'entreguista' no. 1, and a tool of the Standard Oil Company.[68]

In 1968, Petrobras started offshore wildcat drilling. Contrary to the disillusions of onshore exploration, the offshore operations led to good results during the 1970s and 1980s. A first offshore installation was built in the Guaricema field in 1967. Its water depth was 30 m. In 1974, the Garoupa field was discovered in the Campos basin, and the scene was set for a range of discoveries in ever increasing water depths. By 1996, Petrobras had 14 Floating Production, Storage and Offloading systems (FPSO's) in operation, in water depths down to 910 m, and late that year, the deepest major discovery in the area was made in 1853 m. Plans

for production were made and published immediately. The water depth made Petrobras a pioneer of subsea wellheads and floating production.[69]

Petrobras' activities differed greatly from those of other companies which we have described in the preceding sections. The company had to be self sufficient in its operations. The way to achieve this, was by hiring people with good reputations and much experience in the oil world. Contracting foreign oil companies, like Shell, Esso, BP and Elf/Agip, formed part of the strategy for a short while in the late 1970s. For the drilling of wells, specialist firms were contracted. Between 1972 and 1974, Petrobras worked with Penrod, the Offshore Company, Storm Drilling, and Zapata Offshore. In September 1977, a first International Conference on Offshore Structures Engineering was held in Rio de Janeiro. It was supported by the British Council and the Ministry of Trade of the UK, and many of the speakers represented British firms and Universities. For the indispensible subsea technology, Petrobras turned to Lockheed Petroleum Services, who delivered a subsea wellhead in an atmospheric chamber for Garoupa in 1979. Earlier satellite wells at Enchova were equipped with 'wet' trees, and this technology proved satisfactory, so that the Garoupa dry tree remained one of a kind at Campos. Meanwhile, a start was made with building a jackup, and in the 1980s Petrobras operated a fleet of jackups, drilling vessels and semi-submersibles, all Brazilian built. The same road was taken for platforms and equipment.[70]

As far as possible, Petrobras worked with Brazilian contractors, but the development generally was kept under its own control. In this way, Petrobras evolved into an integrated corporation, combining expertise on all aspects of offshore operations. Around it, a group of Brazilian firms grew to carry out construction work. Principal-contractor relations as existed else-where, were not found in Brazil. The government had just one market player to deal with, although during the 1970s some foreign firms were invited as well. And the government still wanted results: in his opening address to the first International Conference mentioned above, the president of Petrobras, General

Petrobras; photo Eliana Fernandes

de Oliveira, mentioned *'the urgency of the Government in initiating production in the shortest possible time.'* Until recently, Petrobras operated more or less on its own, separated from the rest of the oil world. Only when it thought fit, other parties were contacted. For the rest, the doors were kept tight, and only very little information was allowed to come out.[71]
It can be said that the Brazilian government has reached the target it had set after the war. Petrobras provides Brazil with oil and is able to produce on land as well as offshore. In 1966 60% of domestic demand was supplied by Brazilian production, much of it from the 231 subsea trees at Campos. It would be incorrect to say that merely nationalist sentiments have made Petrobras into what it is today. The absence of qualified firms in the area has also compelled Petrobras to vertical integration. In that respect, Petrobras was not different from companies in other industrial sectors outside the oil industry and outside Brazil, who for that same reason started to do for themselves what in other circumstances could have been contracted out.

Petrobras' semi-submersible production platform P25 represents the achievements of Brazil's oil industry development. The platform was the first structure converted with fully Brazilian technology. Petrobras started up operations with the P25 in October 1996 in the Campos basin.

The Gulf of Mexico; offshore Texas

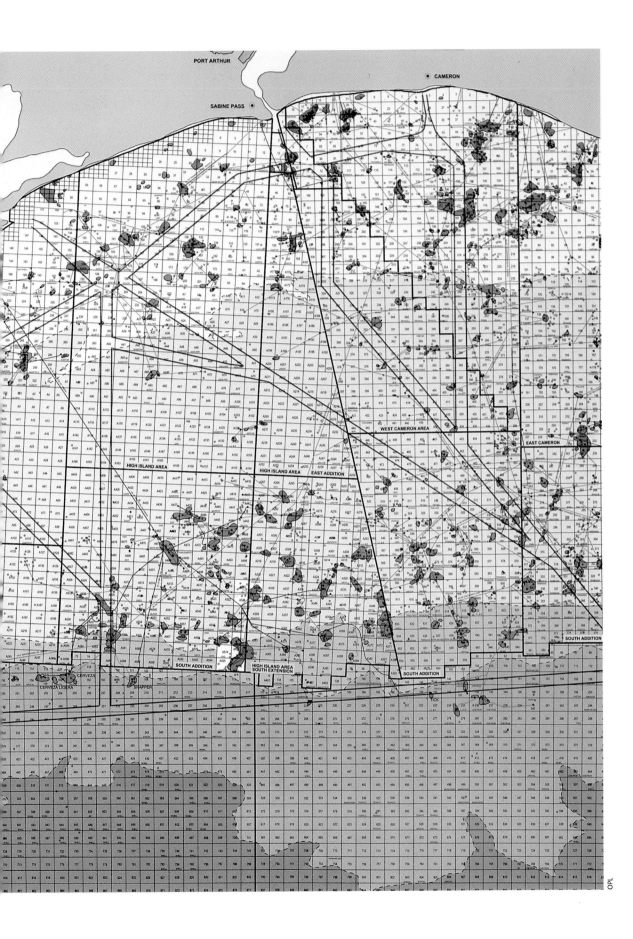

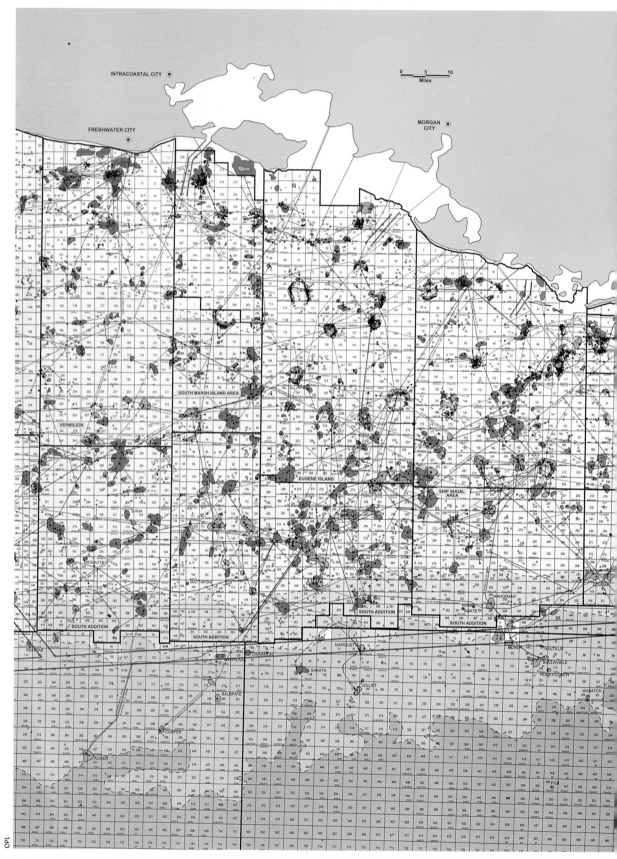

The Gulf of Mexico; offshore Louisiana

The Northern North Sea

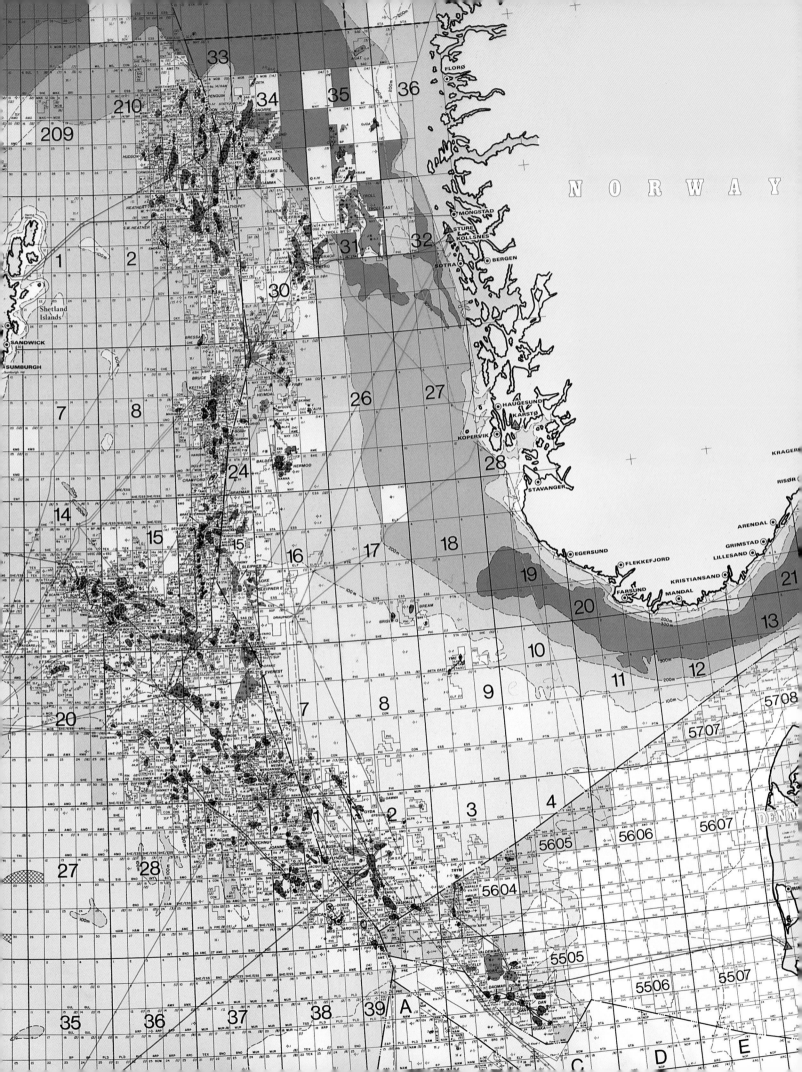

The Southern North Sea

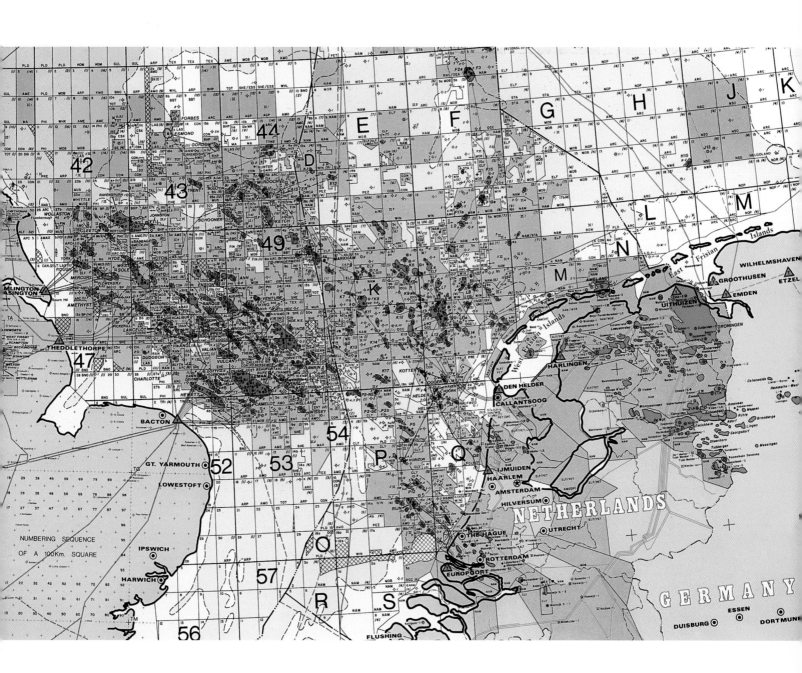

NUMBERING SEQUENCE
OF A 100Km. SQUARE

Chapter 6

The mature offshore sector
The period 1986-1997

'The sharp fall in oil prices in the spring of 1986 made the Americans close 1500 wells, at a cost of two million barrels a day, or 25% of their own production. It simply was cheaper to get the oil in the Middle East, where it was almost for free. A similar argument was used in those days to bring two thirds of the planned exploitation projects in the North Sea to a standstill.'[1]

After the booming years, offshore all over the world was threatened by a crisis. By 1985, 6000 fixed platforms had been installed, and 64000 offshore wells had been drilled. Main areas were the Gulf of Mexico, the North Sea, the Persian Gulf and offshore Indonesia. Offshore areas like Alaska, and California were not as impressive, but technologically they were remarkable.[2] Then, early 1986, the oil price dropped dramatically.

The sudden price fall specially hit the offshore sector. On the Continental Shelf of a relatively small country like The Netherlands, nearly 40 wells were drilled during 1985. In the next years, this number went down to just over 20 every year, to reach a record low of 12 in 1994. The Dutch offshore sector comprised some 300 firms, with a total volume of business of $ 2.5 billion in 1994, of which 60 % originated from the Dutch continental shelf. In an attempt to stimulate exploration, the government adapted its concession policy by granting tax relief and by opening up the total remainder of the continental shelf to exploration drilling in one round. However, expectations were not so high as they had been before. In a situation of a low price level, only very large finds were believed to have commercial potential, and by this time, there were not many substantial discoveries to be expected any more.

'All blocks have been sniffed at once or twice, and major finds are not expected. Now that returns are low and costs are high, there is the oppressive question concerning the oil companies' willingness to invest in exploration and exploitation of those remaining fields, which at most will be marginal.'[3] But the Dutch authorities kept faith, as they proclaimed that second hand blocks offered first rate opportunities. On the other hand, a real bonanza was not expected either: *'We're not like Norway. You have to know your size.'*[4]

Bonanza came back, but not in the North Sea. The Campos Basin in Brazil never ceased to bring in new large finds, and in the early 1990s the Gulf of Mexico went through a strong revival. In both cases, deep water was the key. For the North Sea, the main issues were related to Norway and marginal fields.

The reference to Norway is typifying for the post 1986 situation. Amoung the North Sea countries, Norway behaved as if there never was a crisis. Large scale activities continued, even to the extent that the largest platform ever was built. Most production developments were based on finds that dated from before 1986. Norway appeared to possess enough financial stamina to allow for large investments and long periods to recover the costs.

The concept of a marginal field changed contents after 1986. Before that time, the oil world merely spoke of commercial or non-commercial fields or reserves. Being commercial depended on size, oil price, reservoir properties, technical possibilities, exploitation costs, and factors such as the vicinity of large fields and

A four year old child was asked to look at this picture. She described it perfectly, but did not notice the people on deck and after they were pointed to her, she could not believe they were real people. It shows that even an open minded, young child has difficulty to imagine the scale of offshore operations. The photo shows one of the hooks of the Saipem 7000 semi-submersible crane vessel.

The 1986 oil price fall caused a crisis in offshore exploration. Mothballed jackups in Sabine Pass drive the point home.

George Steinmetz/Transworld

infrastructure facilities. Infrastructure came to play a more dominant role in the second half of the 1980s. Most existing fields saw their production gradually decline, which led to a discrepancy between the capacity of pipelines and onshore treatment plants and the actual production. To use this infrastructure to the full capacity it had been designed for, the exploitation of the smaller, or marginal, fields became interesting.[5] As we will see, the attention of the oil companies began to shift to those 'new' areas, resulting in production concepts that appeared as look-alikes of exploration equipment. The hitherto separate courses seemed to come together.

But first, we will consider two events in the North Sea that have been of great importance to the industry in this period: Piper Alpha and Brent Spar.

1. Offshore and society

Norwegian society had been exposed to the risks of the offshore game when in 1977 Ekofisk had its blow-out and, in 1980, the Alexander Kielland capsized. In California the Santa Barbara blow-out of 1969 was never forgotten, and Mexico was hit by the Ixtoc 1 blow-out in 1979, which spilled 450 000 tons oil into the Bay of Campeche for 9 months. Great Britain was deeply shocked in 1988 when Occidental's Piper Alpha platform burnt out. This disaster affected public opinion in Britain and abroad, on a subject which until then had passed largely unnoticed. A further sharpening in 1995 of the public's suspicions of offshore operations in several other European countries did not even need an accident. The decision by Shell, Esso and the British government to dispose of the floating oil storage platform Brent Spar by sinking it into the deep Atlantic Ocean, caused a general outcry of such magnitude that Shell in the end decided to put plans on ice.

J. Ray McDermott's Morgan City Fabricators simultaneously built jackets for Shell's Boxer and Sohio's Snapper field.

J. Ray McDermott

The Piper Alpha disaster

The Piper Alpha platform had started production on North Sea block 15/17A in December 1976. It was a typical medium-deep water (145 m) North Sea platform: a single jacket with production facilities and living quarters. In July 1988 several maintenance activities were going on; a common situation on any platform. On the evening of 6 July 1988, one of two condensate injection pumps on Piper Alpha stopped working. The night shift crew switched over to another pump, and then a series of incidents began, culminating in the most infamous disaster of the offshore industry ever.

The crew did not know that this other pump had been switched off for maintenance, and that a valve had been removed, and replaced by a flange. And this flange leaked. Condensate leaked out, and caused a first explosion, damaging the separation module located above the pump. The crude oil inside the module caught fire and immediately the fire spread to the adjacent compression module and to the lower level, where the initial explosion had occurred. The fire was also fed by a leakage in the main pipeline to the shore, to which two other platforms, Tartan and Claymore, were linked. A poorly functioning riser on the gas pipeline coming from Tartan caused a second explosion and the fire increased more and more. The rapidly mounting temperatures later caused failure of risers on the gas pipeline from Frigg and Claymore. These two platforms were not yet cut off. The fire spread quickly over the tightly packed modules on the platform, and flames and heavy fumes reached the accommodations on top of the modules where the majority of the personnel remained. Only the night crew, 62 out of 225 staff, was outside the accommodations, the rest was trapped in the fire and the smoke. It was almost impossible to reach or to leave the quarters, let alone that helicopters could land on the helideck on top of the accommodations. And the smoke made it impossible to reach the diesel fire pumps which were set to manual. Of the 225 people on the platform, 167 were killed.[6]

Immediately after the disaster, the British government ordered an inquiry. Led by the Scottish High Court Judge Lord Cullen, it became known as the Cullen Inquiry. In 1990, the final report was issued, in which the causes of the calamity were given and some hundred recommendations were made.[7]

The Cullen Report was critical on many points. Much was related to the *execution* of procedures for safe operations. In spite of the existence of safety procedures and regulations for many parts of the work, it was found that these had been either neglected or applied in a deficient manner, and that personnel was insufficiently trained. The night crew should have been familiar with the fact that repairs of the standby pump were going on; the other platforms that were connected to Piper Alpha, should immediately have been cut off; the fire pumps should have worked automatically; and staff should have been better prepared for escape procedures. A further conclusion

drawn from the events concerned the way the platform was designed. Like many other platforms built in the 1970s, Piper Alpha was a compact platform. The modules were closely linked and stacked in stories. Living quarters were very close to the production modules and even on top of them. In Chapter 5, the reasons for this compact design have been given in general terms. Platform concepts with a hotel on a separate platform, as used in the Gulf of Mexico, were rare in the deeper waters of the North Sea.

The Piper Alpha disaster affected the offshore sector as a whole, as the authorities confronted the offshore industry with entirely new legislation. Lord Cullen's recommendations were accepted in their entirety by the British government. Other countries, too, saw the need to review the prescribed safety procedures. For their new projects, the oil companies looked for solutions that would prevent accidents of this kind.

Piper Alpha before August 1988.

Bob Fleumer Aerial Photography

Safety Cases, a hitherto unknown notion, became mandatory for each and every installation. Outside the offshore sector, consequences were equally important. The whole drama with its numerous explosions and seas of flames had been visible on colour tv for everyone in Europe. Only then, people started to realise what was going on 'out there'. This intensive confrontation of the general public with offshore oil and gas production could not have been worse for the oil companies. Caring for people and protection of the natural environment were issues of increasing importance in the public mind. In both fields, the operator of Piper Alpha was depicted as having been less than diligent, and - justly or unjustly - the example was taken as typical for all offshore operators. The observation that oil platforms could burn out as this one did, represented another reason to put the public's interrogating spotlights on the oil companies. In Britain, the Piper Alpha events long remained part of collective memory, just like the Santa Barbara blow-out stuck in Californian memory, and echoes of the Ekofisk blow-out and the Alexander Kielland disasters rang for a long time in Norway's public opinion. On the European continent, Piper Alpha disappeared from the headlines more quickly. But there, Shell, and with it the entire oil industry, was again confronted with public opinion seven years later. This time, it was not even a disaster but an issue full of mutual misunderstanding.

'Mercedes cars racing through environmentally conscious Germany'[8]

In 1986, some 400 platforms stood in the North Sea. All of them had been designed, built and installed after 1966. In their design, North Sea weather, sea floor conditions, water depth etc. had been incorporated, as far as exact knowledge of these factors had been available. The platforms were intended to operate for the duration of 'their' field's estimated productive life,

Inferno at Piper Alpha.

and this aspect, too, had been made part of the design requirements. As a field's commercial production potential is hard to estimate precisely, some platforms turned out to be still very useful when the field had little left to offer. In such case, the platform became unnecessary at that location, while its technical life-time had not yet expired. Options then were to either scrap or reuse the platform. In both cases removal from its location was needed. However, this was something the designers had often not really taken into account. There are various rationales to be found for this omission. In the first place, it was already considered a technical challenge far above the average to design a structure that could withstand a long spell in the cruel North Sea. In the second place, there was a strong belief in technological developments that would offer the right solution at the right time. And, finally, in the days when these platforms had been designed, factors like environment played a lesser role, or at least its role

was different when the moment came to consider the platform's final hours.

From the start, there had been regulations on the removal of structures standing in water. Already in 1947, Kerr-McGee had to follow US Navy rules stating that abandoned structures must be removed to a certain depth. Later, international legislation developed roughly to the same effect. The most authoritative regulations are those by the International Maritime Organisation, in which it is stated that no structures must remain in water shallower than 75 metres, and that in deeper water structures must be removed to a depth of 55 metres.[9]

International legislation in this area does not specify the way in which removal should take place. In the Gulf of Mexico, by 1997, about 1000 platforms had been removed already. With some 100 of them, a practise developed to take the equipment and the deck from its substructure, and cut the substructure legs to make it

Based on the Cullen recommendations, the later platforms separate accommodations from the production facilities. Shown is Amerada Hess' Scott platform, installed in 1993 in 142 m water depth.

Bob Fleumer Aerial Photography

fall over and use it as an artificial reef. This method was known as the rigs-to-reef approach, and it met with consensus. In other cases, jackets were reused. As early as September 1955, the journal *Offshore Drilling* showed pictures of templates being reinstalled, which had been used three times before.

In the North Sea, however, there was hardly any experience with demolition or dismantling because only a few platforms had been removed. There had been some cases of dumping, which in fact concerned sunken mobile rigs that were not salvaged. In the 1990s, the list of platforms due for demolition was growing, but no action was taken. Costs were high, and in many cases, a platform's redundancy was caused by the low price of oil, so rising prices resulted in reconsideration of the platform's position. All this prevented the oil companies from hurrying.[10]

One of the installations marked for removal in the 1990s was the Brent Spar, a floating oil storage terminal in the Brent field. It was not a production platform, but in terms of removal policies this was immaterial. It had been built between 1975 and 1976 as a temporary facility until a pipeline to the shore would be ready. After its storage capacity had become unnecessary, it had continued functioning just as a tanker loading terminal until decommissioning in 1991. The best way to decommission and remove it was studied extensively. Then Shell and Esso, jointly operating the field, had agreed with the British government that the best option was to tow the Brent Spar to deep water about 150 miles west of Scotland and sink it in a water depth of some 2000 m. According to both parties, this 'deepsea disposal' was a solution that kept the right balance between cost, safety and protection of the environment. Especially the combination of the latter two aspects had dominated the discussion which concentrated on defining the 'Best Practical Environmental Option' (BPEO), in accordance with UK government requirements. An alternative was considered too risky by Shell and Esso. This involved the inverse of the process of building and installation. The Brent Spar had been built onshore and then towed horizontally to a Norwegian fjord, where it had been turned upright. Getting the spar back in a horizontal

Texaco

In the Gulf of Mexico several substructures were pulled over and turned into reefs. Picture shows barnicle growth on a substructure removed from offshore California.

position and dismantling afloat rated several times lower than dumping in the BPEO studies, and its feasibility was in doubt due to old damage to the spar structure.[11]

Only just before the plan was to be carried out, Greenpeace reacted fiercely. In May 1995, Greenpeace activists boarded the Spar in an attempt to prevent dumping and to find data that could be effective arguments against the dumping. Greenpeace announced that dumping was irresponsible from an environmentalist point of view, and that alternative options had been rejected too rapidly. Should dumping of the Brent Spar, after all, turn out to be the best solution, Greenpeace warned that it still would be a very undesirable precedent.[12]

The action by Greenpeace can hardly have surprised Shell and Esso, as many oil companies had already been the object of this organisation's activities. However, the companies were indeed surprised by the general public's reaction to the Greenpeace call for attention. Public indignation spread quickly and, to an objective bystander, soon grew out of proportion. The Brent Spar matter became a discussion in which everyone was right and no one seemed to understand the other party, let alone the subject under consideration. The British government and the operator took a position based on rational arguments: Brent Spar was large, though not extraordinarily so in maritime terms; it contained some residual oil, but not in the quantities estimated by Greenpeace; an environmental effect of this residual was of course possible, but the residues would remain inside the Spar at great depth. On land dismantling was possible, indeed, but such an operation was also, and according to the studies more, hazardous to man and nature. This rational argument by Shell and the authorities was perfectly sound.[13]

Greenpeace, on the other hand, set out from a different premise, viz., *'the sea is not a dumping ground'*.[14] This was an argument that appealed to the public, especially *'in times when you may even be prosecuted for just throwing away a chips bag'*.[15] Public support for Greenpeace being right was demonstrated

by German drivers, who refused to fill up at Shell petrol stations. Ministers told the press that they did the same, and the German Chancellor Helmut Kohl publicly confronted the British Prime Minister John Major. Near Frankfurt, a Shell station was even shot at.[16]

Europe, and especially Germany, was outraged, and the claims made by Greenpeace that Shell underestimated the quantity of oil residual, that the Spar contained radioactive material and that its structure was weakened, stirred up the fire even further.[17] It did not matter whether these statements, repeated in front page articles, were true or not. Every new remark was a direct hit, and Greenpeace seemed to be back in business. *'To Greenpeace* [the intended dumping] *is like manna from heaven, as in the preceding years the organisation dealt with diminishing receipts, violent rows, dismissals, and, consequently, a bad press that pressed the spiral even further down'*[18], observed a journalist. That Greenpeace had been overreacting due to the unexpected success, became clear in September 1995 when the affair was over. It felt obliged to apologise to Shell for the presentation of incorrect facts on the quantity of oil inside the Brent Spar.[19] Some days before the planned dumping and after Greenpeace had managed to reboard the Spar, Shell decided to give in and reconsider the dumping.[20] But then it was the British government that raised its voice, being less inclined to surrender to public pressure.[21]

Shell realised it had underestimated the power of an angry society, and it became increasingly aware of the financial consequences. At first, dumping had seemed the least expensive solution, but when the discussion dragged on, this became an open question: *'for management it is a matter of accounting'*, quoted an editor.[22]

The Brent Spar issue had once again reinforced a public perception that the offshore world 'made profits at the expense of the environment'. Although this argument was largely irrational, it had great power. Inside knowledge of the offshore industry remained as shallow as it had been, as most people, including journalists, continued to call the Brent Spar a drilling platform.[23] This taught the offshore sector the old

Greenpeace

Greenpeace activists posing on the helideck of the Brent Spar.

truth, that the world does not react entirely rationally. For Shell the matter turned into a drama, whereas Esso, being equally involved, remained dead silent and escaped from the public's anger. Shell found itself sandwiched between the British Government, which still supported the dumping option, and the angry public opinion, which was followed by the less directly involved other governments of North Sea states. After the decision to reconsider the dumping, Shell made a deep bow for the (German) public. *'Wir werden uns ändern'* (we will change), it was announced in the press. *'We have [ ] learned that for some decisions, your approval is as important as the opinion of experts or the official consent of authorities'*, Shell admitted.[24] A British Labour party peer however candidly wrote in the Offshore Engineer: *'The volte-face by Shell on its plans to dump Brent Spar in the deep waters of the Atlantic is some kind of a victory for Greenpeace, the German Green Party and the flabby European governments which were persuaded to join in the rumpus which the plans provoked.'*[25]

The offshore service industry took a positive view on the events. Those firms that until then had specialised in construction and installation of rigs, saw a new market opening up for the dismantling of installations. Many replied to Shell's invitation for tenders to demolish the Brent Spar.[26] Early 1997, six proposals were selected for further study. At the time of writing this book, the saga is yet far from finished and the dumping option is still formally open.

2. The last giant

In the history of platform construction, three materials played a dominating role. At the start, wooden piles were used. In the Gulf of Mexico, steel was used as an alternative during the 1930s, and gradually steel jacket foundations became the standard for offshore structures. The third material was concrete. Even before steel structures were developed, concrete was used in Lake Maracaibo to build foundations during the 1920s, and in that region it continued to be a common

Foundations

All permanent structures in the offshore industry have the need for a proper foundation on and in the seabed as a common feature. As with many other aspects, the earliest foundations were extrapolations of land-based methods and experience with piers and jetties. Until the gluttonous Teredo in Lake Maracaibo necessitated a different approach, the platform builders relied on wooden piles to be driven into the seabed. In Maracaibo, concrete (1927) and steel (1934) were introduced and in the course of time steel piling has become the standard method. In the shallow waters of the pre-war years the common concept for building a platform was to drive a certain number of piles into the seabed in a certain pattern, and then build a platform on top.

Superior in the Gulf of Mexico was the first to depart from the in-situ pile-by-pile construction of a platform, by introducing the jacket or template structure. This structure provided the support between seabed and platform decks and could be prefabricated on land, thereby saving costly offshore time. Still, piling was required to provide vertical bearing capacity and to ensure that the template platforms would be capable of resisting horizontal and overturning loads. For this purpose, the hollow legs of the framed structure served as guides for lowering the piles to the seabed and for supporting them laterally during driving.

The piles have grown in size (number, diameter and length) in line with the jacket platforms. Their weight became an important part of the total structural weight. For example, jacket and pile weights of the largest platforms in the Gulf of Mexico are 30400 and 14500 metric tons respectively for Cognac and 44800 and 9500 for Bullwinkle. For small structures in shallow water, the weight of the foundation piles may actually equal or even exceed the steel weight of the template. Almost exclusively hollow, open ended tubular piles are used ever since steel became the principal pile material.

After the piles have been driven, they must be connected to the space frame structure of the template. For piles passing through the jacket legs, this is usually achieved by inserting steel wedges or shims in the annulus between the leg and the pile at the top of the leg, and welding these to both sides. For piles not extending above the pile sleeves at the base of the jacket, it is normally done by grouting the annulus by pumping a special cement into it and letting this harden.

The design of the piles is a function of soil conditions and loads. Soil information and empirical data are indispensable, but sometimes not enough, as in the case of the North Rankin (1982) and Goodwin (1992) jackets offshore Australia. Both platforms are installed on a seabed consisting of notoriously difficult calcareous material. In the first case, the calcareous soil provided too little friction to achieve the required bearing capacity. The second foundation was designed with the first experience in mind. A two stage piling concept was chosen, with the first stage being a driven pile through the rather weak upper layers of the seabed. The second stage was to be a drilled and grouted pile in deeper and more competent layers. However, some of the first stage piles got squeezed during the installation such that the planned drilling through for the second stage became impossible.
Both the Rankin and the Goodwin problem required costly corrective action. Most of the 6000 fixed platforms world-wide have been piled without particular difficulties, however. The need for heavy hammers to drive the large jacket piles has contributed to the development of the semi-submersible heavy lift crane barges, which logged much less downtime in piling than the conventional crane barges and ships. Steam driven hammers were followed by hydraulic hammers, operable under water. A modern, high energy hammer for 8 ft diameter piles typically weighs some 160 tons.

The cost of piling is substantial. Starting in the North Sea with Ekofisk, a different foundation design has been introduced, called gravity platform. Here piles are not needed, since a gravity platform has a large footprint on the sea floor, keeping soil pressures acceptably low and providing sufficient stability against overturning without the need to be 'nailed down'. By its sheer weight it provides for a low ratio of horizontal to vertical loads on the soil, which avoids the need for piles to resist transverse displacement. Most gravity platforms are built in concrete, which automatically brings the heavy weight, but also some steel gravity platforms exist, like Loango, offshore Congo, and Maureen A in the British sector of the North Sea.

The first gravity platforms were designed for hard sea beds and the concept was not considered suitable for soft bottoms. However, the later designs such as the Troll gas platform were provided with long skirts which penetrated the soft seabed under the influence of the weight of the platform itself plus ballast. In this way, sufficient soil resistance was mobilised.

A third foundation type is the caisson, bucket or suction anchor foundation. It may be thought of as an inverted bucket, hence the name. It is pushed into the soil by the pressure difference over the 'bottom of the bucket' when water is pumped out from within the bucket. Suction anchors have in the first place been developed to provide anchoring points for Single Point Moorings (SPMs). With the installation of the large diameter bucket foundations under the Europipe riser platform 16/11E (1994) and the Sleipner Vest T platform (1996) this foundation type has won broader acceptance. The 'bucket' consists of a plate, usually circular, surrounded by a skirt. In the case of Sleipner Vest, the skirts are 5 m high and the plate has a diameter of 14 m. This foundation type has a certain capacity for tension loading and thus combines features of pile and gravity foundations, however without the costly time needed for piling.

With the advent of floating production units, different foundation problems were introduced. A tension leg platform requires an anchoring point with a high tension capacity. A traditional pile may provide this, but combinations of piles and dead weights are also applied to reduce the required length of the pile to be driven. A 'Floating Production, Storage and Offloading' vessel (FPSO) requires the same type of anchors which are used for floating drilling rigs. These may be driven or bored piles, or drag anchors. The latter are designed for horizontal loads and can only hold minimal vertical pull. With the move to deeper water and the introduction of synthetic materials for mooring lines, the need for high slanted pulling on the anchor under an angle to the horizontal plane is now directing the attention to design of appropriate foundations for this purpose.

An obvious, but not too visible factor in all foundation considerations, is the condition of the sea bed. Experience has taught that the variability of soil properties from site to site in the same general area may be high. It is therefore important that sufficient data sampling and proper analysis is done. Specialised companies provide such services with sophisticated apparatus, which usually have been developed specifically for offshore applications.

RWE-DEA

The Schwedeneck-See platforms in the Baltic Sea near Kiel belong to the early concrete offshore structures. They were both monopods, and designed for ice conditions.

Jackets were built on land, towed in a horizontal position, launched or lifted upright and anchored to the seabed with piles before the superstructure was lifted into position. Construction of concrete platforms began with the building of a sheet piling to create a dry dock. In this dock, the base for the structure was built. At a certain point, this base left the dock and was towed to deeper but protected water. The columns were built on top of the base, and with their increasing length, the base was sunk deeper. When the substructure was ready, it was submerged almost entirely, i.e. far deeper than would ever be the case at its location in the field. This allowed for the superstructure to be floated exactly over the columns' ends. Then the substructure was raised again, and both parts were mated. The deep sinking of the substructure was also *'in effect [ ] an inshore pressure test prior to the offshore installation'*. The immense external pressure the hollow legs had to withstand in this procedure, could be fatal, as was discovered with the loss of a platform for the Sleipner field in 1991.[29] Once the superstructure was standing on its concrete foundation, the entire structure was allowed to rise, this time further than its operational position. Then the platform was towed to its location and there it was sunk again, usually penetrating some metres into the seabed due to its enormous weight. Submerging and emerging the platform was done through letting in or pumping out seawater from the platform base and columns.

material until the present day. Although some structures in the Gulf of Mexico were made of concrete, the most important developments took place in the Norwegian part of the North Sea.

The first concrete structure which the oil industry placed in the North Sea was an oil storage tank, designed by the French firm C. G. Doris for the Ekofisk field, where it was installed in 1973. Not much later, the Norwegians, too, began designing concrete platforms for production purposes. In 1976, two platforms were installed: in the Beryl field and in the Brent field. Frigg and Statfjord followed suit in 1977 and 1979, and two near copies of Statfjord followed in that same field in 1982 and 1985.[27]

Between 1973 and 1989, Norwegian firms built 22 concrete platforms.[28] The use of the locally available material and the option to use the gravity base for oil storage were seen as main advantages over steel jacket structures. Over the years, the size of these platforms increased, in order to operate in ever deeper water. The building and installation concepts of these platforms greatly differed from those used for steel jackets.

The first concrete platforms at Beryl, Brent, Frigg and Statfjord were comparable in size to steel ones, but over the years concrete platforms outclassed even the largest steel jacket structures in mass and size. Norwegian government policy, which focused on large fields and consequently scaling up of operations, allowed to spread the high investments in concrete platforms over a long period and a large production. Economies of scale had been a guiding principle in the offshore sector from the 1950s onwards. New waves of concessions opened up fields at ever larger distance from the shore and in deeper water. This led to structures that could only be used profitably when they produced vast quantities of oil or gas. The trend of increasing steel platforms ended with Shell's

Shell International - Photographic Services London

Shell International - Photographic Services London

Shell International - Photographic Services London

Shell International - Photographic Services London

Building and installation of concrete platforms is done in phases. Usually a dam is built to create a drydock for the casting of a concrete base. After that, the dam is opened and the base is floated out to deep water,

where building of the columns starts. During this, the base sinks little by little. When the columns have been cast to full length, the total is further submerged to allow float-over of the topsides. Finally the assembly is

emerged somewhat in preparation of the tow to site.
These pictures show the construction of Shell's Troll platform, installed in 1995 in the Norwegian sector.

J. Ray McDermott

In 1978 McDermott fabricated and installed the substructure for the largest steel jacket platform to that date, Cognac. It was celebrated with the American Society of Civil Engineers Achievement Award.

Shell International - Photographic Services London

The Cognac platform in the Gulf of Mexico with its remarkable two derricks.

Bullwinkle, installed in the Gulf of Mexico in a water depth of 412 metres in 1988. Probably the last concrete giant that was built, was installed by Shell for gas production in the Troll-field. Touchdown in the field took place on 16 May 1995. This structure, 430 metres high, weighing one million tons and installed in 303m deep water, dwarfed all earlier concrete giants, like Brent B (140m), Gullfaks C (216m), and Draugen (251m). Only the Gullfaks C platform has a larger volume, due to its need for oil storage in the base cells. Today, many engineers feel that Bullwinkle and Troll are probably the last of their kind. Technology has shifted towards floating and subsea systems.

To get a better understanding of Troll's size, we make some comparisons. With its 430 m height, it is 120 m taller than the Eiffel Tower. Its highest point (the tip of the flare tower) stands 170 m above the waterline, and the superstructure is 170 m long and weighs 22500 tons. The concrete substructure is made of 245000 m³ concrete and weighs 656 000 tons. Twelve heavy tugs were needed to tow the platform to its location - a journey on which the colossus was known to miss some rock formations on the seabed by only a few metres. After installation, the platform was expected to sink into the soft seabed over almost 30 metres. In spite of its 1 million tons total weight, the experts managed to position the platform within 30 centimetres of its planned location.
A total of 39 production wells were drilled from the platform and each well was planned to produce 2.8 million cubic metres of gas per day. Accommodation on the platform has a capacity of 108 people. The total investment, including the pipelines and onshore gas treatment plant, amounted to 15 billion dollars. *'The builders of Norske Shell [ ] reverently call the platform the eighth Wonder of the World.'*[30]

The Troll gas field, some 80 km off Bergen, was discovered in 1979. The oil price - which was a yardstick for gas pricing - was high, and was thought to continue to rise. The field was declared commercially viable in 1983, and soon concepts for exploitation were developed. In 1986, the oil price fell dramatically, but due to Troll's reservoir size being about half the Groningen field, the project was carried on, and the first gas sale contract was concluded. Only the initial plan for an integrated drilling, production and accommodation platform was abandoned. A relatively simple design appeared on the drawing boards, without the elaborate gas treatment plant which usually is found on platforms. Instead of being dried and compressed on board, the gas is pumped to the shore for further treatment. On the platform, a separator just separates condensed water from the gas, and glycol is added to prevent hydrate formation.

The rocky, uneven nature of the seabed made it necessary to lay the pipes partly in a tunnel, where the bottom climbs up from the deep water to the shore.[31] In October 1996 the first gas was produced. After onshore treatment in Norway, it was again transferred into pipelines, and through the by then existing infrastructure of North Sea pipelines, it was brought to customers all over Europe. Firms in Germany, The Netherlands, Belgium, France, Austria and Spain buy Troll gas, and Norway is hoping to supply gas to Europe for at least 50 years.

While a further increase of large platform size is highly unlikely in view of the trend towards subsea wells with long tiebacks or with floaters, the role of concrete is all but finished. The Hibernia platform, designed for iceberg infested waters off Newfoundland (Canada), is another concrete gravity base oil production platform, which will start operating late 1997.[32]

3. Floating production systems

The 1986 oil price fall made offshore operations less economically viable. In areas like the Gulf of Mexico and the North Sea, infrastructures of production units and pipelines were available, that needed to be used to full capacity to remain in business. However, several fields in these provinces saw the end of their productive years approaching rapidly. It now seemed to make sense to start exploitation of the hitherto disregarded smaller fields, to make up for the loss of supply and continue making use of the infrastructure.

Taking smaller fields into production required relatively cheap production units, as the period of

The Bullwinkle platform decks in the Gulf of Mexico give no clue on the size of the structure underneath.

Bullwinkle's substructure: the largest jacket ever built.

exploitation would be shorter. The size of the fields allowed units to be smaller, too, which fitted in well with the cost specifications. Sometimes existing platforms in the vicinity of a new well might be used. In other cases emphasis was on minimizing the cost of a new production platform by simplifying the design or by re-using a refurbished structure from an abandoned field. Tie-backs of new wells to existing production platforms were another way to replace fading production. None of these ideas, however, was fit for medium size discoveries in deeper water and remote from existing infrastructure. In such cases, floating production provided the answer.

The most significant change in the North Sea technology after the concrete gravity platforms has been the advent of ship-shaped floating production and storage systems. The earliest experiments with ship-shaped floating production date back to 1977, when Shell started drawing oil from a subsea well in 114 m water depth into a tanker moored to an oscillating mooring tower, offshore Spain at Castellon. This technology was followed by several similar projects around the world, in the Garoupa field offshore Brazil in 1979 and in the Nilde field offshore

Italy in 1982. Variants to the principle used surface wells on a jacket platform in combination with a floating production and storage vessel, like Hondo off California in 1981 and Tazerka off Tunisia in 1982. In some cases such systems were installed as temporary facilities only, for extended well testing or early production purposes. In other cases they were designed as regular production units for the full field life.

The common understanding was that such systems were fine for moderate to benign seas, but had no practical value in the North Sea. Even so, they provided a business opportunity to companies like SBM Inc. and Bluewater, who jumped in when an oil company desired to lease rather than own a Floating Production, Storage and Offloading system (FPSO).

Until 1986, all of these FPSOs were based on conversion of second hand tankers, with the exception maybe of the ARCO Ardjuna floater, an LPG storage barge on stream since 1976. Second hand tankers were cheap and seemed well fit for this purpose. The necessary upgrading of structure and coating usually more than outweighed the higher costs of a newbuild.

The principle was of beautiful simplicity. Flexible risers transported crude from one or more subsea well

In the Tazerka field offshore Tunisia, one of the early tanker based floating production, storage and offloading systems (FPSOs) was installed in 1982. With its 210000 deadweight tons, it was the largest FPSO until 1985.

The Petrojarl I demonstrated the ability of ship based production systems to work satisfactorily in the North Sea environment.

SBM Inc.

Golar Nor

The FPSO technology lends itself to fast track developments. The Uisge Gorm conversion was completed in less than one and a half year from contract to first oil.

Bob Fleumer Aerial Photography

completions to the ship. Production equipment placed on the deck of the vessel produced the crude, which was then loaded into the tanks of the ship. Every so many days, a shuttle tanker moored up to the side or the end of the FPSO and the load of crude was discharged into this shuttle.

Then, in 1986, Golar Nor presented a new ship dedicated to production of marginal oil wells in the North Sea. Golar Nor proved that the FPSO was a viable concept in the North Sea environment, that separation of oil, gas and water was feasible in spite of ship motions and that the economics might even support newbuilding.

The North Sea industry was not easily convinced. In other areas of the world, for instance in the Australian waters and the South China Sea, the development of the FPSOs went on and resulted in a range of mooring designs, mostly internal or external turrets, sometimes systems that could be released when a cyclone threatened to pass over the FPSO mooring site. It was not until 1993, when Kerr-McGee installed a permanently moored ship on the Gryphon field in the

northern North Sea, that the ice was finally broken. The FPSO, which had long been regarded as unfit to the North Sea, stole the show in no time and made possible the development of fields which were earlier regarded as 'sub-marginal'.

Bluewater and SBM profited from their earlier reputations to stay ahead of competition and provided systems to Amerada Hess and Shell, respectively. However, the competition came fast and in large numbers. Norwegian oil companies shopped within their country for FPSO contractors. At the start of 1997, 16 FPSOs were in use or coming in the Norwegian an UK sectors. Other application areas were Brazil, West Africa, South East Asia and Australia, or roughly: worldwide. Only the Gulf of Mexico was slow to embrace this technology.

In the Gulf of Mexico, floating production followed two other development lines, which had both been proven originally in the North Sea. The first was based on the use of semi-submersibles. In 1975, Hamilton had installed the Transworld 58 semi-submersible on the

Argyll field, in a water depth of 78 m. It served there until 1984 and then worked on Innes for 4 more years starting in 1985. Two years after Hamilton, Petrobras installed its first semi-submersible, the Sedco 135-D, on the Enchova field at Campos. The advantage of a semi-submersible over an FPSO was perceived to be its quiet motions in seaway, favouring for both the production risers and the separators. On the negative side, a semi-submersible had no storage capacity for produced crude, and thus always required a permanently moored storage tanker near it, a dual shuttle tanker scheme, or a pipeline to shore.

From then on, the use of semi's for production snow-balled, with Petrobras as the main user. In the Gulf of Mexico, Placid was the pioneer, with its use of the Penrod 72 for extended well testing of a Green Canyon

field in 1988-1990. At the time, it was the deepest water ever for such system: 460 m.

The second type of floater and the only one which was more popular in the Gulf than anywhere else was the Tension Leg Platform (TLP). Essentially, this is a semi-submersible anchored to the seabed with vertical, taut steel cables or solid pipes. Contrary to the practise with freely floating platforms such as ships or 'normal' semi-submersibles, wellheads can be placed on deck of a TLP, and production is largely similar to fixed platform production.

In 1974 and 1975, Deep Oil Technology performed large scale TLP model testing offshore California with sponsoring of a group of oil companies. The TLP concept was used for the first time in 1984 by Conoco

Production systems of the 1990s often combine subsea wellheads and manifold centres with several types of floating platforms. The role of fixed platforms, however, is not over.

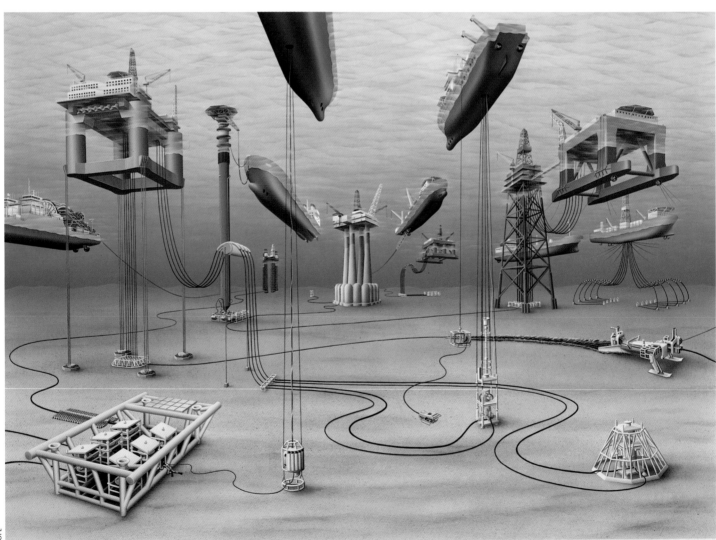

in the British Hutton field in the North Sea. In 1989, Conoco installed the Jolliet TLP in the Gulf of Mexico, merely a wellhead platform without production facilities. Saga followed suit in the North Sea Snorre field in 1992, but the party which really embraced the concept was Shell. While Conoco built a concrete TLP for the North Sea Heidrun field, Shell ordered four steel units for the Gulf of Mexico, resulting in the installation in 1994 of the Auger TLP in 872 m of water at Garden Banks; in 1996 the Mars TLP in 896 m of water at Mississippi Canyon; in 1997 the Ram-Powell TLP in 981 m of water at Viosca Knoll; and the Ursa TLP for about 1200 m of water depth at Mississippi Canyon. Engineers assume that TLP's can be used to a depth of some 2000 metres. The interesting aspect of this concept is that the cost of a unit is not as strongly influenced by the water depth as is the case with fixed platforms. Just like all other floating systems, TLP's can in principle be reused at another location.

In the 1950s and 1960s we saw offshore drilling technology develop much faster than offshore production. But in the 1980s and 1990s, production technology has recovered remarkably. The concepts used for production at large depth look very much like those used for drilling. In deep sea operations both activities nowadays use floating systems, and water depth is becoming less of an obstacle for either kind of operation. The offshore industry of the 1990s is capable of finding and producing oil in places that were formerly thought inaccessible, and it can be concluded that technology has ceased to be one of the most important restricting factors in offshore operations.

4. Deep, deeper and beyond

Within the offshore sector, people became convinced that the direction of technological development was strongly guided by the industry's move into ever deeper waters. Deep, deeper and beyond became the direction which fascinated the minds of offshore men. During the late 1940s, 25 metres of water depth was considered quite deep. The quest for hydrocarbons quickly drove the oil companies beyond 25 metres, into

Saga Petroleum Company

Dockwise NV

The Snorre TLP shows all features of a tension leg platform, except the most important one: the tethered mooring system, which remains completely under water. The water depth at this site is 309 m. Snorre was installed in 1992.

The voyage of the Ram-Powell TLP floater from the Belleli yard in Taranto, Italy, across the Atlantic Ocean to the Aker Gulf Marine yard in Corpus Christi, Texas, took

22 days. The hull weighs 14500 tons and is measuring 87 x 87 x 52 m. The overhang to both sides of the Mighty Servant 2 was 36.5 m.

more remote and deeper waters of the Gulf of Mexico, while in California deeper water was the working area from the start. The Southern North Sea was considered neither shallow nor deep, with water depths ranging from 20 to 100 m. Statfjord, Ninian and Brent in the Northern North Sea are situated in 140 to 150 m of water, but the relatively close Snorre field is in 309 m. The developments in the Campos basin, offshore Brazil, took and take place in waters from 100 to 2000 m depth. In South East Asia and West Africa, the focus of attention originally was in shallow waters, but started to move towards deeper waters in the 1990s. Also, the West of Shetland activity since 1990 is in water depths which before and certainly shortly after 1986 were considered too large for economic production.

Deep had become the buzz word of the industry in the

1990s, as was apparent from the themes of many conferences and engineering conventions. The motive behind this drive is clear: even during the period of low oil prices after 1985, the long term strategy of the oil companies required finding new reserves, and chances to find large extensions were small in the well explored, shallow waters. The deep, however, held the promise of the unknown. The deep waters near Campos (Brazil) cover geological structures with large reserves, and the finds west of the Shetlands, like Foinaven, Schiehallion and Claire, are promising enough to warrant the high investments required. The Gulf of Mexico seemed over-mature in the mid 1980s, until the attention there too shifted to the deeper areas. Wells drilled in the Auger and Mars fields appeared different from the wells in the shallow areas

An animation of subsea systems. The combination may not be realistic, but the congestion at the seabed could be.

of the Gulf, and yielded large production rates like North Sea wells. Encouraged by these discoveries, the search went ever farther and deeper. Mid 1997 the Mensa gas field in 1640 m water depth in the Gulf of Mexico was brought into production as the largest tie-back (100 km) and the deepest subsea completion of this time, but the water depth record will not last long. Already the next record depth had been announced in the Campos basin: the Roncador discovery in 1850 m water depth was planned to start producing oil by the end of 1998.[33]

Moving into deeper areas went with technological progress. The whole train of activities, drilling, the design and handling of drilling risers, the choice of drilling mud specific gravity, the handling and installation of blow-out preventers and later trees, the laying of in-field flowlines and export pipelines, all needed adjustment to the deep.
Dynamically positioned vessels for all kinds of duties, such as drilling, pipelaying and installation work, became indispensable, to the advantage of the contractors who had kept their confidence in this technology also when the rig market was depressed.

For exploration, water depth was not so much of a limit any more. The heaviest jackup platforms can stand in 120 m North Sea, 150 m in benign areas. Moored semi-submersibles and ships can deal with 500 to 1000 m. Dynamically positioned vessels are independent of water depth for their station keeping, but for drilling still require a riser string. Drilling for oil has been done in 2300 m water depth. Riserless drilling for scientific purposes has been performed in over 6000 m.

For production however, the water depth forms a problem as long as large, atmospheric equipment is needed to separate and treat oil, gas, water and sand. This equipment is traditionally placed above water, where it can be designed following proven, land based technology, and can easily be accessed. With water depth increasing past 300 m or thereabout, the bottom supported platforms literally lost ground. Floaters needed subsea wellheads, and experiments

J. Waddell, 'Development trends in deep water', Journal of offshore Technology (May 1996), 10-12.

Waterdepth records

Bottom supported platforms				
Steel jacket	Bullwinkle	Gulf of Mexico	412m	1988
	Magnus	North Sea	186m	1982
Concrete gravity	Troll	North Sea	303m	1995
Compliant tower	Lena	Gulf of Mexico	305m	1983

Floating production				
Spar	Neptune	Gulf of Mexico	588m	1996
Semi-submersible	Marlim 3	Campos Basin	910m	1994
	Troll Oil	North Sea	335m	1996
TLP	Ram-Powell	Gulf of Mexico	981m	1997
	Heidrun	North Atlantic	345m	1995
Ship	Barracuda	Campos Basin	833m	1997
	Foinaven	North Atlantic	540m	1996

Subsea tie-backs				
To fixed platform	Mensa	Gulf of Mexico	1640m	1997
To floater	Snorre North	North Sea	300m	1997

Exploration drilling				
Ship	Alaminos Canyon	Gulf of Mexico	2324m	1996

INTEC Engineering

With the increasing depth of water where oil or gas is produced, subsea production trees have become the standard of the 1990's.

George Steinmetz/Transworld

with such systems had been going on since long off California and in the Gulf of Mexico. In the North Sea several more or less experimental systems were installed, such as the diver assisted installations of subsea trees at Argyll, Buchan and Balmoral in water depth from 75 to 145 m. On the Cormorant field, a diverless approach was choosen. In 1982, an Underwater Manifold Center (UMC) was installed in 150 m water by Shell and Esso, which could accommodate 9 well heads. Some elements of this design made a come back in the Snorre subsea system in 335 m water depth in 1992. The largest wellhead template in this style was placed in Placid's Green Canyon field in the Gulf of Mexico.

For maintenance at Cormorant and Snorre, specific robots were developed. A more general trend in installation and maintenance was to use Remotely Operated Vehicles (ROV's) which became increasingly powerful and sophisticated. Their versatility changed the course of subsea developments towards application of individual wet subsea production trees, some-

times as stand alones, sometimes in clusters. The importance of subsea trees cannot be overrated. By 1996 Petrobras alone had installed 231 subsea trees and was planning for a further 181 until the year 2000. Of course, subsea trees did not stand alone. In deep water they went together with floating production systems which were connected to the wells by risers and needed to be kept in position above the wells. Conventional mooring required heavy steel wire ropes or chains and became increasingly difficult in deeper waters because of dynamic behaviour as well as the weight of winches and lines. Dynamic positioning of production platforms, however, did not seem to be economically viable. BP experimented with the dynamically positioned production vessel Seillean on some smaller North Sea fields from 1990 onwards, but it was never intended to stay at a field permanently, and it still is the only example of this approach. For production platforms, the development of true deep water moorings became important. The TLP type mooring for floating production systems was well proven, and development of the use of light, strong

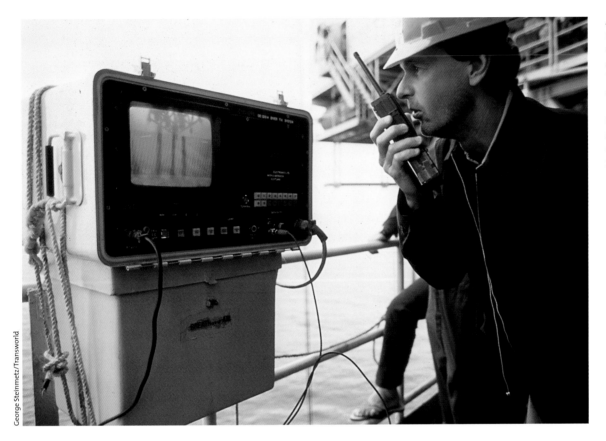

George Steinmetz/Transworld

A 45 tons template is lowered through 24 m of water in the Gulf of Suez, to be placed over three delineation wells. The framework can accommodate six more wells. While the supervisor monitors the underwater tv on deck of the crane ship, divers guide the structure into position.

synthetic ropes for spread moorings was under way in Brazil, the Gulf of Mexico and the North Sea in the mid 1990s. It is not evident when and where this development will cease. Once the shift from bottom supported to floating platforms and from surface to subsea completions had been made, economics rather than technology started to determine the production system lay-out.[34]

5. A new structure of the industry

After the oil price fall of early 1986, the offshore industry as a whole suffered from a drastic reduction of activity. The new reality of a low oil price killed a large number of development plans and postponed others. The notion of 'marginal field' was more clearly than ever before linked to an economic criterion.

In the wake of the reduced investments in exploration and development, the offshore drilling and construction contractors found insufficient work for their staff and equipment. Several renowned firms went out of business, others assumed heavy loans. Renowned names disappeared from the scene. ODECO, for instance, a pioneer from the first hour, merged with Diamond M Company and became Diamond Offshore Drilling Inc. New joint ventures aimed at containing throat-cutting competition. HeereMac has already been mentioned and in the pipelaying world, Brown & Root Ltd. and Saipem UK Ltd. formed European Marine Contractors (EMC). Newbuilding of rigs, which had already almost ceased after the 1986 oversupply, came to a complete standstill. Also less visible changes took place. Inspection of platform jackets, which had traditionally been divers work, was gradually taken over by ROVs because of their lower risks and costs. Specialized diving firms merged with ship owners to provide this new type of service.

Gradually, firms and people in the offshore industry got used to the fact, that no longer the sky was the limit. New designs appeared, which effectively cut costs of developing a field. Typical examples are the increased use of subsea satellite wells tied back to

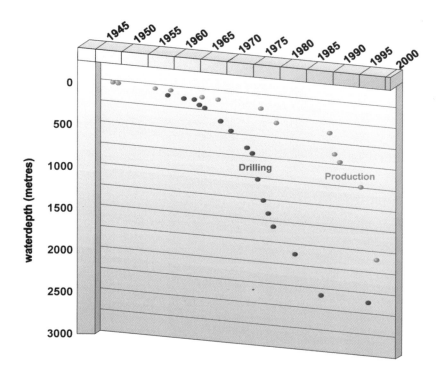

Technology for exploration drilling and production developed separately. The graph shows that drilling developed much earlier to deeper water than production. The shape of the curves, however, is comparable.

existing production platforms, and the introduction of floating productions systems, in particular FPSOs, in the North Sea. The result was a fast growing new sector in the industry where until 1990 only few companies had operated.

Most notable in the 1990s however was a new attitude towards contracting. Conventionally, oil companies would go through extensive engineering detail in house, with help of specialised engineering companies. With the trimming of oil company engineering department size after the mid 1980s came the interest in Engineering-Procurement-Construction (EPC) contracts, in which a large engineering contractor would undertake a project on the basis of functional specifications instead of detail design. The loss of control in the oil companies, and the high risk on the contractor's account made both parties less than happy. A new contract form was found in the 'alliance', in which several contractors jointly undertake a project and jointly share risks and rewards, sometimes including the principal in their team. Sharing the gains and

The Tyra East platform in the foreground and the Tyra West unit in the background stand on the Danish continental shelf.

Mærsk Olie og Gas AS

the pains sounded right, but in the high risk offshore environment it often meant sharing pains only.

With the new contract forms, the emphasis on quality assurance became stronger, since the oil companies exerted less direct control over the contractors, but would get the public blame anyway if something went wrong. Having a quality certificate became a prerequisite for firms operating offshore or supplying equipment. Also engineering companies submitted to quality audits in increasing numbers. The most heard definition of quality in this respect was 'fit for purpose'. Other aspects were traceability of materials, actions and documentation, and doing things right

the first time. The industry, which had started to grow with trial and error methods, went through some pains while adopting these principles, but after a while saw the advantages.

Parallel to these developments were cost reduction efforts by standardisation and simplification of procedures. In the UK, the term CRINE (Cost Reduction Initiative for the New Era), introduced in 1993, became the magic word. In Norway, NORSOK, introduced in 1993, aimed at similar goals. In the Gulf of Mexico, oil companies teamed up together to share the cost of deep water developments in DEEPSTAR, an initiative of Texaco.

The building of BP's Pompano jacket in 1993 to be installed in 400 m in the Gulf of Mexico.

Epilogue

This year, 1997, it was one century ago that a spiritualist by the name of H.L. Williams, exploring on his territory, moved his search for oil some steps into the sea. He built wooden piers to support the kind of derricks he also used on land. This year, 1997, it also was fifty years ago that three oil companies dared to explore out of sight of land in the Gulf of Mexico. Steel, tenders and jackets were their means to face the challenge. Some 25 years ago, skyrocketing oil prices provided for incredible expansion of offshore activities. North Sea offshore became profitable, and due to its environment and location a playground for innovators and investors. This year, about an eighth of a century ago the period of profits seemed over, but offshore industry proved to be mature enough to withstand the hard times. Offshore activities went on, became even more sophisticated, learned from disasters and mingled with society.

The offshore sector, from its early days until the present is in some ways special. Its product is a commodity, known to everyone, a key factor in economics, and a fuel even worth fighting for. Its activities however were generally out of sight. It made people rich and it took peoples lives. It became loved for its products and the political power it could provide, but also hated for what these could do to our world. Offshore became a common industry, creating good things and bad. Offshore also became an industry in extremities: in the importance of its products, as a political factor, in its big investments, in its giant structures, in its daring innovations, in its dangerous activities, in its invisibility to society and also in the attention it ultimately got from society.

As in other sectors the offshore sector was born out of experiments, by people looking for ways to bypass their settled competitors. They took their chances to expand with rising demands. They developed technical means by learning from other industries, adapting such knowledge to the offshore requirements, and eventually creating their own concepts, giving others reason to learn from offshore technology.
Offshore innovators followed certain patterns in their thinking: once concepts had been proven successful, regardless whether or not the concepts as such were the key to the success, they became a standard and a basis for further development. Revolutionary innovations still occurred, but the minds in which they grew, were often with companies blocked from traditional lines by patents, looking for a breakthrough on their own, or aiming at the very long term.

Most remarkable in the development of offshore technology are the separated paths along which exploration and production. Due to American oil policy stimulating companies to increase their reserves, offshore exploration developed fast. Fixed equipment was followed by mobile equipment and to a large degree water depth ceased to be a limiting factor within two decades from getting out in the open sea. Eventually production platforms would follow the same line as exploration units, from fixed to mobile or rather floating units and eliminating water depth as a factor through subsea equipment.

Within one hundred years, offshore became a sector of industry in which several hundreds of specialised companies are involved, which turns over tens of billions of dollars and which obtained world wide presence. Starting off Santa Barbara, California, it spread to several lakes and coastal waters, some even forgotten. After an incubation period of fifty years it expanded into the open sea, and became an international industry with activities in the Gulf of Mexico, the North Sea, the Persian Gulf, California, Alaska, the South China Sea, Indonesia, Australia, Lake Maracaibo and the Gulf of Paria, Africa, the Atlantic margin off Britain, Canada and the U.S.A., in the Adriatic Sea.

Much has changed since the days of Kerr-McGee's Ship Shoal discovery. The industry has become truly international, quality conscious and highly professional. Fortunately, the mentality of the players in the industry has not changed. Most offshore related people enjoy working in an inspiring, challenging and informal environment. Even during the depressed days after 1986, people took pride to build on new ideas and concepts, to advance technology one step further again. And that is what makes the offshore world such a fascinating one.

Chapter 1

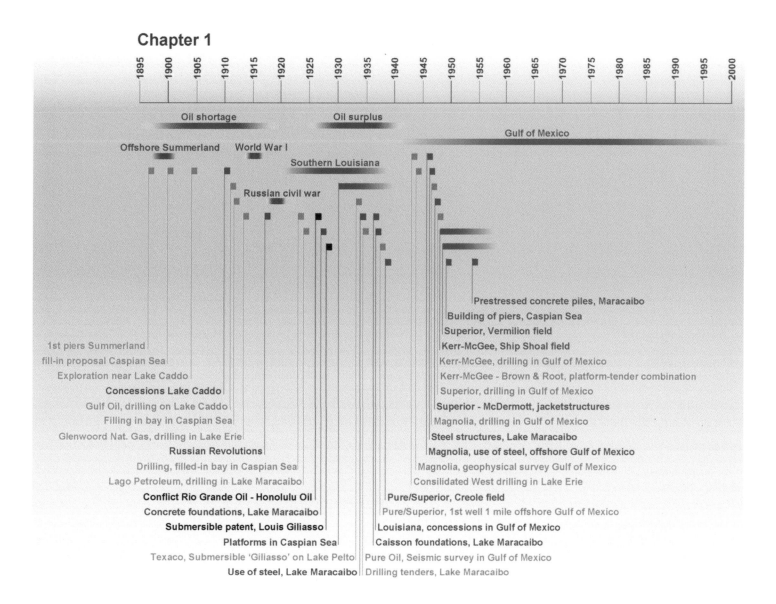

1895 1900 1905 1910 1915 1920 1925 1930 1935 1940 1945 1950 1955 1960 1965 1970 1975 1980 1985 1990 1995 2000

Oil shortage

Oil surplus

Gulf of Mexico

Offshore Summerland   World War I

Southern Louisiana

Russian civil war

Prestressed concrete piles, Maracaibo
Building of piers, Caspian Sea
Superior, Vermilion field
Kerr-McGee, Ship Shoal field
Kerr-McGee, drilling in Gulf of Mexico
Kerr-McGee - Brown & Root, platform-tender combination
Superior, drilling in Gulf of Mexico
Superior - McDermott, jacketstructures
Magnolia, drilling in Gulf of Mexico
Steel structures, Lake Maracaibo
Magnolia, use of steel, offshore Gulf of Mexico
Magnolia, geophysical survey Gulf of Mexico
Consilidated West drilling in Lake Erie

1st piers Summerland
fill-in proposal Caspian Sea
Exploration near Lake Caddo
Concessions Lake Caddo
Gulf Oil, drilling on Lake Caddo
Filling in bay in Caspian Sea
Glenwoord Nat. Gas, drilling in Lake Erie
Russian Revolutions
Drilling, filled-in bay in Caspian Sea
Lago Petroleum, drilling in Lake Maracaibo
Conflict Rio Grande Oil - Honolulu Oil   Pure/Superior, Creole field
Concrete foundations, Lake Maracaibo   Pure/Superior, 1st well 1 mile offshore Gulf of Mexico
Submersible patent, Louis Giliasso   Louisiana, concessions in Gulf of Mexico
Platforms in Caspian Sea   Caisson foundations, Lake Maracaibo
Texaco, Submersible 'Giliasso' on Lake Pelto Pure Oil, Seismic survey in Gulf of Mexico
Use of steel, Lake Maracaibo   Drilling tenders, Lake Maracaibo

Chapter 2

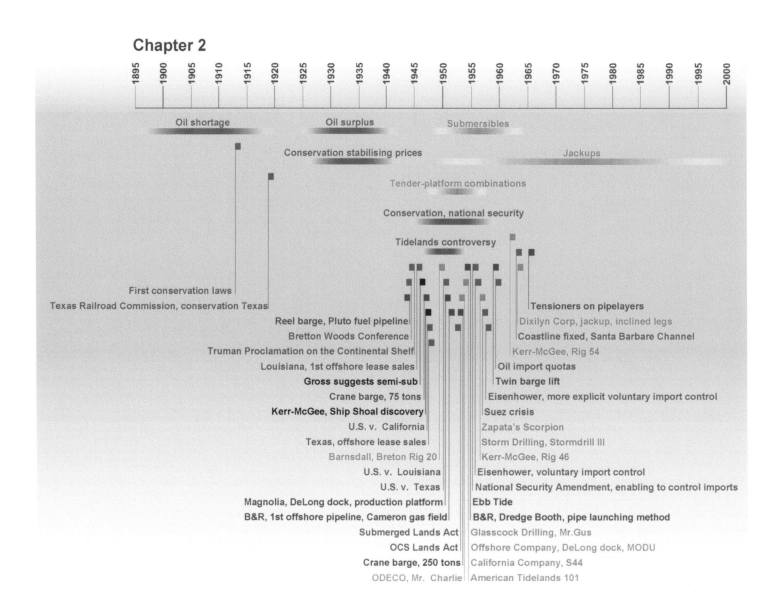

Chapter 3

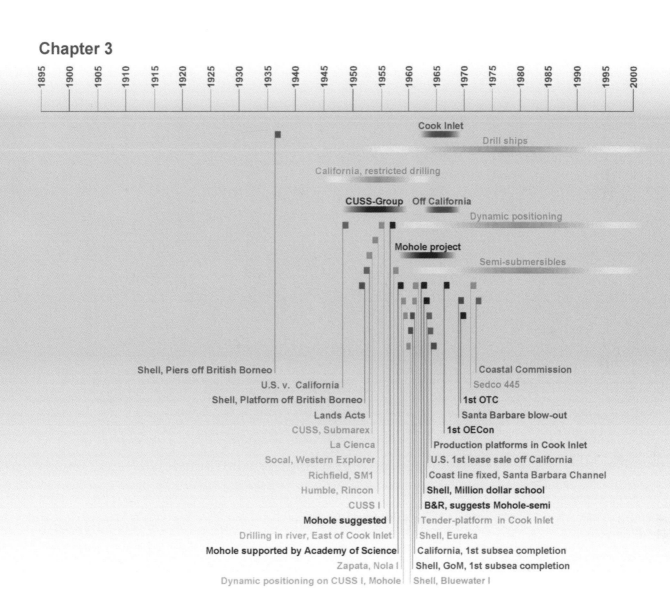

1895 1900 1905 1910 1915 1920 1925 1930 1935 1940 1945 1950 1955 1960 1965 1970 1975 1980 1985 1990 1995 2000

Cook Inlet

Drill ships

California, restricted drilling

CUSS-Group   Off California

Dynamic positioning

Mohole project

Semi-submersibles

Shell, Piers off British Borneo   Coastal Commission
U.S. v. California   Sedco 445
Shell, Platform off British Borneo   1st OTC
Lands Acts   Santa Barbare blow-out
CUSS, Submarex   1st OECon
La Cienca   Production platforms in Cook Inlet
Socal, Western Explorer   U.S. 1st lease sale off California
Richfield, SM1   Coast line fixed, Santa Barbara Channel
Humble, Rincon   Shell, Million dollar school
CUSS I   B&R, suggests Mohole-semi
Mohole suggested   Tender-platform in Cook Inlet
Drilling in river, East of Cook Inlet   Shell, Eureka
Mohole supported by Academy of Science   California, 1st subsea completion
Zapata, Nola I   Shell, GoM, 1st subsea completion
Dynamic positioning on CUSS I, Mohole   Shell, Bluewater I

Chapter 4

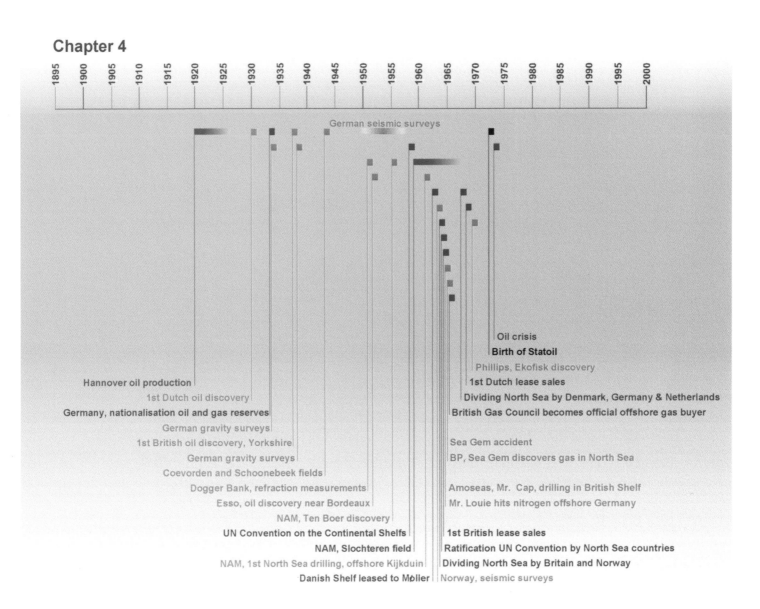

German seismic surveys

Oil crisis

Birth of Statoil

Phillips, Ekofisk discovery

Hannover oil production
1st Dutch oil discovery
Germany, nationalisation oil and gas reserves
German gravity surveys
1st British oil discovery, Yorkshire
German gravity surveys
Coevorden and Schoonebeek fields
Dogger Bank, refraction measurements
Esso, oil discovery near Bordeaux
NAM, Ten Boer discovery
UN Convention on the Continental Shelfs
NAM, Slochteren field
NAM, 1st North Sea drilling, offshore Kijkduin
Danish Shelf leased to Møller

1st Dutch lease sales
Dividing North Sea by Denmark, Germany & Netherlands
British Gas Council becomes official offshore gas buyer

Sea Gem accident
BP, Sea Gem discovers gas in North Sea

Amoseas, Mr. Cap, drilling in British Shelf
Mr. Louie hits nitrogen offshore Germany

1st British lease sales
Ratification UN Convention by North Sea countries
Dividing North Sea by Britain and Norway
Norway, seismic surveys

Chapter 5

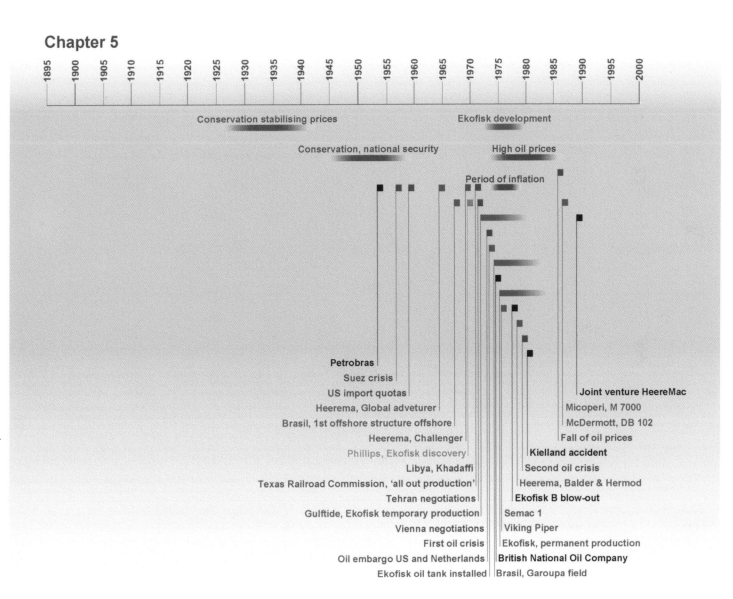

1895 1900 1905 1910 1915 1920 1925 1930 1935 1940 1945 1950 1955 1960 1965 1970 1975 1980 1985 1990 1995 2000

Conservation stabilising prices

Ekofisk development

Conservation, national security

High oil prices

Period of inflation

Petrobras
Suez crisis
US import quotas   **Joint venture HeereMac**
Heerema, Global adveturer   Micoperi, M 7000
Brasil, 1st offshore structure offshore   McDermott, DB 102
Heerema, Challenger   Fall of oil prices
Phillips, Ekofisk discovery   **Kielland accident**
Libya, Khadaffi   Second oil crisis
Texas Railroad Commission, 'all out production'   Heerema, Balder & Hermod
Tehran negotiations   **Ekofisk B blow-out**
Gulftide, Ekofisk temporary production   Semac 1
Vienna negotiations   Viking Piper
First oil crisis   Ekofisk, permanent production
Oil embargo US and Netherlands   **British National Oil Company**
Ekofisk oil tank installed   Brasil, Garoupa field

Chapter 6

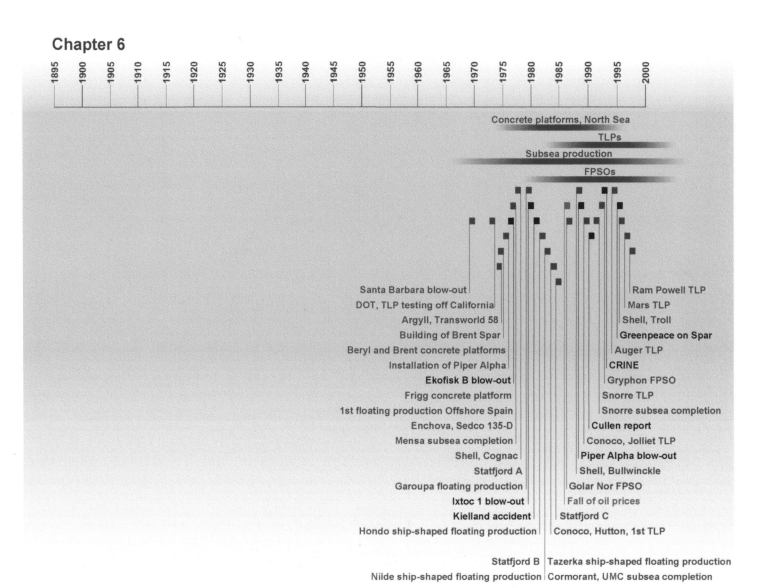

Concrete platforms, North Sea

TLPs

Subsea production

FPSOs

Santa Barbara blow-out

DOT, TLP testing off California

Argyll, Transworld 58

Building of Brent Spar

Beryl and Brent concrete platforms

Installation of Piper Alpha

Ekofisk B blow-out

Frigg concrete platform

1st floating production Offshore Spain

Enchova, Sedco 135-D

Mensa subsea completion

Shell, Cognac

Statfjord A

Garoupa floating production

Ixtoc 1 blow-out

Kielland accident

Hondo ship-shaped floating production

Ram Powell TLP

Mars TLP

Shell, Troll

Greenpeace on Spar

Auger TLP

CRINE

Gryphon FPSO

Snorre TLP

Snorre subsea completion

Cullen report

Conoco, Jolliet TLP

Piper Alpha blow-out

Shell, Bullwinckle

Golar Nor FPSO

Fall of oil prices

Statfjord C

Conoco, Hutton, 1st TLP

Statfjord B | Tazerka ship-shaped floating production

Nilde ship-shaped floating production | Cormorant, UMC subsea completion

Notes

Chapter 1

1. J.S. Ezell (1979), 164.
2. Ibid 169.
3. R. Londenberg (1972), 54.
4. R.L. Lankford (1971), 1364.
5. W. Rintoul (1976), 207-208; R.L. Lankford (1971), 1364-1366; W.J. Graff (1981), 4.
6. W. Rintoul (1976), 208.
7. W. Rintoul (1976), 208; R.L. Lankford (1971), 1366.
8. R.L. Lankford (1971), 1366.
9. W. Rintoul (1976), 208-209.
10. Cited in R.L. Lankford (1971), 1368.
11. Ibid.
12. W. Rintoul (1976), 209-211; E.W. Owen (1975), 672; R.L. Lankford (1971), 1383.
13. W. Rintoul (1976), 211.
    See also: *De Ingenieur 58 (1946)5*, M9.
14. Franks & Lambert (1985), 46-47; W. Rintoul (1976), 211-215.
15. E.W. Owen (1975), 650 describes the Californian oil industry during this period as *'a large, but essentially self-contained regional business'*. California was for a period of time the American state offering the highest oil production. Perhaps this position created a basis for an own or in a way isolated technological paradigm.
16. F.G. Clapp (1915), 162.
17. W.E. Park (June 5, 1913), 32.
18. Ibid.
19. Ibid; F.G. Clapp (1915), 162.
20. *The Oil & Gas Journal (August 21, 1913)*, 28.
21. W.E. Park (July 10, 1913), 26.
22. W.E. Park (June 5, 1913), 32; W.E. Park (July 10, 1913), 26; W.E. Park (August 7, 1913), 32; J.A. Clark (1963), 95; F.G. Clapp (1915), 162.
23. W.E. Park (June 5, 1913), 32; W.E. Park (July 10, 1913), 26; F.G. Clapp (1915), 162.
24. W.E. Park (July 10, 1913), 26.
25. R. Gramling (1996); *The Oil & Gas Journal (August 21, 1913)*, 28.
26. *Offshore (August 22, 1958)*, [c].
27. Franks & Lambert (1982), 35; G. Forbes, 59.
28. G. Forbes, 61.
29. Franks & Lambert (1982), 35-37, 42; G. Forbes, 61-63.
30. Franks & Lambert (1982), 40; G. Forbes, 64.
31. Cited from *Mineral Resources, II, 1907*, 323, 342, 404 in G. Forbes, 61.
    D.T. Day was *'the father of mineral resources studies in the Federal Government'* (J.A. Clark (1963), 93).
32. G. Forbes, 67.
33. *Offshore (September 1957)*, 31.
34. Franks & Lambert (1982), 37; G. Forbes, 61.
35. Franks & Lambert (1982), 41.
36. G. Forbes, 68-69; R.L. Lankford (1971), 1368-1371.
37. Franks & Lambert (1982), 37; G. Forbes, 59.
38. A.B. Thompson (1920), 80; A. Perrodon (1985), 80.
39. A. Perrodon (1985), 83; S. Lewarne (1988), 63-65; *La Revue Pétrolifère (24 Février 1923); La Revue Pétrolifère (1 October 1925); La Revue Pétrolifère (17 Novembre 1928)*; A.B. Thompson; A.B. Thompson (1925), [A]; A.B. Thompson (1925), [B]; *The Oil & Gas Journal (March 5, 1920)*, 74; C.A. Sloan (1919), 62-63.
40. R.L. Lankford (1971), 1420.
41. S. Lewarne (1988), 63.
42. R.L. Lankford (1971), 1422-1425; S. Lewarne (1988), 65
43. R.L. Lankford (1971), 1372-1374; R. Londenberg (1972), 56 (from Lankford); H. Pérez La Silva (et.al) (1995), 2.
44. R.L. Lankford (1971), 1374.
45. Janssen & Kranendonk (1950), M42.
46. R.L. Lankford (1971), 1374-1375; H. Pérez La Silvia (et.al.) (1995), 2-3.
47. R.L. Lankford (1971), 1375; H. Pérez La Silvia (et.al.) (1995), 3.
48. R.L. Lankford (1971), 1375-1376; H. Pérez La Silvia (et.al.) (1995), 2.
49. Janssen & Kranendonk (1950), M41.
50. Ibid.
51. Ibid.
    See also: H. Pérez La Silvia (et.al.) (1995), 3.
52. Janssen & Kranendonk (1950), M43.
53. A. Kranendonk (1953), 3.
54. Ibid M42.
55. R.L. Lankford (1971), 1377.
56. Ibid 1379.
57. E.W. Owen (1975), 446-457, 748.
58. G.F. Shepherd (1947), 1081.
59. Ibid 1082.
60. E.W. Owen (1975), 457-462.
61. R.L. Lankford (1971), 1378; G.F. Shepherd (1947), 1082-1083.
62. Ibid.
63. G.F. Shepherd (1947), 1081-1083.
64. U.S. Patent 1681533 (1928).
65. R.L. Lankford (1971), 1379.
66. Ibid 1380-1381; U.S. Patent 1681533 (1928).
67. R.L. Lankford (1971), 1381-1382; *De Ingenieur 59(1947)13*, M13.
68. E.W. Owen (1975), 446-454; D. Yergin (1991), 208-209, 218, 223.
69. E.W. Owen (1975), 450, 452, 465-467; D. Yergin (1991), 218-219.
70. E.W. Owen (1975), 449, 450.
71. See among others: G.F. Shepherd (1947), 1081-1082.
72. E.W. Owen (1975), 748.
73. Cited by D. Yergin (1991), 233.
74. E.W. Owen (1975), 800; R.L. Lankford (1971), 1383.
75. R.L. Lankford (1971), 1383.
76. R.L. Lankford (1971), 1384; E.W. Owen (1975), 800.
77. E.W. Owen (1975), 800.
78. Ibid.
79. J.S. Toler (1953), 289/3; R.L. Lankford (1971), 1384.
80. *Offshore (October 1963)*, 17.

81. R.L. Lankford (1971), 1384.
82. E.W. Owen (1975), 800.
83. Ibid.
     See also: Herbert & Anderson (1936); I.W. Alcorn (1938).
84. G.F. Shepherd (1945); G.F. Shepherd (1947); W.B. Neill (1948); McBee & Orchard (1949).
85. E.W. Owen (1975), 800-801; W.B. Neill (1948), 1038-1039.
86. D.A. McGee (1949); R.L. Lankford (1971), 1384; W.J. Graff (1981), 8-9; *De Ingenieur 59(1947)13*, M13.
87. *De Ingenieur 59(1947)13*, M13.
88. W.J. Graff (1981), 9.
89. R.L. Lankford (1971), 1383-1384; E.W. Owen (1975), 800.
90. E.H. Short (1947), 82-85, 91; W.J. Graff (1981), 9-10.
91. E.H. Short (1947), 91.
92. Ibid 83.
93. E.H. Short (1947), 82-85, 91; W.J. Graff (1981), 9-10.
94. McBee & Orchard (1949), 986.
95. J.S. Ezell (1979).

96. Ibid 154.
97. Ibid 156-157, 163.
98. Ibid 163.
99. *The Oil and Gas Journal (April 19, 1965)*, 191.
100. J.S. Ezell (1979), 162.
101. *The Oil and Gas Journal (April 19, 1965)*, 191.
     See also: J.S. Ezell (1979), 163; W.J. Graff (1981), 10; R.L. Lankford (1971), 1386-1393.
102. J.S. Ezell (1979), 163-164; *The Oil and Gas Journal (April 19, 1965)*, 191; D.A. McGee (1949).
103. J.S. Ezell (1979), 164.
104. L.S. McCaslin (1948), 82-84, 123-124.
     A lot has been written on the Kerr-McGee oil discovery. Some Examples are: Barnes & McCaslin (1948) and J.W. Calvert (1955). Seale and McGee wrote down their knowledge and experiences in: A.T.F. Seale (1948); McGee & Seale (1948); D.A. McGee (1949).

Chapter 2

1.   W.B. Neill (1948), 1035.
2.   A.T.F. Seale (1948), 16.
3.   W.J. Graff (1981), 9; E.H. Short (1947), 82-85, 91.
4.   See among others E.W. Owen (1975).
5.   J.E. Hartshorn (1962), 218-219.
6.   R.L. Lankford (1971), 1368-1369; E.O. Thompson (1959); D. Yergin (1991).
7.   J.E. Hartshorn (1962), 218-219; E.O. Thompson (1959).
8.   J.E. Hartshorn (1962), 211-222.
     See also: E.W. Owen (1975); D. Yergin (1991).
9.   E.O. Thomson (1959); J.E. Hartshorn (1962), 220; A.P.H. van Meurs (1971), 178.
10. J.E. Hartshorn (1962), 218.
11. Ibid 217-218.
12. Ibid 215.
13. The Texas Railroad commission was initially established to regulate the building of railroads, but gradually developed into a more generally controlling body in various fields.
     See also: D.F. Prindle (1981).
14. A. Sampson (1972); D. Yergin (1991); J.E. Hartshorn (1962); E.O. Thompson (1959).
15. J.E. Hartshorn (1962), 220-221.
16. *Petroleum resources under the ocean floor* (1969), 7
17. Cited in D. Yergin (1991), 233.
18. D. Yergin (1991), 395.
19. Ibid.
20. Ibid 396-405.
21. Ibid 428-430.
22. Freudenburg & Gramling (1994), 17.
23. Ibid 18; Marshall & Zisk (1966), 17.
24. Marshall & Zisk (1966), 14.
25. *Truman Proclamation on the Continetal Shelf* (1945).
26. Freudenburg & Gramling (1994), 18.
     See also: R.B. Krueger (1969).
27. Marshall & Zisk (1966), 15.
28. Ibid 14.

29. Ibid 16; Freudenburg & Gramling (1994), 21.
30. Marshall & Zisk (1966), 17.
31. Freudenburg & Gramling (1994), 20.
32. Ibid 21; A.J. Laborde (1985), 154.
33. R.L. Lankford (1971), 1393.
34. Ibid 1392-1393.
35. Freudenburg & Gramling (1994), 21.
36. H.E. Gross (1946), 189.
37. Ibid.
38. Ibid 189, 192.
39. Ibid 186.
40. R.L. Lankford (1971), 1394-1396.
41. Ibid 1396; Howe & Collipp (1956); R.J. Howe (1966, Part I); R.J. Howe (1968).
42. D.A. McGee (1949).
43. J.S. Ezell (1979), 192.
44. Howe & Collipp (1956); R.J. Howe (1966) Part I.
45. Ibid; R.J. Howe (1968); R.L. Lankford (1971), 1397-1399.
46. R.J. Howe (1966, Part I); R.L. Lankford (1971), 1397; J.S. Ezell (1979), 262-267.
47. R.J. Howe (1966, Part I).
48. Howe & Collipp (1956).
49. Ibid.
50. U.S. Patent no. 89794 (1869).
51. Howe & Collipp (1956); R.J. Howe (1966, Part II); R.L. Lankford (1971), 1407-1412.
52. Ibid.
53. Ibid; L.C. Rogers (1964).
54. G.C. Lee (1968).
55. *Offshore (September 1979)*, 104; J. Dwyer (1968); Desa & Shaw (1979).
56. D. Yergin (1991), 536.
57. Ibid.
58. A.o.: D. Yergin (1991), 427-430, 479-498, 535-536; R. Janssen (1994).
59. D. Yergin (1991), 537-540.
60. Ibid 539.

Chapter 3

1. *The Oil and Gas Journal (April 19, 1965)*, 191.
2. Freudenburg & Gramling (1994), 21.
3. Hester & Evans (1977), 261.
4. R.L. Lankford (1971).
   See also: E.R. Kaplan (1982).
5. W. Bascom (1961), 244.
   R.L. Geer (1973).
6. W. Bascom (1961), 244.
7. Ibid 246.
8. R.L. Lankford (1971), 1399-1407; R.J. Howe (1966, Part III);
   W. Bascom (1961), 244-245; R.L. Geer (1973).
9. W. Bascom (1961), 247 calls it 'landing base';
   R.L. Lankforrd (1971), 'birdcage'.
10. R.L. Lankford (1971); W. Bascom (1961), 246-249;
    Field & Thornburg (1963-64).
11. R.L. Lankford (1971), 1399-1407; R.J. Howe (1966, Part III);
    W. Bascom (1961); R.L. Geer (1973).
12. R.L. Lankford (1971), 1426-1438.
13. Ibid.
14. W. Bascom (1961), 260.
15. Ibid 255-267.
16. R.L. Lankford (1971).
17. Ibid.
18. *Design of a deepsea ocean drilling ship* (1962), v.
19. Ibid.
20. Freudenburg & Gramling (1994), 21.
21. R.J. Howe (1968), 50-52; R.R. McKay (1970).
22. E.P. Danenberger (1991).
23. E.R. Kaplan (1982).
24. Freudenburg & Gramling (1994), 22.
25. G.C. Martin (1921), 9.
26. Ibid 42-55; J.B. Daigle (1968), 21.
27. B.L. Goepfert (1969).
28. J.B. Daigle (1968), 24.
29. Ibid 24-29.
30. Ibid.
31. B.G. Collipp (1993), 586.
    See Also Chapter 2.
32. R.L. Lankford (1971), 1405.
33. B.G. Collipp (1993) , 590; U.S. Patent 3163147 (1964);
    F.G. West (1964), 43-45.
34. D.M. Taylor (1983).
35. Ibid.
36. R.J. Howe (1968).
37. Ibid.
38. B.G. Collipp, 591; D.S. Hammett (1972), II 104.
39. R.L. Lankford (1971); Freudenburg & Gramling (1994), 19;
    E.R. Kaplan (1982).
40. B.C. Carlson (1979).
41. Hansen & Rickey (1994).
42. A. Kranendonk (1953), 17-26; *Mengjangkau enampuluh
    tahum, Sixty years on, 1929-1989*, (1989), 16-20.
43. A. Kranendonk (1953); F.G. West (1964), 30-31.
44. D.M. Taylor (1983).
45. Ibid.
46. These societies were: The American Institute of Mining,
    Metallurgical and Petroleum Engineers, The American
    Association of Petroleum Geologists, The American
    Institute of Chemical Engineers, The American Society
    of Civil Engineers, The American Society of Mechanical
    Engineers, The Institute of Electrical and Electronics
    Engineers, The Marine Technology Society, The Society
    of Exploration Geophysicists and The Society of Naval
    Architects & Marine Engineers.

Chapter 4

1. *The Economist (September 19, 1964)*, 1141.
2. *The Economist (September 25, 1965)*, 1237.
3. Cooper & Gaskell (1966), 1-8; R.J. Howe (1968), 53.
4. J.W. Owen (1975), 1538-1543.
5. J.W. Owen (1975), 1545-1548; *Eén biljoen op onze gasmeter*
   (1982), 17-18; Brouwer & Coenen (1968), 163-176;
   Hoyer & Siccama (1946).
6. J.W. Owen (1975), 1550-1551.
7. N. Kokxhoorn (1974), 182.
8. J.W. Owen (1975), 1551; 'Important dates' (1972).
9. Brouwer & Coenen (1968), 177-194.
10. Ibid.
11. *Gas uit Groningen*, 1994, p. 4.
12. *The Economist (September 19, 1964)*, 1141-1142;
    A. Sampson (1975), 215-216.
13. N. Ely (1969).
14. S.S. Andersen (1993), 39-40.
15. Ibid 40.
16. A. Sampson (1975), 215; S.S. Andersen (1993), 40.
17. S.S. Andersen (1993), 41.
18. See a.o.: N. Kokxhoorn (1974); J. van Ginkel (1978);
    A. Sampson (1975); D. Yergin (1991).
19. Ibid.
20. N. Kokxhoorn (1974).
21. *The North Sea Offshore Drilling* (1965), 10.
22. N. Kokxhoorn (1974), 181-193.
23. *Offshore Adventure* (1982), 22-23, 24; S.S. Kvendseth (1988),
    11-12.
24. *Offshore Adventure* (1982), 40.
25. H.H. Ram (1994); S.S. Andersen (1993), 57-61;
    Offshore Adventure (1982), 40-44.
26. Lubbers & Lemckert (1980), 78-112.
27. Ibid.
28. Ibid.
29. G.H.B. Verberg (1984), 4.
30. 'The contribution of Dutch shipyards to offshore
    operations' (1968); *Energienota* (1974).
    I.L. White (et.al.) (1973) gives a remarkable explaination
    for the observation *'new developments have not been as
    visible'* (p. 11) in The Netherlands, as they are in Norway
    and Denmark: The Netherlands have twice as many
    citizens.
31. *Eén biljoen op onze gasmeter* (1982), 21-27; J.W. de Korver
    (1976); P. Schierbeek (1976); P.E. Kent (1970), 180.
    See also: *Noordzee Almanak* (1995), Ch. 9.
32. A. Sampson (1975), 215; S.S. Andersen (1993), 46-47;
    J.D. Davis (1981), 156-157.
33. A.P.F. van Meurs (1971), 174; S.S. Andersen (1993), 47-50.

34. H. Eisenhans (1974), 202-221.
35. Interview with J. Delacour and M. Ningler, 22 November 1996.
    J. Nauwelaers (1975); H. Eisenhans (1974), 202-221.
36. S.S. Andersen (1993), 51-53; Corti & Frazer (1983); D. Hann (1986); J.E. Hartshorn (1962).
37. Ibid; Cook & Surrey (1983).
38. *Aardgas uit de Noordzee* (1985).
    .W. Owen (1975), 1553; S.S. Andersen (1993), 54-60.
39. Cook & Surrey (1983), 6-20.
40. A.P.F. van Meurs (1971), 173.
    See also: Cooper & Gaskell (1966); S.S. Kvendseth (1988).
41. See also: Cooper & Gaskell (1966); S.S. Kvendseth (1988).
42. The North Sea Offshore Drilling (1965).
43. P.E. Kent (1967), 740; 'The Continental Shelf and North Sea Exploration' (1968), 13; *The North Sea Offshore Drilling* (1965), 13; R.J. Howe (1968), 57.
44. 'The Continental Shelf and North Sea Exploration' (1968), 13; F. Sandmann (1975); R.J. Howe (1968), 57; *The North Sea Offshore Drilling* (1965), 10-12.
45. P.E. Kent (1967), 739-740.
46. L.C. Rogers (1967), 93.
47. K. Hutchinson (1967).
    See also: I.L. White (et. al.) (1973), 48-53; L.C. Rogers (1967).
48. E.W. Owen (1975), 1551; I.L. White (1973), 48-53; K. Hutchinson (1967).
49. Pendered & Taylor (1974), 451.
    See also: I.L. White (1973), 6-7.
50. J.L. Kennedy (1973).
51. S.S. Kvendseth (1988), 9-21.
52. Ibid 21-24.
53. Ibid 31.
54. A special example was the SPM selection for the Louisiana Offshore Oil Port (LOOP) in 1975. After a long selection process, the Single Anchor Leg Mooring (SALM) type, promoted by Esso was choosen, because its vertical anchoring provided less threat to the floating oil hoses, which were pulled under water in the strong tidal current associated with hurricanes.
55. *Ocean Industry (Aug 72)*.
56. I.E. Burrows (1996).

Chapter 5

1. D. Yergin (1994).
2. R. Janssen (1993), 15-52, 66.
3. M. Heikal (1975), 262-263; D. Yergin (1994), 568.
4. J. van Ginkel (1978), 25; D. Yergin (1994), 569, 574.
5. Ibid.
6. See: J. van Ginkel (1978), 28.
7. Ibid 30.
8. D. Yergin (1994), 588.
9. J. van Ginkel (1978), 12.
10. Ibid 17-22; J.A. Akins (1973).
11. R. Janssen (1993), 63-64; D.L. Meadows (1972).
12. D. Yergin (1994), 557-558.
    See also: R. Janssen (1993), 37-52; J. van Ginkel (1978), 41-56.
13. D. Yergin (1994), 577-580; M. Heikal (1975) 266; J. van Ginkel (1978), 28-33.
14. R. Janssen (1993), 60; J. van Ginkel (1978), 33.
15. M. Heikal (1975), 265; R. Janssen (1993), 37, 55, 56, 61-63.
16. J. van Ginkel (1978), 66-68.
17. Ibid 69.
18. M. Heikal (1975), 273-274.
19. R. Janssen (1993), 63.
20. Ibid 61-63.
21. Ibid 63; H. van der Wee (1983), 98.
22. D. Yergin (1994), 654-655; H. van der Wee (1983), 98; R. Janssen (1993), 66; J. van Ginkel (1978), 98.
23. R. Janssen (1993), 66-67.
    Prices are different from one source to the other.
    See also: D. Yergin (1994), 749.
24. R. Janssen (1993), 67.
25. D. Yergin (1994), 720.
26. R. Janssen (1993), 67-68.
    One effect of the second oil crisis was a flood of orders to shipyards for newbuilding of drilling semi-submersibles and jackups, as a consequence of increased demand and increased day rates. By the end of 1980, 31 semi-submersibles were on order. The core of the oversupply in the second half of the 1980s was created.
27. Ibid.
28. D. Yergin (1994), 664-665.
29. R. Janssen (1993), 68.
30. *The Economist (February 22, 1975)*.
31. *Offshore Adventure* (1982), 44-45.
    See also: J.L. Brekke (1975).
32. *Offshore Adventure* (1982), 40.
33. P.L. Eckbo (1981), 277-290; K.W. Dam (1976), 63-69.
    See also: H.H. Ramm (1994); S.S. Andersen (1993), 94-102.
34. *EZ en de offshore-industrie* (1984); M. Ellman (1981), 149-165.
35. J. Howard (1975); J. Smith (1975); S.S. Andersen (1988), 88-94; K.W. Dam (1976), 103-143.
36. 'Future of non-majors in the North Sea' (1975), 54.
37. G.J. Maier (1975); J.D. Dewhurst (1975); B. Collins (1975); G.E. Monteith (1975); J.G.S. Longcroft (1975); 'Future of non majors in the North Sea' (1975).
    In 1974, the British and Norwegian governments increased taxes in offshore oil and caused a cut-back of exploration. Rig rates dropped, many rigs became idle and new uses of the expensive equipment were sought, such as accommodation for offshore construction workers.
38. D. Yergin (1994), 746.
39. Ibid 746.
40. S.S. Andersen (1993), 80.
41. Ibid 47.
42. Ibid 47-48.
43. Ibid 39-43.
44. Ibid 47-49.
45. *Offshore Adventure* (1982), 54-55; S.S. Kvendseth (1988), 47-48.
46. *Offshore Adventure* (1982), 54-55; S.S. Kvendseth (1988), 48, 68.
47. S.S. Kvendseth (1988), 39, 79, 80.
48. Ibid 53-55.
49. Ibid 58-63.

50. Ibid.
51. *Offshore Adventure* (1982), 58-59; S.S. Kvendseth (1988), 57, 69-75; J.E. Lamy (1975), 9.
52. S.S. Kvendseth (1988), 49f, 120f, 64-123.
53. *Offshore Adventure* (1982), 58.
54. S.S. Kvendseth (1988), 142; R.J. Howe (1968), 55; G. Arnold (1978), 23-24.
55. G. Arnold (1978), 22-23.
56. *Offshore Adventure* (1982), 114-115; G. Arnold (1978), 17.
57. *Offshore Adventure* (1982), 114-115; S.S. Kvendseth (1988), 133-140; G. Arnold (1978), 18.
58. G. Arnold (1978), 18.
59. Ibid 21.
60. *Offshore Adventure* (1982), 115; G. Arnold (1978), 22.
61. G. Arnold (1978), 20.
62. Ibid 24-25.
63. Ibid 20.
64. A. Almar-Naess (et. al.) (1982); B. Nilsen (1984).
65. In this section, crane capacities are given in short tons, as was common in the industry, unless explicitly defined differently.
66. *Thirty Years Offshore* (1992); B. de Wit (1994); E.P. Heerema (1982); J.D. Bax (1975).
    Interview with E. Heerema (1997).
67. Concrete platforms are discussed in Chapter 6.
68. E.W. Owen (1975), 1237-1238.
69. E.W. Owen (1975), 1244-1245; Bacoccoli & Bentes (1988); S. Possato (et. al.) (1990); G. Bacoccoli (1982); P.A. Bonesio (1996); *Subsea Engineering News, 13(1996)16.*
70. Hansen & Rickey (1995); E.W. Owen (1975), 1244-1245; G. Bacoccoli & M. Bentes (1988).
71. See: R.L.C. Beltrão (1995); L. Randall (1993).

Chapter 6

1. Former Rotterdam Spotmarket secretary-general J. Oskam, quoted in C. van der Leeuw (1990).
2. R.J. Howe (1986).
3. *Het Financieele Dagblad (31 maart 1993).*
4. Ibid.
5. J.W.A. Coker (1994).
6. Cullen (1990); P. Algar (1990); W.J. Pike (1991).
7. Cullen (1990).
8. J.M. Bik (1995).
9. K. Knip (1995).
10. Ibid.
11. R. Biersma (1995); *Het Financieele Dagblad (15 juni 1995).*
12. *NRC Handelsblad (17 mei 1995); NRC Handelsblad (20 juni 1995);* R. Biersma (1995).
13. R. Biersma (1995); *Het Financieele Dagblad (15 juni 1995).*
14. R. Biersma (1995).
15. H. Jessayan (1995).
16. H. Achterhuis (1995); J.M. Bik (1995); *Het Financieele Dagblag (15 juni 1995); NRC Handelsblad (14 juni 1995); NRC Handelsblad (17 juni 1995); Het Financieele Dagblad ()20 juni 1995).*
17. R. Biersma (1995); *NRC Handelsblad (19 november 1995).*
18. Z.C.A. Luyendijk (23 juni 1995).
    See also: Z.C.A. Luyendijk (21 juni 1995); R. Biersma (1995); J.J. Heij (1995).
19. K. Knip (19 oktober 1995); *Het Financieele Dagblad (6 september 1995).*
    See also: Z.C.A. Luyendijk (14 juni 1995).
20. *NRC Handelsblad (15 juni 1995); NRC Handelsblad (20 juni 1995); NRC Handelsblad (21 juni 1996);* M. Schinkel (1995); *Het Financieele Dagblad (21 juni 1995); Het Financieele Dagblad (28 juni 1995.*
21. *NRC Handelsblad (16 juni 1995); Het Financieele Dagblad (16 juni 1995); Het Financieele Dagblad (22 juni 1995).*
22. R. Biersma (1995).
23. See H. Jessayan (1995).
24. *Het Financieele Dagblad (28 juni 1995); NRC Handelsblad (27 juni 1995).*
25. L. Howie (1996), 17.
26. *Het Financieele Dagblad (23 juni 1995); NRC Handelsblad (10 juli 1995); NRC Handelsblad (5 maart 1996); NRC Handelsblad (4 juli 1996); Het Financieele Dagblad (4 juli 1996).*
27. See Chapter 5.
    Offshore Adventure *(1986), 68-75.*
28. S. Fjeld (et. al.) (1994).
29. J. Moksnes (et. al.) (1994).
30. NRC Handelsblad (16 mei 1996); Troll, Gas for Europe.
31. Troll, Gas for Europe.
32. NRC Handelsblad (16 mei 1996).

Textblocks

Drilling techniques
La Revue Pétrolifère (Novembre 1923); Berger & Anderson
(1992); W. Rundell Jr. (1977); H. Jariwala (et. al.) (1997).

Jackup platforms
R.J. Howe (1968).

Jacket platforms
G.C. Lee (1963); G.C. Lee (1968); A. Cottrill (1996);
Offshore Drilling (September 1955).

The Jennifer Project
C.W. Burleson (1976); Varner & Collier (1978).

Offshore Technology Awards
Data from the OTC organisation

Semi-submersibles
B.G. Collipp (1962).

Foundations
A. Cottrill (April 1994); A. Cottrill (August 1994).

Literature

ABBOTTS I.L. (ED.), *United Kingdom Oil and Gas Fields, 25 Years Commemorative Volume*, London, 1991.

ADAIR RED, D.S. HAMMETT, 'Red I - A New Offshore Fire-Fighting Concept', *6th Offshore Technology Conference*, Houston, 1974, 365-378.

AKINS J.E., 'The oil crisis: this time the wolf is here', *Foreign Affairs*, 1973, 462-490.

ALCORN I.W., 'Marine drilling on the Gulf Coast', *Drilling and production practice, American Petroleum Institute, 1938*, 40-46.

ALGAR P., 'The Cullen Report: A Landmark in Offshore Safety', *Petroleum Management (December 1990)*, 12-15.

ALMAR-NAESS A., P.J. HAAGENSEN, B. LIAN, T. MOAN, T. SIMONSEN, 'Investigation of the Alexander L. Kielland Failure Metallurgical and Fracture Analysis', *14th Offshore Technology Conference*, Houston, 1982, 79-94.

ALVARENGA M.M. DE, 'The strategy employed by Brazil to meet the interantional oil crisis', *Proc. 4th Offshore Structures Engineering*, Rio de Janeiro, 1981.

ANDERSEN S.S., *The Struggle over North Sea Oil and Gas, Government Strategies in Denmark, Britain and Norway*, Oslo, 1993.

ANTIA D.D.J., 'Economic Strategies To Maximise Profits From Satellite Field Developments', *26th Offshore Technology Conference*, Houston, 1994, 89-96.

ARNOLD G., *Britain's Oil*, London, 1978.

ARNOLD K.E., ROOBAERT N.C., 'Comparison of North Sea and Gulf of Mexico Design Philosophies', *21th Offshore Technology Conference*, Houston, 1989, 623-630.

ASAN-NURI A.O., 'Exploration and development of off-shore oilfields', *Techniques of Petroleum Development, Proceedings of the United Nations Inter-regional Seminar on Techniques of Petroleum Development, New York, 23 January to 21 February 1962*, 105-129.

ATWATER G.I., 'Geology and petroleum development of the continental shelf of the Gulf of Mexico', *5th World Petroleum Congress*, New York, 1959.

AUGUSTINE N.R., 'Lessons learned from another industry', *ONS Conference 1996*, Stavanger, 1996.

BAALSRUD T., H.T. GRAM, *RS Platon AS, 1936-1986, Fifty years of shipbroking*, 1986.

BACOCCOLI G., 'Offshore Brazil - Twelfe Years of Oil Exploration', *Studies in continental margin geology AAPG, Memoir No. 34*, 1982, 539-546.

BACOCCOLI G., BENTES M., 'Petrobras and Brazil's Offshore Exploration: 20 Years-A Review', *20th Offshore Technology Conference*, Houston, 1988, 371-377.

BAINBRIDGE C.A., 'Certification of fixed steel platforms in the North Sea', *7th Annual Offshore Technology Conference*, Houston, 1975, 737-755.

BAKER D.G., 'Paul Wolff: Creative Engineer, *Kerr-McGee Resources 2(1980)1*, 17-22.

BANKSTON C.L., G.C. LEE, 'Pipelining Offshore', *Spring Meeting Mid-Continent District API Div. of Production, March 1967*.

BAPTISTA F.G., L. ALCALÁ SUCRE, J. DOMINGUEZ, P. CONRAD, 'Drilling and Producing Operations in Lake Maracaibo', *Fifth World Petroleum Congress, Proceedings, Drilling and Production, Section II*, New York, 1959, 111-124.

BARKER T., V. BRAILOVSKY (ED.), *Oil or Industry?, Energy, Industrialisation and Economic Policy in Canada, Mexico, the Netherlands, Norway and the United Kingdom*, London, 1981.

BARNES K.B., L.S. MCCASLIN, 'Kerr-McGee, Phillips, and Stanolind Develop Spectacular Gulf of Mexico Descovery', *The Oil & Gas Journal (March 18, 1948)*, 96-114.

BARRON P., 'The CRINE Initiative - Cultural Change in the U.K. Oil and Gas Industry', *27th Offshore Technology Conference*, Houston, 1995, 405-409.

BASCOM W., *A Hole in the Bottom of the Sea, The Story of the Mohole Project*, New York, 1961, 239-267.

BAX J.D., R.P DE JONG, W. SCHOONMADE, 'Design, Construction and Operation of the First 2000 Tons Offshore Crane Ship', *7th Offshore Technology Conference*, Houston, 1975, 621-630.

BENDER C.M., 'Some Aspects of Offshore Engineering Concerning Plarform Design', *Offshore Europe, 1st Edition*, London, 1968, 85-86.

BERCHA F.G., 'Evolution of Arctic Marine Structural Forms', *26th Offshore Technology Conference*, Houston, 1994, 415-425.

BERGE G., 'Introduction and Preliminary Findings', *The Ekofisk Bravo Blow Out*, International Council for the Exploration of the Sea, 1977, 1.1-1.17.

BERGER B.D., K.E. ANDERSON, *Modern Petroleum, A basic primer of the industry*, Tulsa, 1992.

BERGSETH S., 'Offshore Northern Europe, the Challenges', *ONS Conference 1996*, Stavanger, 1996.

BERTNESS T.A., F.E. BLOUNT, 'Corrosion Control of Platforms in Cook Inlet, Alaska', *1st Offshore Technology Conference*, Houston, 1969, l524-532.

BIRRELL N.D., 'Offshore industry 1988-1993: regrowth and internationalisation', in: H. BENFORD (ED.), *A half century of marine technology, 1943-1993*, New Jersey, 1993.

BIRRELL N.D., 'Deepwater Engineering Trends', *26th Offshore Technology Conference*, Houston, 1994, 941- 951.

BLAKER F., 'Haltenpipe and Troll oil pipeline, technology at the forefront', *ONS Conference 1996*, Stavanger, 1996.

BONESIO P.A., 'Deep water Developments Offshore Brazil', *Conference on World Wide Deep water Technologies*, London, 1996.

BONNAMY J.M., 'Heavy Duty Long Continuous Flexible Pipes with Built-in Electrical Conductors for Offshore Gathering Lines and Other Applications', *Proceeding of OECON Middle East, The First International Offshore Exploration Conference*, Long Beach, 1968, 405-418.

BOON S.A., 'Constructies voor het boren in water en voor de verdere ontwikkeling van een onder water gelegen olieveld', *De Ingenieur (1962)9*, Reprint.

BOVEN C.J.P. VAN, 'Design Considerations for Permanent-Type Offshore Structures', *Offshore Europe, 1st Edition*, London, 1968, 51-55.

BRAINARD II E.C., 'Towed Underwater Vehicle Applications from 1960 through 1975', *8th Offshore Technology Conference*, Houston, 1976, 539-550.

BRANNON H.R., 'Platform verification - a view from a member of industry', *9th Annual Offshore Technology Conference*, Houston, 1977, 21-32.

BROCHES A., *Verslag van de Monetaire en Financieele Conferentie der Vereenigde Volken, gehouden te Bretton Woods, New Hampshire, van 1 tot en met 22 juli 1944, en in het bijzonder nopens de Nederlandsche deelneming daaraan*, New York, 1944.

BROUWER G.C., M.J. COENEN, *Nederland = Aardgasland*, Amersfoort, 1968.

BROWN R.J., 'Rational Design of Submarine Pipelines', *Proceeding of OECON Middle East, The First International Offshore Exploration Conference*, Long Beach, 1968, 43-90.

BURLESON C.W., *The Jennifer Project*, 1997, Austin, 1976.

BURROWS I.E., 'The North Sea Platform Supply Vessel', *Journal of Offshore Technology (November 1996)*, 5-7.

BURY M.R.C., P.L. DOMONE, 'The role of research in the design of concrete offshore structures', *6th Annual Offshore Technology Conference*, Houston, 1974, 155-168.

BUSH G.H.W., 'The future of the offshore drilling industry', *Drilling (November 1965)*, 46-48.

CABARROU P., 'Bounce Dive at Great Depth', *Proceedings of OECON Middle East, The First International Offshore Exploration Conference*, Long Beach, 1968, 469-480.

CALVERT J.W., 'Louisiana offshore operations', *World Petroleum (November 1954)*, 63-69.

CALVERT J.W., 'A decade of oil progress', *World Petroleum (December 1955)*, 38-43, 74, 91.

CALVERT J.W., 'Gulf Offshore Activity Booming', *World Petroleum (January 1957)*, 48-51.

CARLILE H.B., 'Obtaining Cathodic Protection of Platforms, Cook Inlet, Alaska', *1st Offshore Technology Conference*, Houston, 1969, I533-544.

CARLSON B.C., 'First OCS subsea completion', *Petroleum Engineer (August 1979)*.

CHATEAU G.M., Experimenting a Subsea Wellhead Operated by Tools Through Flow Lines', *Proceedings of OECON Middle East, The First International Offshore Exploration Conference*, Long Beach, 1968, 399-404.

CHENG A.P., J.F. KELEHER, 'First Jack-Up Production Platform in North Sea', *5th Offshore Technology Conference*, Houston, 1973, II621-630.

CLAPP F.G. (ET.AL.), *Petroleum and natural gas resources of Canada, Vol. II, Description of occurrences*, Ottawa, 1915.

CLARK J.A., *The Chronological History of the Petroleum and Natural Gas Industries*, Houston, 1963.

COFFMAN V.T., 'Instrumentation System for Installation of the North Sea Forties Field Platforms', *7th Offshore Technology Conference*, Houston, 1975, 67-76.

COKER J.W.A., 'Marginal Field Development in Mature Areas of the North Sea', *26th Offshore Technology Conference*, Houston, 1994, 109-115.

COLE J.C., 'Operations in water depths greater than 1000 meters', *ONS Conference 1996*, Stavanger, 1996.

COLLIPP B.G., 'A floating drilling platform of optimum design', *Shell Oil EPR Report 83*, 1962.

COLLIPP B.G., 'Floating drilling platform', *U.S. Patent 3163147*, 1964.

COLLIPP B.G., 'Offshore Industry 1950-1965: invention', in: H. BENFORD (ED.), *A half century of marine technology, 1943-1993*, New Jersey, 1993.

COLVIN W.B., 'Report on 89 subsea completions', *Ocean Industry (June 1973)*, 51-57.

COOK L., J. SURREY, *Government Policy for the Offshore Supplies Industry, Britain compared with Norway and France*, SPRU Occasional Paper Series No. 21, University of Sussex, 1983.

COOPER B., T.F. GASKELL, *North Sea Oil - The Great Gamble*, London, 1966.

CORTI G., F. FRAZER, *The Nation's Oil, A story of control*, London, 1983.

COTTRILL A., 'Goodwyn foundations move into the clear', *Offshore Engineer (Arpil 1994)*, 9.

COTTRILL A., 'Bucket foundation debut on Sleipner riser platform', *Offshore Engineer (August 1994)*, 10.

COTTRILL A., 'Large units provide the global challenge', *Offshore Engineer (March 1996)*, 10-11.

COX W.R., S.C. McCLURE, K.H. SORENSEN, 'Settlement of Mat-Supported Mobile Units in Very Soft Clays', *22th Offshore Technology Conference*, Houston, 1990, 391-400.

CRAWFORD D.W., 'A history of protective coatings for the offshore industry: 1947-1972', *4th Annual Offshore Technology Conference*, Houston, 1972, I-671-676.

CROASDALE K.R., 'Structures in ice', *POAC 1991*.

CULLEN W.D., *The Public Inquiry into the Piper Alpha Disaster, Volume One*, London, 1990.

CULLEN W.D., *The Public Inquiry into the Piper Alpha Disaster, Volume Two*, London, 1990.

CURTIS M., 'The Vision and Management of CRINE', *27th Offshore Technology Conference*, Houston, 1995, 399-403.

DAIGLE J.B., 'Cook Inlet drilling and production platforms', *Offshore Exploration Conference*, New Orleans, 1968.

DAM K.W., *Oil Resources, Who Gets What How?*, Chicago, 1976.

DANENBERGER E.P., 'Outer Continental Shelf Drilling Blowouts, 1971-1991', *25th Offshore Technology Conference*, Houston, 1993, 415-425.

DANIELS M., J.C. SWANK, 'Northern North Sea Pipelines - The Brent System', *8th Offshore Technology Conference*, Houston, 1976, 803-818.

DELACOUR J., 'French perfect way to set subsea drilling equipment', *World Oil (May 1972)*, 79-81.

DELACOUR J., 'A review of technical activities carried out within the framework of the C.E.P.M. to develop special offshore hydrocarbon fields exploration and production means and techniques', *Guide Offshore (1981)*, 107-131.

DELACOUR J., 'IFP's Research Program fot the Development of Techniques to Exploit Subsea Hydrocarbons', *Ocean Industry (April 1981)*, 264-270.

DELACOUR J., 'New Technological Concepts and The Profitability of Deep Sea Production', *Pétrole Informations (May 1987)*, 75-78.

DELACOUR J., 'Offshore Outlook: The European Side', *7th International Conference on Offshore Mechanics and Arctic Engineering*, Houston, 1988.

DELACOUR J., 'What's ahead for the North Sea', *Ocean Industry (April 1988)*, 54-56.

DELAUZE H.G., 'Janus '68', *Proceedings of OECON Middle East, The First International Offshore Exploration Conference*, Long Beach, 1968, 281-306.

DELEUIL G.E., M.R. HEYMAN, D.J. MICHEL, 'Behaviour of Offshore Platform Three Dimensional Batter Pile Foundation', *Proceedings of OECON Middle East, The First International Offshore Exploration Conference*, Long Beach, 1968, 131-151.

DESA A.R., J.R. SHAW, 'Marine pipelaying methods defied odds', *Offshore (September 1979)*, 104-109.

DEVANNEY III J.W., J.B. LASSITER III, H.S. LAHMAN, 'The Georges Bank Petroleum Study', *5th Offshore Technology Conference*, Houston, 1973, I103-118.

DRIGGS J.L., 'Deep-water strat drilling - California offshore', *Drilling and production practice, American Petroleum Institute, 1967*, 7-18.

DUNN F.P., 'Deepwater Production: 1950-2000', *26th Offshore Technology Conference*, Houston, 1994, 921- 928.

EDWARDS J.D., 'Offshore Giant Fields, 1950-1990', *22th Offshore Technology Conference*, Houston, 1990, 597-604.

EEK W.H. VAN, 'Boren op zee', *Blokcollege offshore techniek, Cursus 1976-1977*, THDelft, Delft, 1976.

EIDE O.T., L.G. LARSEN, 'Installation of the Shell/Esso Brent B Condeep Production Platform', *8th Offshore Technology Conference*, Houston, 1976, 101-114.

ELLERS F.S., 'Advanced offshore oil platforms', *Scientific American 246(1982)4*, 39-49.

ELSENHANS H. (HRSG.), *Erdöl für Europa*, Hamburg, 1974.

ELY N., 'The Law Governing the Development of Undersea Mineral Resources', *1st Offshore Technology Conference*, Houston, 1969, I19-42.

ERI J., 'Development and implementation of regulations for permanent offshore structures', *7th Annual Offshore Technology Conference*, Houston, 1975, 757-758.

EZELL J.S., *Innovations in Energy, The Story of Kerr-McGee*, Norman, 1979.

FAULDS E., 'Why is Brent Spar Unique?', *The Institute of Petroleum Conference*, Londen, 1996.

FIELD A.J., R.B. THORNBURG, C.R. CROOKE, 'Glomar Challenger - Deep Sea Drilling From Texas To Dakar', *1st Offshore Technology Conference*, Houston, 1969, I165-166.

FJELD S. (ET.AL.), 'The North Sea Concrete Platforms: 20 Years of Experience', *26th Offshore Technology Conference*, Houston, 1994, 427-441.

FLEMMING N.C., 'Diving Technology', *Offshore Europe, 1st Edition*, London, 1968, 91-101.

FORBES G., 'A history of Caddo oil and gas field', *The Louisiana Historical Quarterly 29(....)1*.

FOSS I., 'Concrete gravity structures for the Norts Sea', *Ocean Industry (August 1974)*, 54-58.

FRANKS K.A., P.F. LAMBERT, *Early Louisiana and Arkansas oil, A photographic history, 1901-1946, The Montague history of oil series, number III*, College Station, 1982.

FRANKS K.A., P.F. LAMBERT, *Early California oil, A photographic history, 1865-1940, The Montague history of oil series, number IV*, College Station, 1985.

FREUDENBURG W.R., R. GRAMLING, *Oil in troubled waters*, New York, 1994.

GARRETT R., 'Meals on Rigs', *Offshore Europe, 1st Edition*, London, 1968, 320-322.

GASKELL T.F., 'Offshore Oil and Sea Floor Research', *6th Offshore Technology Conference*, Houston, 1974, 551-560.

GEER R.L., 'Offshore drilling and production technology, Where do we stand and where are we headed?', *3rd Annual Meeting Division of Production American Petroleum Institute, 1973*, Reprint, Shell Oil, Houston, 1973.

GERWICK B., 'Verification of offshore platform design and installation: the marine board panel view', *9th Annual Offshore Technology Conference*, Houston, 1977, 7-14.

GERWICK B.C., *Construction of Offshore Structures*, New York, 1986.

GIBLON R.P., V.U. MINORSKY, 'Super Jack-Up Type Mobil Drill Rig Platform for Operation in 500 to 600-Ft. Water Depths', *5th Offshore Technology Conference*, Houston, 1973, II 509-528.

GINKEL J. VAN, *Het Westen en de oliecrisis 1973-74*, Den Haag, 1978.

GIVENS J.J., G. CARTER, 'A Method for Rehabilitation of Offshore Platforms', *1th Offshore Technology Conference*, Houston, 1969, II 551-556.

GOEPFERT B.L., 'An Engineering Challenge - Cook Inlet, Alaska', *1st Offshore Technology Conference*, Houston, 1969, I511-524.

GOLDSTEIN J., *The politics of offshore oil*, New York, 1982.

GOOSSEN W.J., P. HORSMAN, 'Brent Spar: the continuing story', *Greenpeace (1995)4*, 28-30.

GRAAF F. DE, 'Publieke opinie is belangrijke factor bij milieubeleid van ondernemers', *NRC Handelsblad 13-12-1995*.

GRAFF W.J., *Introduction to Offshore Structures, Design Fabrication Installation*, Houston, 1981.

GRAMLING R., *Oil on the edge, Offshore development, Conflict, Gridlock*, New York, 1996.

GRIFFITHS R.T., *The economy and politics of the Netherlands, Since 1945*, Den Haag, 1980.

GROSS H.E., 'Possibilities and problems of drilling beyond the continental shelves', *The Petroleum Engineer (October 1946)*, 186-192.

GRUPPING A.W., 'Oliewinning op zee', *Blokcollege offshore techniek, Cursus 1976-1977*, THDelft, Delft, 1976.

GUDMESTAD O.T., T.A. WARLAND, B.L. STEAD, 'Concrete Structures for Development of Offshore Fields', *Journal of Petroleum Technology (August 1993)*, 762-770.

HALL J.N., 'Safety Survey Using Piper Alpha Disaster Evidence', *23th Offshore Technology Conference*, Houston, 1991, 651-661.

HALL R.C., *Drilling and producing offshore, 1987*, Tulsa, 1983.

HALVORSEN P.E., '25 years in the North Sea, Pete Silas and Ekofisk at a crossroad', *Kværner Oil & Gas Journal (1994)6*, 9-11.

HALVORSEN T., 'Deepwater Subsea Development', *ONS Conference 1996*, Stavanger, 1996.

HAMMETT D.S., 'SEDCO 445 - Dynamic Stationed Drill Ship', *4th Offshore Technology Conference*, Houston, 1972, II 104-130.

HAMMETT D.S., A.R. McLERRAN, 'Ocean Drilling Program: Vessel/Equipment Capabilities', *17th Offshore Technology Conference*, Houston, 1985, 287-302.

HAMMETT D.S., 'The First Dynamically Stationed Semi-Submersible - Sedco 709', *9th Offshore Technology Conference*, Houston, 1977, 97-111.

HANISCH T.J., *Norsk olje historie, Fra vantro til overmot?, Bind 1*, Oslo 1992.

HANN D., *Government and North Sea Oil*, London, 1986.

HANSEN R.L., W.P. RICKEY, 'Evolution of Subsea Production Systems: A Worldwide Overview', *26th Offshore Technology Conference*, Houston, 1994, 929-939.

HARBEK O., 'Drilling in the Norwegian part of the North Sea', *Journal of Petroleum Technology (October 1969)*, 1259-1262.

HARBONN J., 'Sea floor production system works out in Persian Gulf', *Ocean Industry (July 1972)*, 41-43.

HARTSHORN J.E., *Oil Companies and Governments, An account of the international oil industry in its political environment, 1967*, London, 1962.

HAWKINS M.E., C.J. JIRIK, 'Salt Domes in Texas, Louisiana, Mississippi, Alabama and Offshore Tidelands: a Survey', *Informations Circular Bureau of Mines 8313*, Washington, 1966.

HEEREMA E.P., 'Montage op zee', *Leegwatersymposium (4 november 1982)*, Delft.

HEIKAL M., *The road to Ramadan*, London, 1975.

FILSON J.F., 'Offshore Industry: Introduction', in: H. BENFORD (ED.), *A half century of marine technology, 1943-1993*, New Jersey, 1993.

HENERY D., 'The outer Mexico Gulf', *ONS Conference 1996*, Stavanger, 1996.

HEPPLE P. (ED.), *Petroleum supply and demand*, Report of the summer meeting of The Institute of Petroleum held at Brighton - 1965, London, 1966.

HERBERT W.F., H.E. ANDERSON, 'Proper design of drilling foundation offers problem to coast operators', *The Oil and Gas Journal (March 12, 1936)*, 28ff.

HERITIER F., 'A history of petroleum exploration in France', 29-45.

HESTER F.J., R. EVANS, 'Outer Continental Shelf Development in the Santa Barbara Channel: Lack of Detectable Impact on Fisheries', *9th Offshore Technology Conference*, Houston, 1977, 261-268.

HIRSCH T.J., A.M. KOEHLER, V.J.R. SUTTON, 'Selection of Pile Driving Equipment and Evaluation of Pile Bearing Capacity During Driving for the North Sea Forties Field', *7th Offshore Technology Conference*, Houston, 1975, 37-50.

HOPKINS J.W., B.R. DIXON, 'Lockheed readies subsea system for live well', *Ocean Industry (July 1971)*, 22-24.

HOVE F., KUHLMANN H., 'Troll Phase I Pipelines: Tie-ins to the Subsea Tunnel', *27th Offshore Technology Conference*, Houston, 1995, 125-134.

HOWE R.J., 'Design of Offshore Drilling Structures', *Transactions of the ASME (August 1955)*, 827-851.

HOWE R.J., B.G. COLLIPP, 'Let's look at offshore mobile units, ...as they are today and might be tomorrow', *The Oil and Gas Journal, December 3, 1956*, 91-95.

HOWE R.J., 'Evolution of offshore mobile drilling units, Part I', *Offshore (March 1966)*, 68-90.

HOWE R.J., 'Evolution of offshore mobile drilling units, Part II', *Offshore (April 1966)*, 76-92.

HOWE R.J., 'Evolution of offshore mobile drilling units, Part III', *Offshore (May 1966)*, 102-120.

HOWE R.J., 'Development of offshore drilling and production technology', *ASME Underwater Technology Division Conference*, 1967.

HOWE R.J., 'The history and current status of offshore mobile drilling units', *Ocean Inustry (July 1968)*, 38- 61.

HOWE R.J., 'Evolution of Offshore Drilling and Production Technology', *18th Offshore Technology Conference*, Houston, 1986, 593-603.

HOYER K.H.R., E.L. SICCAMA, 'Het olieterrein Coevorden-Oost', *De Ingenieur 58(1946)7*, A61-A67.

HRUSKA S.J., A.M. KOEHLER, L.K. SHAW, M.J. BOURNE, 'Engineering the Procedure for Installing the North Sea Forties Field Platforms', *7th Offshore Technology Conference*, Houston, 1975, 51-66.

HUBBARD G.A., 'Experience of Arabian Oil Co. with Offshore Loading Facilities with Particular Reference to the Single Buoy Mooring System', *Proceeding of OECON Middle East, The First International Offshore Exploration Conference*, Long Beach, 1968, 171-188.

HUTCHINSON K., 'Hostile environment plagues North Sea pipeline construction', *The Oil and Gas Journal (March 6, 1967)*, 90-91.

ILLINGWORTH R.H. (ET.AL.), 'Proposed offshore production and gathering facilities, Eugene Island area, Louisiana Gulf of Mexico', *American Petroleum Institute, Devision of Production 35(1955)4*, 74-89.

INDERBERG O., E.H. LUNDE, 'Experiences With Respect to Cost-Effective Marginal Field Developments', *26th Offshore Technology Conference*, Houston, 1994, 163-176.

JACOBSEN B., 'The loss of the Sleipner A platform', *Proceedings of the Second (1992) International Offshore and Polar Engineering Conference*, 1992, 1-8.

JANSEN W.A., A. KRANENDONK, 'Nieuw type boortorenfundatie in het Meer van Maracaibo', *De Ingenieur 62(1950)25*, M41-M47.

JANSSEN R., *Erger dan liefde, De internationale economie van Bretton Woods tot Maastricht*, Den Haag, 1993.

JARIWALA H. (ET.AL.), 'Reaching towards the 10 km barrier', *Journal of Offshore Technology (February 1997)*, 35-37.

JOBIN T.J., 'Development program for Ekofisk field - offshore Norway', *3th Annual Offshore Technology Conference*, Houston, 1971, II-897-918.

JOLLES W.H., L. HAMMER, M. HELMER, 'Ploating and bottum founded unit for arctic drilling operations', *Eight International Offshore Mechanics and Arctic Engineering*, 1989, 443-450.

KAPLAN E.R., 'California, Threatening the Golden Shore', in: J. GOLDSTEIN, *The politics of offshore oil*, New York, 1982, 3-28.

KASSLER P., *Energy investment in a greening world, A presentation to the Montreux Round Table, Aspen, Colorado, October 1994*, Shell International Petroleum Company Ltd., London, 1994.

KENNEDY J.L., 'Ocean Victory: one of a new breed of semisubmersible', *The Oil and Gas Journal (December 11, 1972)*, 86-90.

KENNEDY J.L., 'North Sea plans turned into tangibles', *The Oil and Gas Journal (January 8, 1973)*, 65-69.

KENT P.E., 'Progress of exploration in North Sea', *The American Association of Petroleum Geologists Bulletin 51(1967)5*, 731-741.

KENT P.E., P.J. WALMSLEY, 'North Sea Progress', *The American Association of Petroleum Geologists Bulletin 54(1970)1*, 168-181.

KLEMME H.D., 'What giants and their basins have in common', *The Oil and Gas Journal (March 1, 1971)*, 85- 99.

KNECHT R.W., 'How the federal government will help states deal with onshore impacts of offshore operations', *9th Annual Offshore Technology Conference*, Houston, 1977, 549-552.

KNIP K., 'Honderden olieplatforms op Noordzee: slopen of dumpen?', *NRC Handelsblad (5-7-1995)*.

KNIP K., 'Geloofwaardigheid Greenpeace aangetast door studie Brent Spar', *NRC Handelsblad (19-10-1995)*.

KNIP K., 'Slopen Brentspar wordt veel duurder dan Shell berekende', *NRC Handelsblad (18-11-1995)*.

KOBUS L.C.S., H.M. MEYERS, S.W. HAINES, 'Super-Sized Semisubmersible Performance in the North Sea', *9th Offshore Technology Conference*, Houston, 1977, 113-126.

KOEHLER A.M., S.J. HRUSKA, R.C. WALKER, 'Development of the North Sea Forties field platform concept', *7th Annual Offshore Technology Conference*, Houston, 1975, 9-20.

KORVER J.W. DE, 'Mijnreglement voor offshore installaties', *Blokcollege offshore techniek, Cursus 1976-1977*, THDelft, Delft, 1976.

KRANENDONK A., *Marine operations of the Royal Dutch/Shell Group*, 1953.

KRUEGER R.B., 'The State of International Law as Applied to Ocean Mining and an Examination of the Offshore Mining Laws of Selected Nations', *1st Offshore Technology Conference*, Houston, 1969, I334- 374.

KVENDSETH S.S., *Giant discovery, A history of Ekofisk through the first 20 years*, Tananger, 1988.

LABORDE A.J., *My Life abnd Times*, 1985.

LAGERS G.H.G., C.R. BELL, 'The Third Generation Lay Barge', *6th Offshore Technology Conference*, Houston, 1974, 35-46.

LAGERS G.H.G., 'Offshore activiteiten in de Noordzee', *Maritiem Journaal (1974)*, 122-128.

LAGERS G.H.G., 'Windinvloeden of offshore constructies', *De Ingenieur (1993)3*, 32-37.

LAGUILHARRE L., 'The Contribution of Turbodrilling to the Offshore Development in the Light of the North Sea Experience', *Proceedings of OECON Middle East, The First International Offshore Exploration Conference*, Long Beach, 1968, 307-330.

LANKFORD R.L., 'Marine Drilling', in: J.E. BRANTLY, *History of Oil Well Drilling*, Houston, 1971, 1358- 1444.

LEE G.C., 'Offshore platform construction extended to 400 foot water depths', *Journal of Petroleum Technology (April 1963)*, 383-388.

LEE G.C., 'Offshore structures, past, present, future and design considerations', *3rd Offshore Exploration Conference, 1968*, 169-196.

LEE G.C., 'Verification of platform design and installation - a constructor's view', *9th Annual Offshore Technology Conference*, Houston, 1977, 15-19.

LEE G.C., '"Deep" thoughts on conventional concepts', *Offshore (April 1978)*, 90-98.

LEEUW C. VAN DER, 'De Golfcrisis: oliemaatschappijen winnen, banken verliezen', *Management Team, 22 oktober 1990*, 12-18.

LELIVELD H., 'De rol van de overheid in de offshore, algemene jaarbijeenkomst IRO 1986', *IRO-journaal (1986)12*, 5-11.

LEWARNE S., *Soviet Oil, The move offshore*, Boulder, 1988.

LITTLEWOOD S.K., 'The CRINE Initiative - Education and Training', *27th Offshore Technology Conference*, Houston, 1995, 423-427. ·

LLOYD S.H., G.E. JARLAN, 'A New Drilling Vessel Concept', *Offshore Europe, 1st Edition*, London, 1968, 87-90.

LOCKE E.R., 'Offshore search for oil becomes key activity', *World Petroleum (March 1955)*, 62-63.

LODEWIJKX M., 'Brent Spar: Keerpunt in milieudenken?', *Greenpeace (1995)3*, 6-8.

LOHSE A., J.M. SHARP, C.H. OPPENHEIMER, D.E. FERAY, 'Gulf of Mexico Environmental Program', *2th Offshore Technology Conference*, Houston, 1970, I41-48.

LONDENBERG R., 'Man, oil and the sea', *Offshore (1972)10*, 54-55.

LØSET Ø., K.O. HAAKONSEN, 'Troll Oil: The First Concrete FPS', *27th Offshore Technology Conference*, Houston, 1995, 977-986.

LØSET Ø., 'Floating prodruction systems (FPS): Troll oil and Kvœrner concrete semis', Offshore and Arctic Operations, 1995, 179-188.

LOWE E.A., ODONE A.J., 'The History of the Piper-Claymore-Flotta Pipeline System', *12th Offshore Technology Conference*, Houston, 1980, 415-429.

LOWRIE W.G., 'After more than a decade of restructuring, what have we learned, where are we heading?', *ONS Conference 1996*, Stavanger, 1996.

MACGREGOR HUTCHESON A., A. HOGG, *Scotland and oil*, New York, 1975.

MACLEISH W., 'Far out in the Baltimore Canyon, oil companies play for high stakes', *Smithsonian (December 1979)*.

MAIER G. (ED.), *Case histories in offshore engineering*, Vienna, 1985.

MARQUES NETO J., 'Present and future of offshore developments in Brazil', *Proc. Offshore Structures Engineering, Rio de Janeiro*, 1977.

MARSHALL H., B. ZISK, *The Federal-State Struggle for Offshore Oil*, Inter-University Case Program #98, Indianapolis, 1966.

MARTIN G.C., 'Preliminary report on petroleum in Alaska', *U.S. Geological Survey, Bulletin 719*, Washington, 1921.

MASTENBROEK F., 'Werkterrein van een raadgevend ingenieursbureau offshore', *Leegwatersymposium (4 november 1982)*, Delft.

McBEE W., P. ORCHARD, 'Developments in Louisiana Gulf Coast in 1948', *Bulletin of the American Association of Petroleum Geologists 33(1949)6*, 979-989.

McCASLIN L.S., 'Large-scale LST conversion program under way on Gulf coast', *The Oil and Gas Journal (November 25, 1948)*, 82-84, 123-124.

McCLELLAND B., J.A. FOCHT, W.J. EMRICH, 'Designing and constructing heavily loaded pipe piles - part 1', *Ocean Industry (1969)1*, 56-61.

McCLELLAND B., 'Problems in design and installation of offshore piles', *Journal of the Soil Mechanics and Foundations Division, American Society of Civil Engineers (November 1969)*, 1491-1514.

McCLURE A.C., 'Offshore industry 1966-1973: development', in: H. BENFORD (ED.), *A half century of marine technology, 1943-1993*, New Jersey, 1993.

McGEE D.A., A.T.F. SEALE, G.O. DANIELSON, 'Offshore drilling developments', *Drilling and production practice, American Petroleum Institute, 1948*, 9-21.

McGEE D.A., A.T.F. SEALE, 'Oil in the Gulf of Mexico', *American Institute of Mining and Metallurgical Engineers*, 1948.

McGEE D.A., 'A Report on Exploration progress in the Gulf of Mexico', *Drilling and production practice, American Petroleum Institute (1949)*, 38-59.

McKAY R.R., 'Offshore Property Insurance', *2th Offshore Technology Conference*, Houston, 1970, I663-666.

McLEAN J.G., 'The transition from domestic to international oil operations', *Journal of Petroleum Technology (December 1968)*, 1339-1343.

MEADOWS D. (ET. AL.), *The Limits to Growth*, New York, 1972.

MELENHORST P.P.W., 'Waarom nog geen Europees energiebeleid?', *Intermediair 10(1974)13*, 19-21.

MELLBYE P., 'Troll on stream, The Story and its perspectives', *ONS Conference 1996*, Stavanger, 1996.

MERCIER J., 'Offshore industry 1974-1982: the age of expansion', in: H. BENFORD (ED.), *A half century of marine technology, 1943-1993*, New Jersey, 1993.

MEURS A.P.H. VAN, *Petroleum economics and offshore mining legislation, A geological evaluation*, Amsterdam, 1971.

MINOR L.E., 'Improving Deep Sea Pipeline Techniques', *Offshore (June 1966)*, 53-57.

MIREUR TH., 'Texas offshore exploration', *World Petroleum (November 1954)*, 70-75.

MOKSNES J., HOFF G.C., GUDMESTAD O.T., FJELD S., 'Concrete Platforms: History, Technological Breakthroughs, and Future', *26th Offshore Technology Conference*, Houston, 1994, 953-966.

Moore J.D., *Comparison of offshore drilling costs with various types of operation, Discussion,* Humble Oil & Refining Company, Houston, 1956.

Mowell R., 'Offshore industry 1983-1987: consolidation and increased cost consciousness', in: H. Benford (ed.), *A half century of marine technology, 1943-1993,* New Jersey, 1993.

Narimanov A.A., I. Palaz, 'Oil History, Potential Converge in Azerbaijan', *Oil & Gas Journal (May 22, 1995),* 32-39.

Neill W.B., 'Developments in Louisiana Gulf Coast in 1947', *Bulletin of the American Association of Petroleum Geologists 32(1948)6,* 1032-1039.

Nerheim G., [A], 'The Condeep Concept: The Development and Breakthrough of Concrete Gravity Platforms', in: G. Hollister-Short, F.A.J.L. James, *History of Technology, Volume 16,* London, 1994, 15-34.

Nerheim G., [B], 'The offshore drilling business, 1950-1990, Some development patterns', *11th International Economic History Congress,* Milano, 1994, 137-149.

Nicolson K.M., 'Deep-water mooring systems for Santa Barbara Channel drilling operations', *Drilling and production practice, American Petroleum Institute, 1969,* 184-189.

Nilsen B., *Gjenferd i Nordsjøen, Kielland-ulykken i norsk oljepolitikk,* Oslo, 1984.

O'Connor D.M., 'Coastal Region Law: A Preliminary Analysis', *2th Offshore Technology Conference,* Houston, 1970, I345-350.

Oates J.A., 'The Laying and Maintenance of Offshore Pipelines', *Offshore Europe, 1st Edition,* London, 1968, 287-294.

Odell P.R., *Olie en Macht,* Utrecht, 1971.

Odell P.R., *The Western European energy economy, The case for self-sufficiency 1980-2000,* Leiden, 1976.

Owen E.W., *Trek of the Oil Finders: A History of Exploration for Petroleum,* Tulsa, 1975.

Park W.E., 'Canadian gas field', *The Oil and Gas Journal (June 5, 1913),* 32.

Park W.E., 'Canadian gas field', *The Oil and Gas Journal (June 12, 1913),* 32.

Park W.E., 'Canadian gas field news', *The Oil and Gas Journal (July 10, 1913),* 26.

Park W.E., 'Canadian gas fields', *The Oil and Gas Journal (August 7, 1913),* 32.

Park W.E., 'Canadian gas fields', *The Oil and Gas Journal (September 25, 1913),* 33-34.

Pavia A.P. P.K. Yin, P.R. Corder, 'Effect of design, fabrication, and installation on the structural reliability of offshore platforms', *9th Offshore Technology Conference,* Houston, 1977, 451-458.

Peebles M.W.H., V.H. Pass, J. Salkeld, *The development of Groningen gas, A short history of the development of Groningen gas up to end 1969,* Shell International Gas Ltd., 1971.

Pendered J.W., 'Education for the offshore industry in Europe', *6th Annual Offshore Technology Conference,* Houston, 1974, 513-520.

Perez La Salvia H. (et. al.), 'Venezuela Offshore Oil and Gas Production Development: Past, Present and Future', *27th Offshore Technology Conference,* Houston, 1995, 189-201.

Perrodon A., *Histoire des grandes découvertes pétrolières,* Paris, 1985.

Peyton H.R., 'Ice and Marine Structures, Part 1 - The Magnitude of Ice Forces Involved in Design', *Ocean Industry (March 1968),* 40-44.

Peyton H.R., 'Ice and Marine Structures, Part 2 - Sea Ice Properties', *Ocean Industry (September 1968),* 59- 65.

Peyton H.R., 'Ice and Marine Structures, Part 3 - The Importance of Design Alternatives', *Ocean Industry (December 1968),* 51-63.

Pike W.J., 'Lord Cullen's report on Piper Alpha', *Ocean Industry (December 1990/January 1991),* 32-35.

Planeix J.M., J. Ciolina, J. Delueil, J.Y. Heas, 'Are offshore structures over-designed?, Relative influence of environmental parameters', *11th Offshore Technology Conference,* Houston, 1979, 269-280.

Possato S., Rodrigues S.M., Scarton J.C., Figueiredo A.M.F., 'The Discovery and Appraisal History of Two Supergiant Oil Fields, Offshore Brazil', *22th Offshore Technology Conference,* Houston, 1990, 621-634.

Prindle D.F., *Petroleum politics and the Texas Railroad Commission,* Austin, 1981.

Prydz R., 'Troll Oil Development Concept', *25th Offshore Technology Conference,* Houston, 1993, 421-435.

Rabinowitz P.D. (et. al.), 'The Ocean Drilling Program: The Next Phase in Scientific Ocean Drilling', *16th Offshore Technology Conference,* Houston, 1984, 443-449.

Rabinowitz P.D. (et. al.), 'Scientific Ocean Drilling: An Overview of the Ocean Drilling Program', *17th Offshore Technology Conference,* Houston, 1985, 279-286.

Radlinski W.A., 'U.S. offshore regulations', *7th Annual Offshore Technology Conference,* Houston, 1975, 758-759.

Raj A., C.N. White, 'Trends in offshore towing and supply vessel designs', *11th Offshore Technology Conference,* Houston, 1979, 281-293.

Ramm H.H., '25 years of change: Industry moves from indifference through protection to internationalisation', *Kvaerner Oil & Gas Journal (1994)6,* 4-8.

Raustein O., L.E. Abrahamsen, G. Einang, 'The Potential for Satellite and Marginal Field Developments on the Norwegian Continental Shelf', *26th Offshore Technology Conference,* Houston, 1994, 117-123.

Reimering W.Th.B., 'De ontwikkeling van het aardolieveld Schoonebeek na de bevrijding', *De Ingenieur 60(1948)53,* M75-M83.

Rettedal W.K., O.T. Gudmestad, T. Aarum, 'Design of concrete platforms after Sleipner A-1 sinking', *Offshore Mechanics and Arctic Engineering,* 1993, 309-319.

Rey-Grange A., 'Pentagone 81, Semi-Submersible Drilling Unit', *Proceeding of OECON Middle East, The First International Offshore Exploration Conference,* Long Beach, 1968, 225-237.

Reynolds J.M., Submarine Pipelines, *Offshore Europe, 1st Edition,* London, 1968, 297-309.

Rintoul W., *Spudding In, Recollections of Pioneers Days in the California Oil Fields,* San Francisco, 1976.

Robinson R.J., 'Offshore regulations and their impact on permanent offshore structures', *7th Annual Offshore Technology Conference,* Houston, 1975, 761.

Rogers L.C., 'Tallest jackup platform joins offshore fleet', *The Oil and Gas Journal (February 3, 1964),* 88-92.

Rogers L.C., 'Giant platforms tame Cook Inlet', *The Oil and Gas Journal (August 29, 1966),* 70-71.

Rogers L.C., '...No Bonanza Yet', *The Oil and Gas Journal (February 27, 1967),* 93-98.

Rogers L.C., 'Independents jump on the drilling 'fund', bandwagon', *The Oil and Gas Journal (March 31, 1969),* 31-33.

Rønnevik H.Chr., 'Exploration Technology', *ONS Conference 1996,* Stavanger, 1996.

ROTHERMUND H.C., 'Out of sight, out of mind - societal considerations in offshore development', *ONS Conference 1996*, Stavanger, 1996.

RUCKER F.H., 'Packaged Process Equipment Design for Offshore Operation', *Offshore Europe, 1st Edition*, London, 1968, 223-226.

RUITER J. DE, D.A. FOX, 'Site Investigations for North Sea Forties Field', *7th Offshore Technology Conference*, Houston, 1975, 21-36.

RUNDELL W., *Early Texas oil, A photographic history, 1866-1936, The Montague history of oil series, number I*, College Station, 1977.

RUUD M., 'The Troll Olje Platform', *25th Offshore Technology Conference*, Houston, 1993, 439-456.

RYNEWICZ J.F., 'The Submersible Deep Quest - A Step Forward in Offshore Technology', *2th Technology Conference*, Houston, 1970, I527-534.

SAGA B.P., 'Natural gas and energy security', *ONS Conference 1996*, Stavanger, 1996.

SAMPSON A., *The Seven Sisters, The Great Oil Companies and the World they Shaped*, Third edition 1984, New York, 1975.

SAWDON W.A., 'Deep sea drilling on an island of steel', *The Petroleum Engineer (December 1932)*, 26-27.

SCHEFFER R.W., 'De rol van het bedrijfsleven in de offshore, algemene jaarbijeenkomst IRO 1986', *IRO-journaal (1986)12*, 11-16.

SCHIERBEEK P., 'Mijnrechtelijke systemen op het continentale plat van de Noordzee', *Blokcollege offshore techniek, Cursus 1976-1977*, THDelft, Delft, 1976.

SCHNEIDER W.P., 'Dynamic Positioning Systems', *1st Offshore Technology Conference*, Houston, 1969, II183- 190.

SEALE A.T.F., 'Discovering oil 12 miles offshore in the Gulf', *World Oil (May 1948)*.

SHARE J. (ED.), *The oil makers, Insiders look at the petroleum industry*, Houston, 1995.

SHARP J.M., J.W. TYSON, 'The Offshore Ecology Investigation', *7th Offshore Technology Conference*, Houston, 1975, 499-504.

SHEPHERD G.F., 'Developments in Louisiana Gulf Coast in 1944', *Bulletin of the American Association of Petroleum Geologists 29(1945)6*, 792-802.

SHEPHERD G.F., 'Developments in Louisiana Gulf Coast in 1946', *Bulletin of the American Association of Petroleum Geologists 31(1947)6*, 1078-1083.

SHORT E.H. JR., 'Prefabricated offshore drilling platform sets up in record time', The Oil and Gas Journal (August 9, 1947), 82-91.

SHORT T.A., N.S. NEIDELL, 'Economics of Ecology', *3th Offshore Technology Conference*, Houston, 1971, II363-367.

SIMMONS M.R., 'Winners and losers, What are the criterias for success? The Service Industry', *ONS Conference 1996*, Stavanger, 1996.

SJOUKE J., G. LAGERS, 'Development of dynamic positioning for IHC drill ship', *3th Annual Offshore Technology Conference*, Houston, 1971, II-798-812.

SLOAN C.A., 'Oil conditions in the Russian fields', *The Oil & Gas Journal (September 26, 1919)*, 62-63.

SMEITINK M., M. VERBEEK, 'Nogmaals: de Brent Spar', *Greenpeace (1996)1*, 35.

SMITH B., [A], 'Offshore line construction methods examined, Offshore pipeline construction - 1', *Oil & Gas Journal (May 4, 1981)*, 154, 158-159.

SMITH B., [B], 'A look at pipeline riser installation techniques, Offshore pipeline construction - Conclusion', *Oil & Gas Journal (May 11, 1981)*, 105-108.

SMITH D., 'Redeveloping a giant Ekofisk II Experience', *ONS Conference 1996*, Stavanger, 1996.

SMULDERS L., 'New concept in offshore oil storage', *Ocean Industry (February 1972)*, 42-43.

STEELE J.E., 'Offshore industry: early years', in: H. BENFORD (ED.), *A half century of marine technology, 1943-1993*, New Jersey, 1993.

STERLING G.H. (ET. AL.), 'Construction of the Cognac platform, 1025 feet of water, Gulf of Mexico', *11th Offshore Technology Conference*, Houston, 1979, 1169-1184.

STERLING G.H., B.E. COX, R.M. WARRINGTON, 'Design of the Cognac platform for 1025 feet water depth, Gulf of Mexico', *11th Offshore Technology Conference*, Houston, 1979, 1185-1198.

STOCKARD D.M., 'Case Histories - Pile Driving in the Gulf of Mexico', *11th Offshore Technology Conference*, Houston, 1979, 737-746.

STOLL J.E., 'Drilling ... from bayou to ocean', *Brownbilt (1988)*, 19-27.

STOLTENBERG J., 'The North Sea, Its prospects and competitive position', *ONS Conference 1996*, Stavanger, 1996.

STREET W.R., 'United Kingdom regulations for permanent offshore structures', *7th Annual Offshore Technology Conference*, Houston, 1975, 731-736.

STULLER J., 'They call him the father of the semisubmersible', *Shell News (1950)1*, 4-7.

TAYLOR B.G.S., I.G. WALLACE, A. WARD, 'The Response to Piper Alpha: Recent Offshore Safety Developments in the U.K.', *23th Offshore Technology Conference*, Houston, 1991, 641-649.

TAYLOR D.M., 'RED 1 - semi-submersible for North Sea emergencies', *Ocean Industry (September 1973)*, 117- 122.

TAYLOR D.M., 'Shell's million-dollar school of offshore technology, 20th Anniversary of ...', *Ocean Industry (1983)3*, 35-38.

TESSON P.A., 'Laying pipe from a reel', *Offshore (July 1963)*, 33-36.

THALER J., R. GEMINDER, 'Offshore Insurance - Is Anyone The Winner?', *4th Offshore Technology Conference*, Houston, 1972, II387-392.

THOMAS O.D., 'North Sea oil boom', *Ocean Industry (March 1972)*, 11-15.

THOMAS W.A., 'Floating production and subsea completions', in: *A guide to North Sea oil and gas technology, Proc. Institute of Petroleum*, 1977, 79-88.

THOMPSON A.B., 'Immense yield of Russian oil wells', *The Oil & Gas Journal (December 10, 1920)*, 80-87.

THOMPSON A.B., [A], 'Russian oilfield developments', *The Petroleum Times (August 1, 1925)*, 203-205.

THOMPSON A.B., [B], 'Russian oilfield developments', *The Petroleum Times (August 8, 1925)*, 235-237.

THOMPSON E.O., 'Conservation of Oil and Gas in Texas', *Fifth World Petroleum Congress, Proceedings, Drilling and Production, Section II*, New York, 1959, 13-21.

TIELEMAN H.J., (ED.), *Conflicten tussen actiegroepen en ondernemingen, De democratisering van het moreel gezag*, Den Haag, 1996.

TIMMERMANS W.J., 'Designing pipelines for extreme water depths, Deepwater pipelining - 1', *Oil & Gas Journal (December 17, 1984)*, 78-82.

TIMMERMANS W.J., 'Pipe-joining techniques for deepwater lines, Deepwater pipelining - Conclusion', *Oil & Gas Journal (December 24, 1984)*, 57-58.

TOLER J.S., 'Offshore petroleum installations', *Proc. American Society of Civil Engineers*, New York, 1953.

TRODAL L., O. NILSEN, 'The Troll Oil Pipeline Project: a Welcome Challenge to Survey Technology', *27th Offshore Technology Conference*, Houston, 1995, 347-354.

TUFT V., 'The CRINE Initiative - Producing the Engineering Tools (Functional Specifications and Common Working Practices)', *27th Offshore Technology Conference*, Houston, 1995, 411-422.

TURNER E.R., 'Status of oil and gas development - offshore Texas', *3th Annual Offshore Technology Conference*, Houston, 1971, I-125-127.

TWOMEY B.G., 'Abandonment: Technological, organisational and environmental challenges', *ONS Conference 1996*, Stavanger, 1996.

VARNER R.D., W.R. COLLIER, *A matter of risk*, New York, 1978.

VEEN C. VAN, 'Openingsvoordracht, algemene jaarbijeenkomst IRO 1986', *IRO-journaal (1986)12*, 3-5.

VROUWENVELDER A., 'Veiligheid van offshore constructies', *Leegwatersymposium (4 november 1982)*, Delft.

VUGTS J.H., *In woelig water*, Intreerede Delft, 1993.

VUGTS J.H., *Mapping out Offshore Technology*, Delft, 1994.

WALKER D.B.L., 'A technical review of the Forties field submarine pipeline', *8th Annual Offshore Technology Conference*, Houston, 1976, 819-829.

WALKER M.A., E.E. CASTOR, L.J. MARQUETTE, 'Design and Performance of Subsea Production Units for Ekofisk', *4th Offshore Technology Conference*, Houston, 1972, I191-196.

WARD D.R., 'Laying large diameter offshore pipelines', *Offshore (June 2, 1967)*, 52-56.

WATKINS B.J., 'Deep-water drilling operations, An integrated subsea drilling system', *Drilling and production practice, American Petroleum Institute, 1969*, 190-194.

WEE H. VAN DER, *De gebroken welvaartscirkel, De wereld-economie, 1945-1980*, 1985, Leiden, 1983.

WERK K.J.C., 'Floating type production unit', *Ocean Industry (December 1972)*, 19-21.

WEST F.G., *Practices and devloments in off-shore oil exploration and production*, The Institution of Engineers and Shipbuilders in Scotland, 1964.

WEST F.G., 'The Design and Construction of Offshore Oil Drilling Outfits', *Offshore Europe, 1st Edition*, London, 1968, 29-50.

WESTERWOUDT TH., 'Alliantie aannemer en Shell drukt prijs oliewinning', *NRC Handelsblad (11 november 1996)*.

WHITE I.L., D.E. KASH, M.A. CHARTOCK, M.D. DEVINE, R.L. LEONARD, *North Sea Oil and Gas, Implications for future United States development*, University of Oklahoma Press, Norman, 1973.

WICKIZER C.L., 'Challenges of future deepwater operations examined', *Oil and Gas Journal (October 24, 1988)*, 61-68.

WILKINSON H.M., J.P. FRASER, 'Pipeline laid in record water depth', *Offshore (June 1966)*, 58-63.

WILSON G.J., 'Integrated Approach to Deep Water North Sea Drilling', *5th Offshore Technology Conference*, Houston, 1973, II351-360.

WILSON R.O., M.R. MARTIN, 'Deepwater Pipelining for Central North Sea', *5th Offshore Technology Conference*, Houston, 1973, II305-314.

WILSON T.J., 'Concrete versus steel for tension leg platform hulls', *Deep Offshore Technology, 5th International Conference and Exhibition*, 1989, B1-f 75-89.

WIPKINK J., 'Design and Development of the Semi-Submersible Drilling Plarform "Norrig 5"', *Offshore Europe, 1st Edition*, London, 1968, 67-77.

WIT B. DE, [A], 'Offshore-land Nederland', *IRO-journaal 10(1986)25*, 1-7.

WIT B. DE, [B], 'Offshore-land Noorwegen', *IRO-journaal 10(1986)27/28*, 1-25.

WIT B. DE, [C], 'Offshore-land Groot-Brittannië', *IRO-journaal 10(1986)29/30*, 1-15.

WIT B. DE, [D], 'Offshore-land Denemarken', *IRO-journaal 10(1986)31/32*, 1-15.

WIT B. DE, [E], 'Offshore-land Duitsland', *IRO-journaal 10(1986)34*, 1-11.

WIT B. DE, 'Gas wordt een belangrijker brandstof dan olie, Offshore land Maleisië', *IRO-journaal 11(1987)10*, 1-9.

WIT B. DE, *Strategie bouwen op de golven, Een onderzoek naar strategieën in cyclical industries, met als case- study de offshore drilling industry*, Delft, 1994.

WIT P. DE, 'Alle reden voor trots, niet voor arrogantie', *Shell-venster, mei/juni 1996*, 3-5.

WOLFF P., 'Barnsdall-Hayward barge, A development for offshore drilling', *World Oil (August 1949)*, 87-96.

WOLTERS J.G., 'O.T. 3.1, Uitgangspunten voor het ontwerp', *Civiel-technische offshore technologie, PATO cursus*, Den Haag, 1984.

YERGIN D., *The Prize, The epic quest for oil, money and power*, London, 1991.

YERKES R.F., H.C. WAGNER, K.A. YENNE, 'Petroleum development in the region of the Santa Barbara Channel', *Geological Survey Professional Paper 679-B*, 1969.

ZANOYAN V., 'Pipelines, the political dimension', *ONS Conference 1996*, Stavanger, 1996.

Aardgas uit de Noordzee, N.V. Nederlandse Gasunie, Groningen, 1985

Aardgas, Shell, 1963.

'Slopen Brent Spar wordt veel duurder dan Shell berekende', *Archimedia (18-12-1995)*, 13-14.

'Mohole scoreboard', *Brownbilt 1(1966)1*, 16.

'There is where the oil is', *Brownbilt (Fall 1972)*.

De Geschiedenis van Shell, Shell Nederland B.V., Rotterdam, 1990.

'Ook op de bodem van de Noordelijke IJszee ...', *De Ingenieur 80(1968)36*, A489-A490.

'De ontginning van olielagen onder den Oceaanbodem in Californië', *De Ingenieur 58(1946)5*, M9.

'De eerste boring op volle zee', *De Ingenieur 59(1947)13*, M13.

'Diepboormogelijkheden op zee buiten de randen der continenten', *De Ingenieur 59(1947)30*.

Design of a deep ocean drilling ship, The technical Staff of the AMSOC Committee Division of Earth Sciences, Washington, 1962.

Eén biljoen op onze gasmeter, Ministerie van Economische Zaken, Den Haag, 1982.

Energienota, Tweede Kamer der Staten-Generaal, Zitting 1974-1975, Den Haag, 1974.

'Platform comes in on beer budget', *ENR (August 27, 1981)*, 50-51, 54.

'Brent Spar: Both sides of the story', *Euroil (June 1995)*, 4.

Forties, The story of Britain's first major oilfield, London.

Gas uit Groningen, NAM brochure, 1994.

'De geschiedenis van de offshore', *HCG-krant, Bijlage (april 1985)*.

'Waarom laat Shell de Brent Spar afzinken?', *Het Financieele Dagblad (15-6-1995)*.

'Shell volhardt in dumping ondanks groeiend protest', *Het Financieele Dagblad (20-6-1995)*, [A].

'Deze onvrede is niet een keurige aanklacht...', boekbespreking, M.J. VAN RIEMSDIJK, 'Actie of dialoog, over de betrekkingen tussen maatschappij en onderneming', *Het Financieele Dagblad (20-6-1995)*, [B].

'Grote interesse in Nederland voor Brent Spar', *Het Financieele Dagblad (4-7-1996)*.

History of Petroleum Engineering, American Petroleum Institute, Dallas, 1961.

Humble ST-9 class drilling tender, Humble Oil & Refining Company, Houston, 1957.

Impact of new technology on the U.S. petroleum industry, 1946-1965, National Petroleum Council, Washington, 1967.

Integrated production operations, Shell Briefing Service, No. 3, 1995, Shell International Petroleum Company Ltd., London, 1995.

'Olie en gas in Nederland 1993', *Jaarverslag Ministerie van Economische Zaken*, Den Haag, 1993.

Kerr-McGee Resources 2(1980)1.

'Boren in de Zuid-Chinese Zee', *Koninklijke/Shell-Nieuws 5(1952)6*, 1-3.

'Comblement artificiel de la Baie de Bibi-Eibat (Bakou)', *La Revue Pétrolifère (24 Février 1923)*, 19.

'Procédés d'exploitation en usage a Bakou avant et depuis la nationalisation des champs pétrolifères', *La Revue Pétrolifère (Novembre 1923)*.

'Procédés et méthodes de forage a Bakou', *La Revue Pétrolifère (1 October 1925)*, 13-19.

'L'histoire de l'industrie pétrolière russe', *La Revue Pétrolifére (17 Novembre 1928)*.

'Fabricage van componenten voor offshore platforms', *Leegwatersymposium (4 november 1982)*, Delft.

Lessons in rotary drilling, Unit V - Lesson 3, Buoyancy, stability, and trim, University of Texas, Austin, 1976.

Menjangkau Enampuluh Tahun, Sixty Years On, 1929-1989, Tahun Minyak Dan Gas, Brunei, 1989.

Mr. Charlie, International petroleum museum & exposition, Morgan City.

Nederlandse on/offshore dagen 1985, Syllabus, Symposium "Vernieuwing in de technologie / vernieuwing in de markt", Groningen, 1985.

Netherlands Offshore Catalogue 1995, Oil - Gas - Environment, IRO, Rotterdam, 1995.

Noordzee Energie, Werkgroep Noordzee, Amsterdam, 1981.

Noordzee-Almanak 1995, Den Haag, 1995.

'The future of subsea production', *Noroil (September 1984)*, 59-69.

'Constructie Brent Spar is verzwakt', *NRC Handelsblad (19-11-1995)*.

'Offshore wil uit dieptepunt door lastenverlichting', *NRC Handelsblad (7-2-1996)*.

'Veel overtollige platforms op Noordzee, Sloop-consortium wil olieplatforms opruimen', *NRC Handelsblad (5-3-1996)*.

'Shell publiceert lijst gegadigden sloop Brent Spar', *NRC Handelsblad (4-7-1996)*.

'Deep-water exploration pushes demand for seabed production gear, Part I', *Ocean Industry (May 1972)*, 26-29.

'Report on 72 subsea completions', *Ocean Industry (June 1972)*, 42-45.

'Phillips Ekofisk million barrel oil storage tank nears completion', *Ocean Industry (July 1972)*, 33.

'Shell makes subsea completion in 375 ft water off Louisiana', *Ocean Industry (August 1972)*.

'Shell's deep seafloor completion is in operation', *Ocean Industry (November 1972)*, 45-47.

'Seafloor completions hold the key to deep areas', *Ocean Industry (February 1973)*, 74-76.

'Seal develops a low cost seafloor completion system for 100-450-ft. water', *Ocean Industry (April 1973)*, 161-162.

'Hughes Glomar Explorer begins sea test of mining systems', *Ocean Industry (March 1974)*, 32-34.

'Future of non-majors in the North Sea, Hugh Harvey interviews Dr. Norman A. White', *Ocean Industry (February 1975)*, [A], 47-55.

'Huge pipelaying barge under construction for North Sea operations', *Ocean Industry (February 1975)*, [B], 117-119.

'Underwater well completions', *Offshore (September 1957)*, 45-47.

'Concrete pile supports', *Offshore (July 1958)*, 37, 40, 52.

'Third annual marine rig round-up', *Offshore (August 22, 1958)*, [A], 19.

'Marine oil round up: Lake Maracaibo', *Offshore (August 22, 1958)*, [B], 37, 40.

'Lake Erie', *Offshore (August 22, 1958)*, [C], 41-42.

'Drilling from a floating vessel, Part II', *Offshore (December 1958)*, [A], 19-25.

'Lake Erie Wildcat Hits', *Offshore (December 1958)*, [B], 51-52.

'How the Russians produce offshore oil', *Offshore (August 1959)*, 36-37.

'First Well In Gulf Of Mexico Was Drilled Just 25 Years Ago', *Offshore (October 1963)*, 17-20.

'Drilling assault on the North Sea', *Offshore (May 1964)*, 15-16.

'Persian Gulf production sears', *Offshore (June 22, 1964)*, 51-53.

'Betsy's damage will surpass Hilda's', *Offshore (October 1965)*, 26-28.

'Brown & Root will lay North Sea line, 50-mile carrier will feed gas from BP discovery to England's coast', *Offshore 25(1966)4*, 31.

'North Sea gamble looks better', *Offshore (June 20, 1967)*, 93-100.

'Marine pipelaying methods defied odds', *Offshore (September 1979)*, 104.

Offshore Adventure, A Pictorial History of the Norwegian Petroleum Industry, Universitetsforlaget, 1982.

Offshore development, Volume one, Engineering and supply, The Financial Times, London, 1975.

Offshore development, Volume two, Exploration and production, The Financial Times, London, 1975.

Offshore development, Volume three, Finance, taxation and government, The Financial Times, London, 1975.

'The building of an offshore platform, a step by step study', *Offshore Drilling (September 1955)*.

'Working up to a perfect lift', *Offshore Engineer (September 1987)*, Reprint.

'Azeri Initiative', *Offshore Engineer (August 1992)*, 22-25.

'The Continental Shelf and North Sea Exploration', *Offshore Europe, 1st Edition*, [A], London, 1968, 9-14.

'Legal and Concessional Aspects of Drilling Activities on the Dutch Continental Shelf', *Offshore Europe, 1st Edition*, [B], London, 1968, 16-27.

'The Contribution of Dutch Shipyards to Offshore Operations', *Offshore Europe, 1st Edition*, [C], London, 1968, 61-64.

'Progress in the Design of Plarform, Barges and Other Craft used for Drilling Operations', *Offshore Europe, 1st Edition*, [E], London, 1968, 78-83.

'Diving to Six Hundred Feet', *Offshore Europe, 1st Edition*, [F], London, 1968, 103-105.

'Deep-Diving Techniques at the Service of Industry', *Offshore Europe, 1st Edition*, [G], London, 1968, 117- 119.

'Automatic Station Keeping and Telemetry', *Offshore Europe, 1st Edition*, [H], London, 1968, 171-174.

'The Development of Hoisting Gear', *Offshore Europe, 1st Edition*, [I], London, 1968, 239-241.

'Supply Boats for All-Round Rig-Servicing', *Offshore Europe, 1st Edition*, [J], London, 1968, 311-315.

Outer Continental Shelf Lands, Cross References, Submerged Lands, 43 USCS par. 1331, 199-278.

Outer Continental Shelf Lands Act, Chapter 345, Public Law 212 (August 7, 1953).

'It's very expensive offshore', *Petroleum Press Service (January 1969)*, 27.

Petroleum Resources Under the Ocean Floor, National Petroleum Council's Committee on Petroleum Resources Under the Ocean Floor, Washington, 1969.

Report of the joint Brazil - United States technical commission, Washington, 1949.

'Ekofisk Jack-Up', *RIQ Special RE 09 634 / 10.87*.

'Brent Spar - the way forward', *Shell UK Reports (October 12, 1995)*.

'Gulf of Mexico oil play', *Shell News (October 1949)*, 4-9.

'Offshore Activity is booming again', *Shell News (November 1953)*, 1-4.

'Rivalry for underwater land', *Shell News (May 1960)*, 18-19.

'A giant step to the deeps', *Shell News (October-November 1962)*, 5-10.

Shell Group deepwater technical expertise, Shell International Exploration and Production B.V., The Hague, 1995.

Statfjord, The Statfjord Group.

The North Sea Offshore Drilling, Cazenove & Co., 1965.

'Piping North Sea gas ashore is historic operation', *The Yorkshre Post (March 2, 1966)*.

'North Sea: Les Jeux Sont Faits', *The Economist (September 19, 1964)*, 1141-1142.

'At the first try', *The Economist (September 25, 1965)*, 1237-1238.

'The Norwegians gave the oil companies hell - and then concessions', *The Economist (February 22, 1975)*, 91- 92.

'Canadian gas fields', *The Oil and Gas Journal (August 21, 1913)*, 28.

'Bolsheviks take Baku and Grozny', *The Oil & Gas Journal (March 5, 1920)*, 74.

'From Gulf Coast to North Sea, Kerr-McGee's operations executive recalls those early days when offshore rigs were "built by brute strength", Profile A.T.F. Seale', *The Oil and Gas Journal (April 19, 1965)*, 191- 192.

The North Sea - A Province of Excellence, Petroleum Economist, London, 1995.

The offshore challenge, Shell Briefing Service, No. 2, 1993, Shell International Petroleum Company Ltd., London, 1993.

The North West European Continental Shelf: areas under concession, Cazenove & Co., 1974.

The deep offshore: dream or reality?, A special address to the Deep Offshore Technology Conference 'Managing economic opportunities today and tomorrow', Monte Carlo, 8 November 1993, Shell Internationale Petroleum Maatschappij, The Hague, 1993.

Thirty Years of Innovation, 30 Years Heerema, 1962-1992, Leiden, 1992.

Troll, Gas for Europe, Developing Europe's largest offshore gas field, A/S Norske Shell.

Truman Proclamation on the Continental Shelf (1945).

Vendor profiles of suppliers to the offshore industry, Norway, London, 1976.

Vendor profiles of suppliers to the offshore industry, United Kingdom, [A], London, 1977.

Vendor profiles of suppliers to the offshore industry, France, [B], London, 1977.

Vendor profiles of suppliers to the offshore industry, Netherlands, [C], London, 1977.

'Technical breakthroughs displayed in offshore drilling', *World Oil (July 1968)*, 90-95.

'Aramco wildcat in Persian Gulf finds cretaceous production', *World Petroleum (August 1951)*, 32-33.

Glossary

The Oil and Gas Yearbook 1996 (Financial Times International, London) lists 384 upstream and integrated oil and gas companies and 418 downstream companies. The following selection is made to help understanding who is who in this book. It is not, and is not intended to be exhaustive.

Large integrated companies with international operations are called majors. Independents are usually smaller companies with less widely spread activities. The borderline between the two categories is vague.

Companies with an asterisk (*) are one of A. Sampson's Seven Sisters.

Amoco
Standard Oil of Indiana, incorporated in 1889 and renamed in 1985. Amoco is fourth in the USA in assets and seventh in oil production (1995). Original owner of Creole in Venezuela and inventor of the crude cracking process. Purchased Pan American Petroleum with its Maracaibo interests in 1925 but sold all foreign operations to Esso in 1932, after which SO of Indiana was the largest single stockholder in SO of New Jersey.

Aramco
Arabian American Oil Company, originally a joint venture of Texaco and Socal (Chevron), later joined by Exxon and Mobil. In 1988 the Saudi Arabian Oil Co. was formed to take over responsibilities from Aramco.

ARCO
Atlantic Richfield Company, a descendant of the Atlantic Refining Co. (1870) which formed part of the Rockefeller group. In 1966 Atlantic merged with Richfield Oil Corp. which determined the present name. Later acquirements were Sinclair Oil Corp.(1969) and Anaconda Corp. (1977). ARCO holds ovber 80% of Vastar Resources Inc.

BP*
Burmah Oil was main share holder in the Anglo-Persian Oil Company (1909) until 1914, when the British Government obtained a 51% interest. In the middle of the first World War, Anglo-Persian bought a distribution company named British Petroleum, but this name was only adopted for the whole company in 1954. Meanwhile in 1935 the name had been changed to Anglo-Iranian. The US company Sohio was teamed up with in 1970 and later merged in 1987.
Measured by assets, BP was the third biggest oil company in 1995. It is no longer controlled by the British Government.

Burmah
Burmah Oil started operations in 1886 and was registered in Edinburgh in 1902. In the 1970s it was bought by BNOC, which was dissolved in 1985.

Caltex
Refining and retailing joint venture of Socal and Texaco since 1936.

CFP
Compagnie Française des Pétroles, see Total.

Chevron*
In 1895 Rockefeller bought Schofield's oil company which dated back to 1880. Standard Oil Co. (California) was formed in 1906 and renamed Socal in 1926 upon merger with the Pacific Oil Co. Earlier it had absorbed Standard Oil of Kentucky, also a Rockefeller company. In 1984 Gulf (originally Guffy Petroleum Co., 1907, but really started at Spindletop 1901) was acquired and the name was changed in Chevron.

Conoco
Continental Oil was a smaller Rockefeller's company. In 1929 it merged with Marland Oil (Oklahoma) and since 1979 it is named Conoco Inc. During the 1950s and 60s it expanded internationally. In 1981 it was taken over by DuPont.

ELF
Incorporated in 1941 as Société Nationale des Pétroles d'Aquitaine. Until 1994 controlled by the French government. It incorporated over time the French BRP and RAP after which the name was Elf-ERAP. Since 1994 operating as Elf Aquitaine.

Exxon*
Exxon Corporation, incorporated 1882, originally named Standard Oil (New Jersey) or Esso and the major descendant of the Rockefeller empire. Second largest private oil company in the world (1995) by all standards. The Anglo American Oil Company, also a Rockefeller company, joined Esso. The name Exxon was assumed in 1972. Humble Oil and Refining Company was merged into Exxon in the 1970s. Exxon and Shell have several 50/50 joint ventures in the North Sea: Nederlandse Aardolie Maatschappij (NAM, 1947) and Shell UK Exploration and Production (Shell Expro, 1964).

Gulf*
See Chevron

Humble
See Exxon

Magnolia
See Mobil

Marathon
The Marathon Group was originally incorporated in 1887 as Ohio Oil Company. It is a subsidiary of United States Steel (USX) Corporation since 1981.

Mobil*
Originally named Vacuum Oil Co. (1866) and in 1882 incorporated in Standard Oil (New York) or Socony, after its telegram address. Since 1911 Socony and Vacuum were two of the 33 companies into which Standard Oil was broken up. In 1925 Socony fully acquired Magnolia Petroleum Co. in which they already had an interest. In 1931 Socony and Vacuum joined forces and became Socony-Vacuum. The name was changed to Socony Mobil Oil Co. Inc. in 1955, Mobil Oil Corp. in 1966 and Mobil Corp. in 1976. Acquired Superior Oil Co. in the 1980s. Third largest private company in revenue and profit, or fourth in assets (1995).

Murphy
Independent oil company, incorporated in Louisiana, 1950; major shareholder in ODECO until its sale to Diamond M Corporation in 1992.

Pennzoil
Incorporated as Pennzoil in 1968, but originally a Rockefeller company: SW Pennsylvania Pipelines. Lost competition with Texaco to take over Getty Oil and successfully sued Texaco as a result.

Pure Oil
Pure Oil Company was formed in 1895 by a number independents - that is producers and refiners independent from Standard Oil. Early Gulf of Mexico player.

Shell*
Royal Dutch/Shell Group, formed in 1907 by merger of Royal Dutch (60%) and Shell Transport and Trading (40%). In 1995 Shell's assets were valued at $ 117.7 billion and its revenue at $ 151.7 billion. Shell is the largest privately owned oil company by these two criteria as well as by net profit (1995 data). If state oil companies are included in the ranking, Saudi Aramco is first, Petróleos de Venezuela SA is second and Shell is third.

Sohio
Standard Oil of Ohio, the original company of Rockefeller and the basis of the Standard Oil Trust; see BP

Standard Oil
The oil company created by John D. Rockefeller in 1870 and dissolved in a number of independent companies in 1911. The major descendants of Standard Oil still existing in 1997 are Exxon, Mobil, Chevron, Amoco, Conoco, Arco, Marathon Oil and Pennzoil.

Superior
See Mobil

Texaco*
Incorporated in 1902 as The Texas Company, became Texas Corporation in 1926 and Texaco in 1959. Texaco acquired Getty Oil in 1984. Number 7 in asset value (1995)

Total
Total SA, since 1991 the name of the former Compagnie Française des Pétroles (CFP), which was incorporated in 1924. Originally state owned, but in 1992 the French government diluted its interest to under 6%. CFP was regarded as the eighth of the Seven Sisters due to its interest in Middle East oil.

Unocal
Union Oil started in 1890 in California and survived the take-over tactics of Standard Oil. Since 1983 its name is Unocal Corporation.

Vastar
See ARCO

The following selection is made to help understanding what is what in this book. It is not, and is not intended to be exhaustive.

ABS
American Bureau of Shipping, a classification society. These societies provide checks of design calculations of seagoing structures. Their design approval is a prerequisite for obtaining insurance. ABS started in 1862 as the American Shipmasters Association. In 1968 it issued the first 'Rules for building and classing offshore mobile drilling units' which were used as the basis for the later IMCO rules.

AMSOC
American Miscellaneous Society, a body funding research projects.

Appraisal well
A well drilled as part of a drilling programme conducted to determine the extent, reserves and likely yield of an oil field.

Barrel
Unit of measurement used for oil quantities.
One barrel = 35 Imperial Gallons = 159 liters = 42 US gallons

Blow-out
Uncontrolled escape of gas, oil or water from a reservoir as a result of a release of pressure in a reservoir or a failure of the containment systems.

BOP
Blow-out preventer: equipment to close a well being drilled around or across the drill string

Christmas tree
Arrangement of pipes and valves at a wellhead which controls the flow of oil and gas and enables a number of manipulations with the well.

Conductor
Largest diameter pipe in the casing program, cemented into the seabed and extending to above water in the case of a fixed production platform. In subsea completions, the wellhead is set on the conductor and the connection from the wellhead to the surface is called riser.

Continental shelf (CS)
The shallow submerged area bordering the land of a continent. Water depth up to 200 m.

CUSS
Partnership of four oil companies: Continental, Union, Shell and Superior. Formed in 1948 to develop deep water drilling technology.

Derrick
A structure used to support the drill string and other equipment which has to be raised or lowered during well drilling operatyions. Originally wood, since many years steel.

Deviation well
A well drilled at an angle to the vertical, to cover the maximum area of an oil or gas field that can be produced from a single spot.

Diamond M
One of the MODU contractors and the largest semi-submersible owner in 1997 after acquisition of ODECO and Arethusa. Now named Diamond Offshore Drilling Inc.

Directional drilling
Producing deviation wells. The state of the art is capable of drilling horizontal or even somewhat upward to best penetrate a reservoir.

Downstream
Activities relating to oil product trading, transport, refining, distribution and marketing.

Drill bit
The part of the drill that actually cuts through the rock.

Drill string
Steel pipes of 30 ft (9.15 m) length joined together to form a continuous tube from the rotary table at the drilling rig down to the drill bit.

Dry hole
A well which shows no signs of oil or gas.

DWT
Deadweight tonnage: the weight of cargo + bunkers and other stores and supplies which a ship can carry when loaded to its mark.

Flaring
Burning off gas produced in association with oil which can not be utilised for technical reasons. Flaring for lack of commercial value is mostly history.

FPSO
Floating Production, Storage and Offloading vessel.

Gusto
Originally a shipyard, subsidiary of the IHC Holland Group. After the yard was closed in 1978, Gusto Engineering came into being and ultimately became a full subsidiary of IHC Caland.

GVA
Gotaverke

HeereMac
Joint venture between Heerema and McDermott, to jointly operate four semi-submersible crane vessels.

IFP
Institut Français du Pétrole, a French research institute. IFP has produced several important innovations, which were commercialised by starting firms like Coflexip. IFP is financed by the revenues of its patent licenses as well as by a surcharge on gasoline sold in France.

IHC
Industriele Handels Combinatie, a Dutch company, originally shipbuilders specialised in dredging and offshore equipment. The offshore yard, IHC Gusto was closed in 1978 as part of the restructuring of shipbuilding in the Netherlands. The name Gusto persisted in Gusto Engineering. The dredger building division had a difficult time around 1980 but made a come back in the mid 1980's and was ultimately fully re-acquired by IHC Caland, a holding. IHC Caland also owns SBM Inc, Imodco, Gusto Engineering and Marine Structure Consultants (MSC).

IMCO
International Maritime Consultative Organization, an adjunct of the United Nations and the international body best placed to assure quality in all aspects of maritime activity.

LST
Landing Ship Tank, a World War 2 vessel type.

Majors
The collective nameused for the world's alrgest oil companies; often referring to Shell, Exxon, BP, Mobil, Chevron and Texaco.

MARIN
A ship model basin and research institute in The Netherlands, which has played a pioneering role in many aspects of offshore hydrodynamics as well as in commercial testing of a large variety of offshore designs.

Micoperi
Operator of offshore cranes, taken over by Saipem in the 1990s.

Midstream
A seldom used term for the borderline between upstream and downstream, usually referring to transport and pipelines.

Moonpool
A cut-out in the center of a vessel, through which riser handling and drilling take place. The term is also used on other than drilling vessels for similar cut-outs, for instance for handling diving bells or ROV's.

Mud
A mixture of clays, water and chemicals used in drilling operations to lubricate and cool the drill bit, carry drilling wastes to the surface, prevent the walls of the well from collapsing and keep the upward flow of oil or gas under control. It is circulated continuously down the drillstring and up to the surface through the annulus between the drill string pipes and the wall of the hole.

Natural gas
A mixture of mostly methane and ethane found in the earth's crust, often in association with oil.

ODECO
Offshore Drilling and Exploration Company, one of the pioneering MODU contractors. Acquired by Diamond M. in the early 1990s and since operating as Diamond Offshore Drilling Inc.

The Offshore Company
One of the pioneering MODU contractors. Later renamed Sonat and ultimately merged with Transocean.

Operator
The company which manages and controls the development of a field. Usually the largest shareholder in a field becomes operator, but sometimes a smaller partner assumes operatorship.

Proved reserves
The quantity of oil and gas estimated to be recoverable from known fields under existing economic and operating conditions.

Reservoir
Underground rock formation containing oil or gas

SEAL
Subsea Equipment Associates Ltd, a company formed to develop atmospheric as well as wet subsea wellheads.

Sedco
South Eastern Drilling Company, a MODU contractor. Originally based in Dallas. Taken over by Schlumberger and merged with Forex of Paris to become Sedco-Forex.

Sonat
See The Offshore Company

Ton
Unless otherwise specified: metric ton, equivalent to 1.1 short ton or 2205 lbs or 9810 Newton

TLP
tension leg platform: a semisubmersible type platform moored by means of vertical tension legs or tethers. The mooring arrangement results in zero vertical movement of the platform, which makes possible the use of hard piped well risers to wellheads on board the TLP.

Upstream
Activities relating to crude oil exploration, production and delivery to export terminals.
Wellhead
The control equipment fitted to the well where it reaches the surface, consisting of valves, blow out preventers etc.

Wildcat
A well drilled on speculation. The term is said to be derived from the early days of oil drilling, when prospectors in the American wilderness shoot wildcats and hung their skins for drying near their drilling sites. A more formal definition is: a well drilled without reference to technical surveys or with little or no knowledge of the chances of striking oil (Shell Petroleum Handbook, 1948)

YF, YNFB
Yard Fighter, a World War 2 navy ship type.

Index

Index of persons

Index of companies and institutes

Geographical index

Index of oil and gas fields

Index of offshore structures